To Rosemary & Frank
With Best Wishes

THIRTY YEARS IN
Wilderness Wood

Chris & Anne

CHRIS YARROW

Matador
9 Priory Business Park,
Wistow Road, Kibworth Beauchamp,
Leicestershire. LE8 0RX
Tel: 0116 279 2299
Email: books@troubador.co.uk
Web: www.troubador.co.uk/matador
Twitter: @matadorbooks

ISBN 978 1784624 934

British Library Cataloguing in Publication Data.
A catalogue record for this book is available from the British Library.

Printed and bound in the UK by TJ International, Padstow, Cornwall
Typeset in 11½pt Fairfield by
www.chandlerbookdesign.co.uk

Matador is an imprint of Troubador Publishing Ltd

To Anne, Joanna and Kate

CONTENTS

ACKNOWLEDGEMENTS

A part from the occasional article for a magazine, and professional reports, writing has played a minor part in my working life. It was therefore essential that I had help from the start, and it is to my wife Anne that I owe so much. Not only did she correct errors of grammar and a myriad of inconsistencies, but imposed structure and flow on what might otherwise have been the random ramblings of a grumpy old man. She graciously stepped back from joint authorship when recommended, despite having already written the foundations of several chapters. Had she not been so busy, this would have been her own, much better, book. However, it is her loyalty and enthusiasm over 45 years of marriage that enabled the Wilderness Wood project to be conceived and nurtured to success, and to this I owe my greatest debt.

Many staff and others were involved in the thirty years, and little would have been achieved without their efforts and contributions. Some are mentioned in the text, and I apologise that it was not possible to name them all. My family must at times have been sorely tried by the process of living in the wood, or having me as an often obsessive relation. My thanks to them for their forbearance.

Several friends have helped during the writing, and especial thanks must go to Esmond Harris MBE, for his heroic efforts assessing the first draft and correcting errors of fact. John Pye, of The Bookshop in East Grinstead, gave very sound advice on cover design and the publishing process. Another hugely appreciated input was made by Nicholas Roe, who helped me better address my audience. John Stoney kindly read an early draft. Prof. Julian Evans OBE, a prolific writer on all aspects of forestry, encouraged me to pen this account soon after he published the first book about his own wood, and has kindly written a foreword. Finally, I would like to thank Martin Toseland, who helped so much with constructive editorial advice.

All the photographs were taken by the Yarrow family, with the exception of two which have been reproduced by kind permission of Country Living and Cris Barnett. I would also like to thank John Eliot for permission to use his sketch of the New Inn, and Peter Gillies for the use and dating of the old postcard of the Main Road.

Chris Yarrow

FOREWORD

I t's a long time since I've enjoyed a book so much. Chris and Anne Yarrow have crafted a masterpiece. I've owned a wood half the size of their Wilderness Wood, and written about it with some success in a popular way, but what Chris and Anne did, and did for nigh on 30 years, was for their 60-plus acres to be their livelihood. They recount the experience in an engaging style, with humour, and with the wisdom of the years culled from the experience of having actually done it.

While perhaps not unique, it must come close to own and actually live off a smallish wood. What is recorded for us fits that genre of books which for me began when my mother gave me Thomas Firbank's 1940's classic, *I Bought a Mountain*. What the Yarrows have done in these pages is tell us all the ups and downs, all the fun, finance and foibles, and all about neighbours and narrow escapes. And they do it in an utterly unpretentious way.

Britain's woodlands, especially smaller ones in the lowlands, still suffer great neglect. Data suggest that at least half are ignored by their owners and lie unmanaged and unloved. This is rarely best for a wood and its wildlife, as it becomes dark and dense. Such neglect also fails to offer produce, even something as simple as firewood, which is so sought-after today. The best woods are where there is light and dark, small trees and large, coppice and high forest, and a variety of species native and, dare I say it, a few non-native too, that usually enrich not harm our impoverished tree flora.

We hear today much about woodlands having multi-uses – something foresters have always known – and how they afford so many benefits and not just timber. Wilderness Wood has been an exemplar. Visitors come for all sorts of reasons, and many return again and again. The variety of produce marketed, though not always successfully, puts most owners to shame – moss, chestnuts, foliage, pea-sticks, bean-poles, fence posts, as well as Christmas trees, timber for local use and for sale, and much more.

We learn all this, and about the Yarrows' passion for being green and recycling everything possible, even visitors' BBQ left-overs to feed the chickens! We learn how to handle the public who flock to Wilderness Wood to follow the trails, enjoy a cuppa, or camp in a quiet corner. Kids play on the 'death-slide', dogs are welcome, while rabbits and grey squirrels aren't. We learn that the Christmas tree business, so superficially attractive, is fraught when it comes to marketing, to the point that a chapter is entitled 'A wholesale mistake'. And we learn how, right in the path of the Great Storm of 1987, their newly acquired investment was assailed.

It really is all here. The reader is led safely in the hands of experts: a chartered forester and an ecologist who developed a special expertise in fungi for food and forays. Chris and Anne complement each other, and have brought to us a treasure in these pages that will amuse, inform and excite, though not necessarily in that order. It has made me almost want to start my career over again and emulate their remarkable achievement as told in '30 Years in Wilderness Wood'.

Professor Julian Evans OBE FICFor
President,
Institute of Chartered Foresters

PREFACE

For thirty years an unusual experiment in sustainable living was taking place in a small Sussex wood. This experiment came about because my wife Anne and I needed a new challenge before we sank into middle-aged torpor, and, like many other foresters, it was my dream to run my own woodland. I was concerned that the average Briton's right of access to the countryside was abysmally restricted in comparison with many other countries. What's more, half our lowland woods were neglected as uneconomic, and yet here was a resource which was uniquely able to absorb people unobtrusively. It seemed crazy to me, a chartered forester who had specialised in countryside recreation, that in our crowded country such land was going to waste, while it could meet so many needs if properly managed.

When in 1980 Anne and I bought Wilderness Wood, we intended to show that we could make our small wood pay. Not only that, we also required it to meet a wide range of purposes that included recreation, education, and wildlife and landscape protection. All this would be within the context of its remaining a productive working woodland, where we harvested useful timber and other products. We wanted to practice what the forester calls "multiple use".

Until then we had made our living advising other landowners, but now we wanted to take on our own personal challenge, and success or failure would be entirely ours.

Fortune shone on us. Despite planning policies to the contrary, we gained permission to build a house, which became home for us and our two daughters. As the woodland equivalent of a smallholding, Wilderness Wood evolved into a much-loved place, with thousands each year coming to enjoy and learn about it, and buy what we had to offer. It won several prestigious forestry prizes, largely because of its uniqueness (which is a way of saying there was not much competition!), and continues under new ownership with similar and equally worthwhile aims.

When we retired, friends told us we should write down what we had done, not just because many could learn from it, but because it was a good story. The woodland venture had been a joint effort, and we intended to write the book together, each producing alternate chapters; but Anne had other calls on her time, and her output did not keep up with mine. Although her writing was better, it was in a different style, so we agreed that I should become the book's author.

Writing did not come easily, with the temptation of straying down immensely interesting sidetracks, which Anne quickly pointed out would make the book tiresome and unreadable. Any structure, and certainly all the style, is due to her meticulous and repeated editing. We submitted what we hoped was a near final draft to a consulting editor, who recommended excising a whole chapter, and trying to address more closely our intended audience. Publication was thus set back by several months.

So who should read this book? Visitors to Wilderness Wood can learn the story behind this unusual place, and may find it hard to imagine that, not long ago, it was just an inaccessible area of coppice and young plantations. I hope it will inspire all those who own, intend to buy, or dream of buying, a small wood. Owners and managers of estates large and small will gain an insight into running a small woodland business. I am honest about the mistakes we made, and the financial and other commitments that were needed to make it work. The increasing numbers of the public who love the countryside will better understand why England's woods appear the way they do, and read how one small woodland-owning family made its contribution to their survival. Paraphrasing Donne, no wood is an island, and my assessment of Wilderness Wood's historical and current roles may interest students of estate management, planning and the rural economy. I greatly admire the many woodland businesses springing up to meet demands for firewood, charcoal, and other woodland products, and hope the details of how we worked the wood, and not least the "Money matters" chapter, will offer helpful advice on avoiding bankruptcy. However, this is not a textbook, and the reader must look elsewhere for guidance on using a chainsaw, tree planting, and the wealth of knowledge that a competent forester must absorb. Finally, Wilderness Wood exists firmly in the embrace of a special Sussex village, and I trust some of its inhabitants will enjoy having a record of our time at what is in many ways the village wood.

As someone who is self-employed (some might say unemployable), I have always felt free to express personal views on changing forestry fashions, and the reader may find the chapter "A stableful of hobbyhorses" at variance with teachings from those whose prime interest is preserving wildlife habitat. I would be disappointed if it did not engender debate, or at least reflection.

We never kept a journal, and had to resort to the many leaflets we produced, dates on the back of fading photographs, and press-cuttings, to remind ourselves of the sequence of events. The first seven chapters cover the period until we completed building the house, in roughly chronological order. Thereafter, different aspects are covered by subject, though there is inevitably a great deal of overlap, and to-ing and fro-ing up and down the years.

This is no coffee-table book. Unless he is a keen photographer, any autobiographer will be dismayed at the accumulated shoeboxes and albums of blurry family snaps, and we are no exception. The few colour photos are reproduced to give a contemporary impression of our story. Our graphic designer friend Colin Lumsden kindly undertook to capture the essence of some scenes by interpreting photos of inadequate quality. Other small line drawings peppering the text were created over the years for our many leaflets and children's activity sheets by Anne and her colleague Sarah Wilesmith, who also drew the map.

Anne and I discussed at length whether we should use metric or imperial units. Most of us use both, in a glorious English muddle. Professionally, I think and talk of tonnes per hectare, and trees with a diameter of 20 centimetres, but consider myself as five foot eight inches tall. Although children had been taught in metric for some decades, we were selling our produce to an older population, so a rustic pole might be labelled "8 foot long, 3 inch top", and we sold Christmas trees in feet. Likewise, road signs are still in miles; but, despite Anne's protestations, apart from distances the book is almost entirely metric. I have tried to avoid forestry jargon, but traditional terms such as "cant" and "sned" are too useful to discard for bland modern equivalents, as well as being a valuable connection to our past. The Glossary explains some of the less familiar words.

I hope this book will be an inspiration to some; amusing or interesting to many; and to those buoyed with enthusiasm and good intentions, a gentle reminder that woods are complicated to manage, and sound advice is worth seeking.

Chris Yarrow
May 2015.

MAPS

Wilderness Wood at purchase

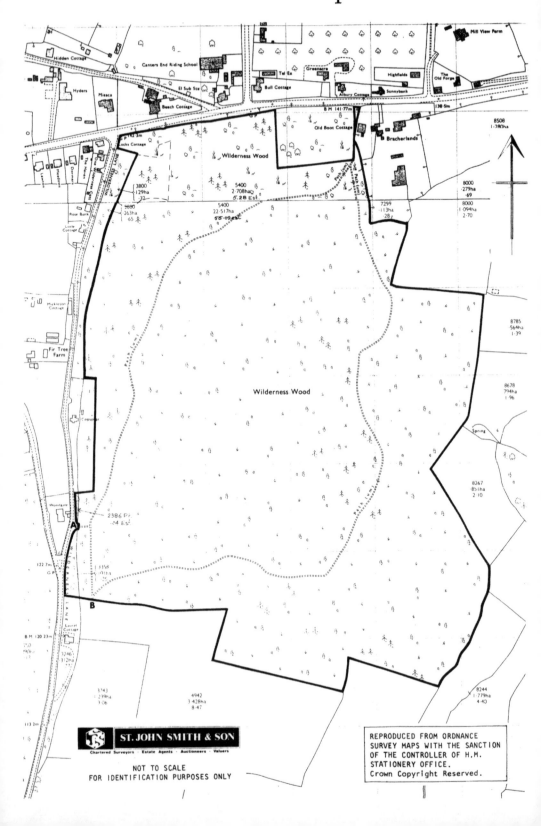

Wilderness Wood as it became

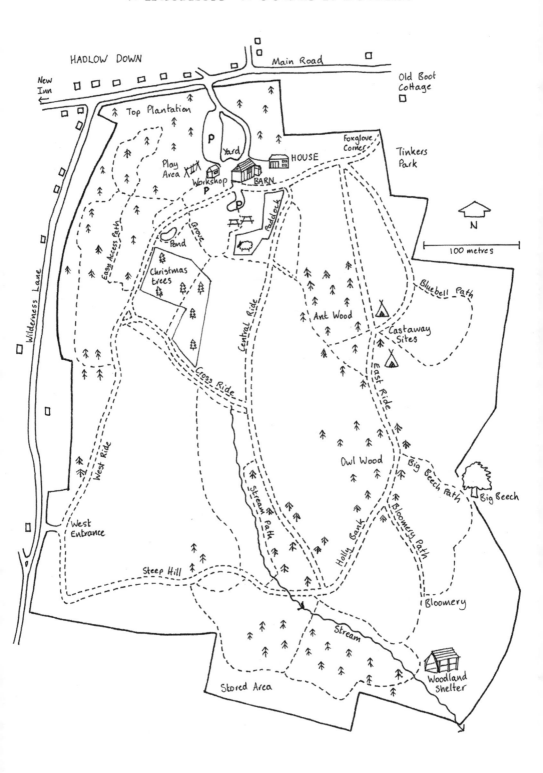

BUYING THE WOOD

I had never spent money so quickly. Each wave of my hand cost me £1,000, and I was already promising more than I had ever earned in a two-year period. Bidding had started at £12,000, and had quickly risen to £20,000 between a young, good-looking lady and an older man, possibly a land agent or woodsman. The latter dropped out, and I started a fresh onslaught against that just-too-nice lady, whom I imagined was investing a legacy in something Granny would have approved of. Heads turned in my direction as I again waved my copy of the sales particulars to catch the auctioneer's eye. Never wanting to prolong the agony, I immediately trumped her every bid by an extra thousand, until "I have twenty-eight thousand pounds from the gentleman in the third row. Any advance? Once. Twice. Sold for twenty-eight thousand pounds". And with that an assistant led me to a table at the front of the crowded church hall in Uckfield, the auctioneer congratulated me, and I got out my chequebook for a deposit of ten percent.

Elation? Panic? Mixed emotions certainly, as I made my way to a public telephone in the High Street, to 'phone Anne at her part-time job in the County Planning Department. Ever supportive, and unable to believe that at last we had actually bought the thing we had sought for years, a warm hug and kiss winged down the wires from Lewes, eight miles to the south.

Three years earlier, in July 1977, we had been only able to afford a holiday away by renting out our home and going camping. That had been three years into a deep recession. Work as a forestry and tourism consultant had been non-existent, and a loan on a property-based venture was sucking up what scarce resources we possessed. Our daughter Joanna had just turned three, and Anne was six and a half months pregnant. We had initially toyed with the idea of a trip along the South Downs Way, hiring a pony to carry Anne, the bags and sometimes Jo, whilst I, Joseph-like, would walk alongside to the next destination in a remote coombe or friendly farmer's paddock. Ponies for hire were not a category in the Yellow Pages, and the internet was still eighteen years away. My call to the Pony Club of Great Britain was listened to with increasing disbelief. "And how much riding experience does your three-year-old have? I've never heard such a ridiculous idea."

Realising we might be reported to the RSPCA, if not the NSPCC, should we pursue the concept further, I hit on the idea of carrying the whole entourage of wife, child, and baggage in a canoe instead, and we set off to explore Midland canals and rivers. Anne's father, a wise and generous-hearted man, on hearing of our holiday proposal stated that it was a crazy idea, but as he knew us well, he thought we were just mad. History does not record what he and Mother-in-Law thought when we announced we had bought a sixty-three acre wood and intended to try and make a living from it.

This is the story of how in October 1980 we bought Wilderness Wood, and over the next thirty years built a house there, raised a family, and transformed the wood into a successful and much-loved woodland park.

SEARCHING FOR
A WOOD

So where did it come from, this crazy idea of living in a wood? By the late 1970's we were living with our two young daughters in the centre of Lewes, in a delightful little house that we had converted ourselves from three derelict terrace cottages. I was a forester by training. Too cussed and impatient to work for others, I was trying to build up a business as a forestry and recreation consultant, but often saw my recreation feasibility studies bastardised out of all recognition, or left to a slow death from neglect; and the long 1970's recession meant that work was hard to come by. Anne, with degrees in geography and conservation, was working part-time in East Sussex County Planning Department on countryside and tourism projects, but several years in local government were enough for her. Middle-age threatened (or so it seemed to us 30-somethings), and we were anxious to stir up our life, rather than sink into a comfortable small-town existence. We dreamed of having our own project, where we could be our own boss, make our own mistakes, create our own destiny.

Bright lights had never held much appeal for either of us, and we both enjoyed getting our hands dirty. Anne's childhood dream had been to marry a farmer (this was pre-feminist days), and we already had runner beans and bottle-fed lambs in the back yard, and vegetables, bees and chickens in a neighbour's garden. So it would have to be a countryside venture. The zeitgeist was with us: John Seymour's *Self-Sufficiency* was our bible, *The Good Life* was on TV, the Welsh Marches were scattered with middle-class back-to-the-landers, and we were tempted to join the flow. We knew about projects involving hard work and risk. The house conversion had taken all our free time for almost two years. Evenings and weekends would see us demolishing, wheel-barrowing, brick-cleaning, right through to putting on the last coat of paint, and cycling home at 11pm to my parents' house , where we were lodging . De-robing our filthy clothes in the garden, we would creep upstairs to the bathroom for an initial rinse, followed by a second wash in the shared bath. And as well as our efforts at vegetables, chickens, sheep and bees, we had partnered Anne's father in creating and tending a half-acre family vineyard in Surrey's outer suburbia, fifty miles away.

We were looking for a project that would give us both a place to live and a living. Ideas were chewed over and binned. Country walks were peppered with sightings of possible vineyard sites, or streams where a trout farm might be developed. But we kept coming back to woodland. After all, woodlands were what I was supposed to know about. I had returned in 1966 from two years in Montana, USA, brandishing a master's in Forest Recreation and convinced I was God's gift to Britain if not mankind, but had quickly concluded that bodies such as the Forestry Commission and National Trust had yet to see the light. I was certain that the way forward was "multi-purpose" forestry, where the land could play many roles. In the States, vast tracts of land were owned by the people, who had the right to enjoy it. Hadn't Woody Guthrie penned *This Land is Your Land, This Land is My Land*? And in the Kennedy years of the post-war boom, things just kept on getting better and more democratic. Over there, millions were visiting their forests as never before, and all manner of facilities were provided for them. How much more important were our limited woodland resources in Britain, especially the crowded South-east! In the absence of free public access to good facilities, maybe Anne and I could make a business from running our own woodland? We had heard of a place that seemed to be what we had in mind, and a visit to Brokerswood in Wiltshire helped us clarify our ideas. Here, Tony Phillips had created a venture that combined productive woodland management with tourism – a campsite, fishing lake, trails, tea-room, museum – all run as a family business. If Tony could do it, so could we!

So our dream crystallised as a woodland where we would harvest wood and timber, add value by making wood products, and welcome - and charge - the visiting public. Forestry alone would make us little money, but the combination of activities should be financially viable. We would need to live on the spot for the same reasons that a corner-shopkeeper lives over the shop – for security, and so that we could be open all hours, and combine our family and working lives. Who was it who spoke of the masochism of the middle-classes? From the start, we expected also to continue part-time consultancy, that would provide what John Seymour called "foreign exchange," to supplement our self-sufficient lifestyle.

We knew that the project was going to need quite a lot of capital. In the early 1970's we had conceived a holiday village on Speyside in Scotland, to demonstrate our consultancy skills. Tasteful timber buildings for self-catering visitors would be sensitively located with minimal impact on the vegetation or the visual scene, and as far from the concept of a holiday camp as could be imagined. All had been going well, until the oil crisis of 1973 pulled the rug from under the project, and for four desperate years creditors were kept at bay while we scoured the globe for finance. By the skin of our teeth we emerged in 1978 with a tenant to build it, our first grey hairs, and a useful source of income. In Lewes, all the hard work we had spent converting three derelict cottages into a lovely home had also paid off, and it would be worth several times what we had spent on it.

With no need to bother the bank manager, we could start looking for our woodland. Our wish-list comprised: 20-40 hectares (50-100 acres), i.e. big enough to feel like a proper woodland, and give us an income from wood products, but small enough to be affordable and workable; not too steep or too wet; with harvestable timber and wood to give some immediate income; with a lake or a potential lake site to develop as a tourist attraction; with visual appeal; with road access for visitors' cars and coaches; and, last but not least, with a house, or at least a ruin for conversion. It was unlikely that any wood would meet all these criteria, but listing them clarified our priorities and objectives.

There are land agents who specialise in woodland sales, but many of the particulars that landed on our doormat featured young plantations located in the most forested parts of Britain, i.e. the North and West. Undoubtedly they were cheaper, and the sort of forests I had been trained to manage, and probably their local planning authorities would be sympathetic to our ideas. However, we decided that we wanted to stay in our comfort-zone of southern England, where there were plenty of small woods and where we would be reasonably near our Sussex- and Surrey-based families. We also judged it unlikely that our concept would work in areas with a low density of population, extensive freely-accessible public forests, and a difficult climate that ruled out year-round visitors.

For two years we pored over particulars, and traipsed round woodland plots from Kent to Somerset. Is it a trick of memory, or did we do most of our searching in winter? Images blur into one another; of leafless branches, maps held in icy fingers, and muddy and overgrown tracks, which in the gathering gloom required our best navigational skills to emerge from the wood remotely near its entrance. Sometimes we dragged along Jo, by then aged four to five, and Kate, three years younger; but often they were left in the warm with Granny and Grandpa. We didn't want to put them off before our woodland adventure had even started. Our transport was my parents' tinny little red Renault 4. Doggedly "green" before the term had been invented, we ourselves did without a car for eight years; until with the acquisition of a wood we became country people, and found that, like wellingtons, a car is sadly a countryside essential.

We investigate yet another wood

It quickly became apparent that patience would be needed, and that to find a piece of land that ticked all our boxes was an impossible dream. This was before widespread demand for small amenity woods had inflated prices, and so affordability wasn't the problem. We had a pretty realistic idea of land prices, and knew that 20 to 40 hectares should be within our price range, although some vendors did seem to have an optimistic view of what their inaccessible and scrubby woodland would fetch. However, few woodlands passed the accessibility test. Most were a residual piece of land, tucked away in the corner of a farm and reached by a long and muddy track, that might have served in the days of horse and cart but would need a fortune spending on it to take a modern timber truck, never mind the visitors' cars and coaches that we had in mind; and, when you emerged onto the tarmac, it was a tiny country lane that, again, couldn't accommodate our planned traffic.

An even bigger problem was the house. Woodlands with accommodation just didn't come on the market. A farm has a farmhouse, but a traditional wood doesn't need constant on-the-spot supervision, and seldom has any buildings at all. The gamekeeper's cottage is the only home you are likely to find in a wood; and that would be on a large estate, which wasn't in the business of selling plots of land to the likes of us. With our planning background, we knew there was a general presumption against new houses in the countryside, so the chances of building one were remote. We clutched at straws, visiting anything with accommodation. A smallholding near Dallington, some fifteen miles away, had a nice little house and outbuildings, but we couldn't pretend its two small copses would be the basis of a woodland venture. We dumped the girls with Anne's parents, and drove in their car all the way to Somerset to look at a plot on the edge of the Levels; again, a nice cottage, but the woodland was impossibly steep, full of dead elm-trees, and tucked away down tiny lanes that were quite unsuitable for visitors' cars or coaches.

A cottage looked unattainable, and we needed to loosen our criteria. A building – any building, even a ruin – could perhaps be the lever for getting planning permission for a house. We had received particulars of a farm that included a 40-hectare wood with the derelict remains of a cottage in one corner. Balneath Wood, at Chailey, turned out to tick several of our boxes. It was the right size, a compact shape, and only a short track separated it from a reasonably wide and straight country road. Gently undulating and on clay, there could be potential for a lake. It was only a few miles from Lewes, so we would be near family and friends. If we could persuade the planners that the derelict cottage could be transmogrified into a house near the access track, we would have our house, and in the right place for control and supervision. Of course nothing is perfect, and Balneath had a couple of drawbacks. It was on Weald Clay, so the tracks were extremely muddy, and an awful lot of hardcore would be needed to make them useable in wet weather. And the woodland was 100 percent coppice, with few large trees for either visual variety or timber value. The coppice was mainly oak and hornbeam: interesting historical relics, as oak used to be coppiced for tan-bark and hornbeam made fine charcoal for the gunpowder industry, but nowadays their poles would just be slow-growing firewood, with few other obvious uses.

Despite the drawbacks, Balneath looked a real possibility. We explored more, finding ancient oak "stools" (coppice stumps) over three metres across, and a chequers tree, another indicator of ancient woodland. Plenty of historical and wildlife interest here. We roughly planned the layout of a house and garden, working area, and car park, and began to imagine a life at Balneath. First we had to buy the wood, and early steps were hopeful. Like many modern farmers, the recent purchaser was really not interested in the woodland, and we settled on a good price for it. But we needed a house, so the sale was agreed subject to our obtaining planning permission. We submitted an application to Lewes District Council, with a three-page explanation of our intentions. Shortly thereafter we had a 'phone call from the local paper – they thought our planning application looked interesting, and would like to run an article about it. Pleased with this opportunity to tell the world of our plans, we poured out our ideas to a local reporter, and an up-beat and reasonably accurate article duly appeared, complete with photograph of eager young couple and their two little girls.

We had anticipated a rough ride with the planners and planning committee, but, in our naivety, were completely unprepared for what came next. The good folk of Chailey and Barcombe, the two nearest villages, had read the article and panicked. We were proposing hundreds – no, thousands – of visitors to *their* countryside, and lots of these would be from towns and cities. There was horrified talk of charabancs, transistor radios, candy floss – perhaps we were Billy Butlins in disguise? As one, very pleasant, lady said: "I believe that you are genuine in what you say, but in practice I don't believe that you will stop there". In vain we offered to explain ourselves in more detail, and pointed out that anything beyond our tabled plan would need further planning permission. Letters of protest poured into the council: "The lane is very quiet, and would be spoiled by more traffic", "The lane is busy, and can't take more traffic". A "Keep out the Yarrows" meeting in the village hall had standing room only. The upshot was that his neighbours let the vendor know just what they would think of him if he sold to us and, understandably, he backed out of the sale.

A little older and a lot wiser, we crept back to Lewes and licked our wounds. Henceforth, we weren't mentioning anything to anyone. We would buy a wood first, and gamble on getting planning permission later. The postscript to the Balneath episode was a sad one: the Nature Conservancy Council would have declared it a Site of Special Scientific Interest if there had been the time, and the County Wildlife Trust would have been interested in it as a nature reserve if they had had the money; but in the meantime the farmer cleared all but the fringes of the wood to make a couple of badly-drained, rush-infested fields, so the locals lost their wood which had been there since long before the Domesday Book.

Another eighteen months passed, with a trickle of property particulars to read, and in many cases to look round. For Jo, "moving to a wood" became one of life's background themes, something that adults talked about endlessly but never actually happened. Twice, we came within a whisker of a purchase. I went along, cheque-book in hand, to the auction of an attractive wood just over the border into Kent, with plenty of mature broadleaved trees and a stream running through it, but had to drop out of the bidding when it soared above our estimate of what the woodland was worth (and what we could afford). We had based our valuation on the underlying land, plus the timber on the site, and it was an object lesson to us on the growing amenity value of woodlands in south-east England – a figure which has totally eclipsed timber worth in the subsequent decades. Some months later, and following protracted negotiations, our offer was accepted for an attractive oak woodland south of Tunbridge Wells. At last the dream seemed about to become reality, and we again dared to start planning where we would try for a house site, where we would have our car park and workshop, and where the girls would go to school. This time, the owner suddenly decided to withdraw his woodland from the market, leaving us only with lawyer's bills.

So when, in the autumn of 1980, I said that something called "Wilderness Wood" was coming up for auction and might be worth having a look at, Anne didn't take it too seriously. This wood was in the village of Hadlow Down, north-east of Uckfield, which jogged a memory. Years previously, we had made a cold Sunday winter walk from Uckfield bus station with infant Jo in a back-pack, trudging up a muddy track through coppiced woods to a pub which resembled a semi-derelict Victorian railway station, where we had sat outside and eaten our sandwiches, watching passing traffic on the main road. A visit confirmed this recollection that Hadlow Down was hardly a "pretty" village, and our suspicions that Wilderness Wood was not a pretty woodland: the sales particulars listed chestnut coppice and fairly young pine plantations, and there didn't seem to be any areas of large trees such as the public likes to see. No tick, then, in the "visual appeal" box, nor in the box for timber to give an immediate income. However, there were lots of plusses. The name "Wilderness Wood" was a good start: attractive, memorable, inviting. At 24 hectares, the wood just scraped into the 20-40-hectare range we had set ourselves, and the lack of large trees, or immediate visual appeal, should mean that the price would be affordable. If we were to have coppice, chestnut, with its ready market, would be the best type. The map told us that the wood was a compact, regular, shape, minimising the boundary to be maintained. Unlike many woods we had looked at, it was south-facing, and at the top of a hill; so there must be views, if there weren't so many trees in the way. A small valley ran down through the wood, and there seemed to be some sort of a stream, so maybe we could make a fishing lake. There were no public rights of way, so that we could control – and charge for – access. Hadlow Down was only 12 miles from our Lewes base, so we wouldn't lose touch with family and friends. The wood was on a main road, so there shouldn't be objections from the highways authorities to our plans for visitors' cars and coaches. Most important of all, we would be on the edge of a village, which must give us as good a chance as we would get of gaining planning permission for a house; and, if we failed, we should be able to find a nearby cottage to live in.

They say that people spend more time agonising over buying clothes than over choosing their house, and the same probably applied to our woodland purchase. A read of the sales particulars, and after a single brief visit to the wood, I set off to the auction with cheque book in pocket – and, a couple of hours later, our future was pinned to Wilderness Wood.

WE HAVE A WOOD !

What was it like, this patch of Sussex on which we had pinned our future? What exactly had we bought, with a wave of the hand and a stroke of a pen? The sales particulars and our lightning pre-auction inspection had given us an approximate idea of what we were getting, but, from today's perspective, we bought Wilderness Wood in a breathtaking state of ignorance. We might be the legal owners, but it would take more than the transfer of money and a land registry entry to make us feel that we had a "right" to the land: 24 hectares (or about 30 football pitches) of chestnut coppices, poplars and pine plantations, according to the particulars. That felt quite a responsibility, coming from a nine-metre-square back garden.

Our first priority was to investigate and explore our piece of Sussex countryside, to give us a better idea of its potential and drawbacks. We parked at the entrance on Wilderness Lane that first Saturday morning after the auction, and, as I climbed out of Mum's old Renault 4, and Anne disgorged Jo and Kate from the back, a wave of trepidation swept away the relief we had both felt when the searching was over. Three-year-old Kate struggled to open the five-bar gate that six-year Joanna was already climbing.

We felt our first responsibility was to introduce them to the wood in such a way that it would be seen as a fun place; somewhere they could make camps and play, while Mum and Dad did boring things like chopping wood or planting trees. With only an ancient six-inch Ordnance Survey map as a guide, the first walk round "our" wood would be truly a joint adventure.

Getting around that late October day proved quite a challenge. There were two entrance tracks into the wood: the one where we had parked in the south-west corner, on Wilderness Lane, and the other in the north-east, on the main A272. The map showed a circular track linking these, but this had evidently been used in wet weather by forestry contractors' heavy machinery, and in places we had to carry Kate over knee-deep water-filled ruts. Gradually we noticed other tracks and paths that weren't on the map, and which were in places all but obliterated by birch saplings. Like rabbits in a cornfield, we pushed our way through young chestnut stems no thicker than one's arm: hardly the most attractive form of woodland, especially in the drab colours of early winter.

We knew that chestnut coppice should theoretically be cut on a rotation of about fifteen years, so that, within the 15 hectares of Wilderness Wood coppices, there should be about one hectare in each age-class. But we found little older than five years. We had purchased it from the executors of a London surgeon, who had owned the wood since 1956 as an investment, and whose physical involvement had been limited to an annual inspection. It had been run on his behalf by a local woodland management company, and they had cut the coppices when prices were good, rather than in rotation, taking advantage of recent high prices. In fact, the badly rutted tracks and extensive recent cutting showed all the signs of a woodland run for short term gain rather than its long term health. One of our early tasks would be to even-out the coppice rotation, but there was little immediate prospect of income.

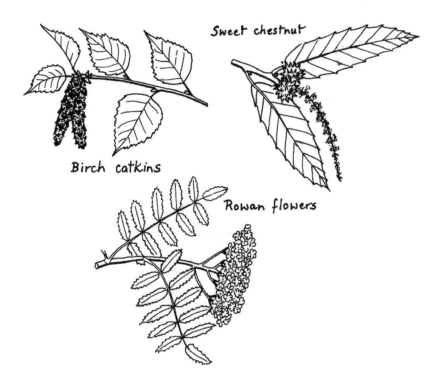

Sweet chestnut

Birch catkins

Rowan flowers

The girls were drawing our attention to mysteries better spotted with their eagle eyes closer to the ground, but, as we slowly worked our way through the coppices, I could see they were not of good quality. My conventional forestry training had hardly covered coppicing, and I had not previously grasped that there is a big variation in the quality of chestnut coppices. It soon became apparent that ours included a good many trees that weren't chestnut, in particular birch; and they were not well stocked, i.e. the stools were too far apart. But you get what you pay for, and the price had been reasonable.

It was quite a trek for small legs to the upper end of the circular ride. I checked the map later, and found a height difference of 65 metres from the lowest point, where the stream flows out, to the highest, up by the Main Road. Looking back southwards, the views over the recently-cut areas revealed a sea of browning chestnut leaves, broken by taller patches of greyish-green pines and the bright yellow leaves of autumn birch. A closer look did uncover some variety. Besides the ubiquitous birch, here and there we spied rowan, willow and sycamore. Hazel is the totemic English coppice tree, but we only noticed a handful, at the top and bottom of the wood. Another typical Wealden coppice tree is the hornbeam, but it was many weeks before Anne spotted the only two in Wilderness Wood. There were a couple of crab apples, and holly growing in abundance, but it was quite clear our wood would take no prizes for diversity.

We expectantly made our way back down the course of the stream to locate an area described in the sales particulars as "two acres of poplar plantation". Eventually we did find a few struggling poplars, far smaller and thinner than would be expected for their age. Disappointed, we re-classified this area rather vaguely as "mixed woodland". As well as the inevitable scattered chestnut stools, not cut for many years, it contained a great deal of birch, quite a lot of alder, and scattered western hemlock, an attractive feathery conifer from the west coast of North America. It looked like an area where our predecessors had tried poplar, replanted with hemlock, and in recent years had given up. This could be explained by the drainage - or lack of - and soil that was very obviously too infertile for poplars, which are most at home on rich meadowland. Pushing through fallen branches, we squelched into quite extensive bogs, where no trees were growing but alder and birch. The moss underfoot was *Sphagnum*, or bog-moss, which carpets vast areas of moorland in upland Britain, confirming our suspicion that we were taking on some very acid and infertile soils.

The particulars also listed conifer plantations, and we found they varied in extent from a few metres square to the size of three football pitches. These areas had mostly been established in 1958 or 1960, and, at around twenty years old, were still very obviously young plantations, with straight lines of similar-sized trees, evenly spaced at intervals of less than two metres. Most were of Scots pine which had reached a height of about ten metres, with a diameter at chest height of around ten centimetres, indicating the trees were growing well. The largest plantation, across the northern and highest part of the wood, was a mixture of pine and beech, with four lines of pine alternating with two of beech, and typical of the forestry planting of its time. Unfortunately most of the beech trunks were forked, and would never yield good timber. The plantation had quite recently been line-thinned: every fourth row of pine trees had been removed, next to a line of beech, to give tractor access within the plantation and to allow the remaining trees more light, especially the beech. It was good to see that the pines had been "brashed", that is, their dead lower branches had been cut off, allowing easy foot access between them. Less happily, I noticed that many showed signs of severe damage three to five years previously by that *bête noire* of foresters, the grey squirrel (more about this in chapter 14). Despite the poorly-formed beech, and the obvious squirrel damage, we had some "proper forestry" that I could at last get my teeth into.

Not far from the stream at the bottom of the wood, we found a young pine plantation about ten years old. Like a similar belt along the Main Road, this was quite impenetrable, the lower branches interlaced with brambles yet to be shaded out. Progress on foot through these areas would require stout boots, gloves, and a slasher to cut back brambles and impeding lower branches, and they would be off-limits for some time yet. Near the west boundary stood a small area of dense and branchy lodgepole pine, a tree that seven years earlier we had seen blanketing hundreds of square kilometres of Yellowstone National Park. This tree also grows on the coast north to Alaska, and unfortunately our predecessors had planted the coastal variety, with its heavy branches and habit of crowding out its neighbours. In the far north-east corner we discovered a small patch of Sitka spruce, the pre-eminent forestry tree of northern and western Britain. It looked pretty unhappy, despite the mist dripping off its needles that damp afternoon, and I remembered it could not tolerate the relatively dry and balmy summers of south-east England. And near the west boundary was a little group of western hemlock, another North American coastal conifer. We had the feeling that the planting contractors working at Wilderness Wood had taken advantage of an absent landowner, and got rid of their odds and ends here at the end of the planting season. I told Anne I was determined not to make the mistake of planting the wrong species. How I would later eat my words!

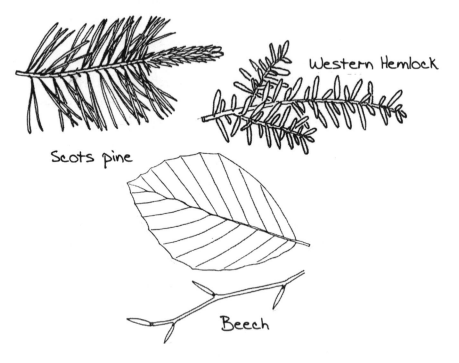

Scots pine

Western Hemlock

Beech

As we retraced our steps towards the south-west entrance, we devised a challenge to see if Jo and Kate could lead us back. With several years of country walks between them, they showed an unerring ability to find the security of Granny's car and the promised slices of cake. Never ones to waste transport, in the fast-descending gloom of an autumn dusk Anne and I loaded up the tiny boot with dead sticks for burning on the woodstove back home: the first of "our own" produce.

On our next visit we attempted a walk - or more accurately a scramble - along the boundaries. They say that "good fences make good neighbours", and my consulting work had shown me how boundaries and boundary trees can bring out the worst in people. Fortunately, the wood's rectangular shape meant that its boundary was relatively short in relation to its area, and the line of the boundary seemed in most places clearly defined, although fences were notable by their absence.

Much of our northern edge fronted the A272, the Main Road running east-west through Hadlow Down village, and this boundary was an overgrown and gappy agricultural hedge. Running down the east side, separating us from unkempt pasture, was a hedge of holly trees perhaps 10 metres tall. Also on that boundary stood what we quickly realised was the largest tree in the wood: a beech standing 35 metres high, which we unimaginatively christened the "Big Beech". Branchy, gnarled and romantic, the Big Beech is what most non-foresters like large old trees to be, although my initial reaction was to dismiss it as "just firewood". With beauty in the eye of the beholder, it was not long before our visitors remarked on its unruly splendour. Our southern edge had more boundary trees, mainly middle-aged oaks to which lazy farmers had over the years nailed fence wire, thereby ruining the lower trunk as timber.

Our west boundary mostly ran parallel with Wilderness Lane, and again was marked by large trees, many of them beech. Much of this western boundary was represented by a considerable bank a few metres from the lane, and I was relieved to note that the aging beech trees were growing on its western flank, and therefore outside our ownership. When, some years later, a couple of heavy limbs fell westwards towards the lane, it would be the responsibility of our neighbour to clear away their remains (and the liability for any damage or accident would have been theirs).

The village of Hadlow Down is in a typical Wealden hill-top location, draped over an east-west ridge at about 140 metres above sea level. Framed by tall boundary trees and the plantation along its highest, northern, edge, our south-facing valley of recently-cut coppices was pleasingly enclosed and self-contained visually - a quality we quickly decided to emphasise by our woodland management. We had seen many dank north-facing woods in our searches, but even in winter it was clear that ours was in a lovely sunny location; although the disadvantages of a ridge-top were to be demonstrated on the night of the Great Storm in October 1987, which we cover in its own chapter.

From the upper part of the wood we could catch tantalising glimpses of southerly views to the distant South Downs, beyond typical Wealden farmland – small hedged pastures, grazed or cropped for hay in a rather desultory way, and dotted with farmhouses and oasts. This quintessential landscape was the reason for the High Weald's Area of Outstanding Natural Beauty status, and we felt privileged now to be part of it. A few years earlier Anne had helped define its southern boundary, and Wilderness Wood lay solidly within it. Less well known than a national park, the High Weald AONB stretches from Horsham in the west to Rye in the east, and is predominantly, as the name suggests, on the high land between the North and South Downs. Its 1,450 square kilometres are almost 25 percent wooded - almost three times the national average. The wood we had bought was just one of many, and even the name "Wilderness" indicated how our forbears must have viewed it. With steep-sided valleys and poor soil, the land was hardly worth farming, but still very valuable as a source of timber, game and iron.

Our explorations revealed no completely flat land in the wood, and this would have implications for any roads or buildings we proposed. On the other hand, no slopes were too steep for forestry work. The geology map showed the underlying rock as "Upper Tunbridge Wells Sand", described as "mudstones, siltstones and silty sandstone". Two dotted lines on the map indicated beds of mudstone, which turned out to be a geological euphemism for sticky clay, with spring lines at these levels explaining the worst ruts in the tracks. Unfortunately, the site we would later choose for our house turned out to be just uphill from one of the spring lines. We soon realised that bogs along the lower spring line were waterlogged year-round, and it would obviously be sensible to zone these as "wildlife habitat", rather than try forestry there.

To Jo and Kate's disappointment, the only standing water in the wood was a tiny pool near the stream. This little stream, running down the lower half of the valley, was a popular spot for early explorations, and the girls had plenty of practical lessons in the relationships between height of welly, depth of water, and wet feet. I had designed several trout fishing lakes in the past, and was mentally putting time aside to carry out a topographic survey of the valley bottom, and working out how a fishing syndicate might fit into the overall scheme of things. Sadly, come spring, the water disappeared into the porous rock and the stream ceased to flow; we now realised why the stream wasn't marked on the Ordnance Survey map. We would have to abandon our idea for a stream-fed pond producing home-grown trout.

As winter gave way to our first spring, we were able to make more relaxed and comfortable visits to the wood, and the girls could be left for a while to play, with the security of our small tent as shelter in sudden showers. Green shoots started pushing up through the drab leaves of the woodland floor, and we began to discover what plants our woodland had to offer. The trefoil leaves and little white flowers of wood sorrel appeared here and there, and more extensive carpets of wood anemones, both signifiers of ancient woodland. Suddenly, in late April, there were pools of bluebells. Jo insisted on taking Granny back a bunch she had picked, which inevitably drooped before she received them with obvious delight.

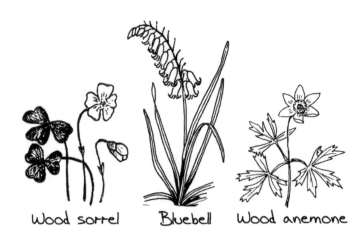

Wood sorrel　　Bluebell　Wood anemone

We roughly plotted the bluebell areas on our new map base. Their distribution turned out to be distinctly patchy, but no particular pattern emerged. Few of the bluebells were really lush, and their areas ended quite abruptly, for no apparent reason. We had already noticed patches of dead bracken fronds, and of heather, and as the year advanced these heathy species were joined by others, such as wood sage and the little yellow tormentil. With much of the coppice cut only a couple of years previously, in June there was a riot of foxgloves, whose seed had lain dormant in the soil, awaiting the sudden flood of light to germinate.

We invited David, our contact at the Nature Conservancy Lewes office, to come and have a look round, and he drew our attention to the bogs, the shady streamside mosses and liverworts (bryophytes), and a small heathy area, all worth protecting as comparatively unusual habitats. The heavy shade and poor soil permitted big patches of white cushion moss (*Leucobryum glaucum*) to spread between and onto the chestnut stools. We still use David's tip for remembering the moss's scientific name – a cushion for that Irishman, "Luke O'Brian". Chestnut, birch, pine, heather, bracken, struggling bluebells – all these indicated infertile and acid soils, and this impression was confirmed by a soil survey undertaken for us by Alan Furneaux, a soil scientist friend and colleague with long experience of Wealden soils. He told us that the Upper Tunbridge Wells Sands underlying the wood gave rise to poorly-drained soils of low fertility, which were the first to go out of production during downturns in the farming economy, such as the 1930's. At spring-lines and where water collected, we would probably find peat being formed, and our bogs and much of the relatively flat Top Plantation confirmed his prediction.

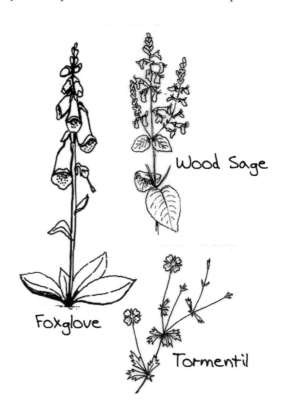

The best soil yielding to Alan's auger was in a shallow, east-facing bowl near the southern boundary, full of lush bluebells and growing some of the better chestnut. He suggested that this might be derived from wind-blown loess, dating from an inter-glacial period. But over most of the wood the thin, acid and impoverished soil would seriously limit the choice of tree species that we could successfully grow – although we would find, to our cost and frustration, that it allowed rhododendron seeds to flourish, blown in from neighbouring shrubberies. A soil test showed an extremely acid pH of 3.9 (a desirable "neutral" level is 7), with no measurable phosphate and little potash or magnesium. We wondered how anything managed to grow at all. Where rainwater could drain downwards, it would leach minerals from the upper layers, depositing them as a hard pan below the surface; this "podsolisation" process leaves a very acid layer of slow-to-decay leaves and twigs on the surface, typified by deep accumulations of needles under the pines, totally indigestible to any remaining earthworms. Traditional diagrams of trees show roots reaching deep into the ground, but the 1987 storm would reveal that our trees, like the majority elsewhere, were balanced on horizontal root-plates, their roots unable to penetrate the badly-drained and infertile rock below.

We would later also realise that one of the keys to plant growth in such inhospitable conditions lay in the toadstools that Anne noticed that first autumn, in an inviting and bewildering variety of colours, shapes and sizes. Her nascent fascination with fungi was certainly going to be nourished by owning Wilderness Wood.

Eager to construct a history for our new acquisition, we seized on clues to its past. Anne's imagination had been caught by Oliver Rackham's recently-published book *The History of the Countryside,* essentially a book about woodland history. He wrote of the physical clues to a woodland's past, and we spotted a massive bank and ditch on or near the northern and western boundaries, and smaller internal banks, which would have been topped by a fence to protect young coppice from deer and livestock. Medieval boundary banks? Who knows? That first winter, she made visits to the County Records Office round the corner from our Lewes house, and started researching the wood's history. It was clearly shown on a 1789 map with more or less its modern boundary, but her efforts ground to a halt when it became clear that earlier investigations would involve trips to London, and a working knowledge of Medieval Latin. The wood had evidently been used for a very long time; an early ferreting exercise with a father and son from nearby Buxted unearthed copious amounts of heavy cinders from a rabbit warren near the bottom of the wood, which the County Archaeologist identified as waste "slag" from an iron-smelting "bloomery" (simple charcoal-fired furnace), probably from Roman times. Further exploration revealed a second site, and a dig a few years later by the Wealden Iron Research Group found pieces of Romano-British pottery at both. Woods like ours provided iron ore and fuel for an industry crucial to the Roman Empire, and a significant reason for its occupation of the Weald, and one can scarcely walk in any wood in the High Weald without stumbling across iron ore workings.

A bank augmented to exclude deer and livestock

As well as the two bloomeries, several other flattened terraces showed up clearly on the winter woodland floor. We guessed that they were charcoal hearths, where kilns had been sited. This was confirmed by a villager who lent us a photo of charcoal-burning in the wood just after World War II. It was charcoal that fuelled the Wealden iron industry, from pre-Roman times to the water-powered valley furnaces and forges of Tudor times and later. Quite by chance, a friend researching the local iron industry came across several references to Wilderness Wood supplying (cart-)loads of "cole" (charcoal) to Heathfield furnace: in 1750 a Thomas Mallion sent 201 loads, "valued at 2 shillings and eightpence, with Tho. Fielder, a carrier".

Anne's efforts at historical research tailed off after a year or two, as our own personal Wilderness Wood story began to accumulate; although we did later devise a historical trail to celebrate the Millennium Year.

Both Anne and I find maps fascinating, and we pride ourselves as proficient map-readers. Anyone can make a sketch map, but as a tool for management, such maps might as well have "here be dragons" engraved, for all the use they are. Woodland management maps must be accurate enough to measure areas and distances. My consulting work often included mapping clients' trees, so making my own map daunted me not at all. With an Ordnance Survey map as a base (ancient enough to be out of copyright), I used a surveying compass and pacing to locate our other paths and tracks. We next added the boundaries of the various plantations, and other features in time fleshed out the picture: the Big Beech and other large trees, boggy zones, the small pond, notable concentrations of rabbit holes, boundary banks and bloomery sites. After trips to the wood, evenings would find me at the kitchen table plotting out the measurements with protractor and scale.

Such a survey with compass and pacing can be surprisingly accurate, and quite adequate for forestry purposes. On completing the one-mile circuit round the main rides, I found the "error of closure" to be less than five metres. In other words, through mud and other obstacles, my stumbles had brought me to within a few paces of where I calculated I should be. Over the years I added the boundaries of coppice cut each year ("cants"), and new paths and plantings, and this base map, plotted on an ever-frailer sheet of tracing paper, was an invaluable source of information, especially when it came to calculating areas. Recent advances in GPS map-making would cause present-day managers to throw up their hands at the time-consuming nature of this process, but it suited our means, and self-reliant approach.

Our predecessors may have had names for different parts of the wood and its tracks and paths, but existing maps offered no clues – just "Wilderness Wood". So we gradually invented names. The earliest were utilitarian rather than imaginative: West Ride, East Ride, Central Ride (a "ride" is a woodland track). We seized on any distinctive features: Holly Bank was a steep track with four large holly trees, Steep Hill, Stream Path, and so on. As the seasons passed, we added more: Bluebell Path was a narrow trail through a fine carpet of bluebells, and a grove of foxgloves in the sunlight of recently cut coppice suggested Foxglove Corner. The plantations gave structure and variety to the woodland, but we never got round to thinking up anything more imaginative than "Top Plantation" for the largest, and several of the smaller ones remain nameless to this day. Owl Wood plantation got its name from an early school visit, when the children had the excitement of disturbing a tawny owl trying to have a quiet nap overhead in a pine tree. Ant Wood commemorates an early attempt to introduce wood ants. These large ants build impressive nests of pine needles, and prey on insect pests of conifers, and we were told that there used to be wood ants in our plantations. Armed with a collecting licence from the Sussex Wildlife Trust, we descended on a nearby local nature reserve, shovelled part of a colony into a dustbin with a tight-fitting lid, tipped the dustbin onto a likely looking spot under the pines, and optimistically named the area "Ant Wood". A wood ant nest contains several queens, and the success of our colony would depend on whether we had managed to scoop up some of them. The ants did begin to build a mound of needles for their new home, but gradually their population dwindled, and evidently they lacked a queen to replenish their numbers. Thereafter we always seemed to be too busy to re-attempt the introduction, but Ant Wood it remains.

Each passing season added to the picture, and not until we had seen the wood through twelve months did we feel that it was really ours. Anne, an inveterate list-maker, started a notebook informally recording its plants, fungi, and birds, and this provides an invaluable reference for others interested in the wood's natural history. Never an ardent botaniser, I left Anne to her studies. It would soon be clear that there was an amazing variability in fungi from one year to the next, whereas the only variation in the bluebells and wood anemones was in their timing. In short, they stayed put. On the other hand, foxgloves appeared in full glory two years after coppicing, to be overtaken in subsequent years by brambles which were in turn suppressed by the shade of the growing coppice.

Only time would tell if we had bought a "Goldilocks" wood: not too small, and not too big. Its compact shape, easily-worked coppices, potentially valuable plantations, and ride system, would mean we could practise self-sufficient forestry. The beautiful setting and hilly landform boded well for attracting the visitors we would depend on for the success of our venture. Clearly it had been a productive woodland for many centuries, providing a changing range of valuable products, and now was our chance to make our mark. It looked as if it would suit us. But where should we start?

WHAT WE DID FIRST

ithin weeks of our purchase it was clear that we could no longer keep borrowing my parents' little Renault. We had lived in Lewes for eight years without a car, within easy walking distance of shops, office, school, grandparents and station. In a town developed on the human scale, centuries before the car, this anti-social personal transport was unnecessary, but modern life in the countryside was another matter, and we succumbed to acquiring a battered but practical Saab 95 to get to and from the wood.

Although in this first year we were still getting to know the wood, we lost no time in getting to work. To feel that we really owned it, we needed to begin making our mark, and patience is not one of my virtues. We would drive up from Lewes at weekends, bringing the girls and a picnic, park in one of the muddy entrances or on the verge by a gap in the front hedge, and, armed with billhooks and bow-saws, set about reclaiming the rides from the invading thickets of birch saplings. Perhaps everyone's reflex is to "do good" to a woodland by planting trees in it, and we were no exception. The trouble was that Wilderness Wood, like most others, was full of trees already. It was the winter planting season, and in our impatience we planted a few ride-side ash in the sunlight of recently-cut coppice. The absence of this species in and around the wood should have been a warning, and if we had waited for our soil survey we would have saved our efforts – most of the trees died, and the remainder lingered for a few years, little larger than when we planted them, overshadowed by the re-growing coppice and sulking in the unsuitable acid soil.

We had rather more success with wild cherries: a tempting proposition in that it's an attractive tree that can grow valuable timber within fifty years, given reasonably fertile soil and plenty of light. The cherries that we planted that first year in better soil may eventually be useful timber trees, and in the meantime provide a valuable demonstration to schoolchildren that trees have flowers.

Also that first winter we established our first Christmas tree plantation, putting little Norway spruce seedlings at one-metre spacing in an area of under-stocked and recently-cut coppice by the stream, and protected within a new rabbit-proof fence. The trees would start giving us an income in three to four years' time – instant riches, in forestry terms. At the same time we cut a path between the plantation fence and the stream, with the aim of creating a shady stream-side walk: the first new path to add to our map.

We set about improving our Main Road frontage by planting up gaps in the front hedge, using both nursery-grown hawthorn plants and seedlings of beech and holly scavenged from the wood. It was during this planting that Anne discovered a hibernating dormouse. She carefully returned the delicate ball-shaped nest to the base of the hedge and hoped for the best. Perhaps this was an ancestor of the animal whose furry tail was left on the doormat a decade later by Moss, our cat, which evidently had failed to read the dormouse protection legislation.

An obvious way to both make our mark, and start the wood paying its way, was to cut coppice. I already had a chainsaw and, like all new woodland owners, was dying to use it. Earlier experience in Lewes, where we had cut small poles on the Castle Mound behind our house, had shown that there was a ready market for bean-poles and pea-sticks, and so we set about cutting an area of five-year-old coppice with a high proportion of thin, drawn-up birch. Anne would trim off side branches with a light billhook, while I bundled and humped the produce to the roadside. The results of these efforts were transported on a groaning roof-rack back to Lewes, where we sold them from our house.

Anne wields a billhook to make our first bean-poles

We needed large quantities of string to tie up the bundles and so, with our ethos of frugality, scrounged loops of used hay-bale twine from a nearby farmer. We also made do with used fertiliser sacks for bagging logs. It was well into our second decade of ownership before we actually bought new twine, and commissioned, at 20p each, new fifty-litre sacks printed with our woodland logo.

The roadside was at least 120 metres uphill from the coppice cutting area, and the need for vehicle access into the wood was immediately evident. Although the exercise was good for both body and soul, it was inherently inefficient, and costly in time. Consequently, within weeks of purchase we acquired an ancient, small and cheap Zetor tractor, which theoretically had four-wheel drive but, as we soon found out, lacked a half-shaft to the front left wheel. With a logging trailer built from a lorry chassis by a local handyman, complete with gearbox to transfer power from the tractor to its wheels, we could now extract two tons at a time from almost anywhere in the wood, and extraction productivity increased hugely.

Within the year, with some part-time help, I had thinned out, or "stored", a twelve-year-old area of well-grown coppice at the bottom of the wood, measuring half a hectare. (Storing is a way of growing on coppice to larger sizes, and is explained in Chapter 11.) By carefully recording all the produce and the costs, I could show a net income of £650; when two years later we applied for planning consent for a house, we used this figure as part of our case that the wood could be viably worked.

In recent years, it has again been accepted that woods can provide other harvests as well as timber, just as they did down the centuries. For the first couple of years we collected chestnuts and sold them at the Lewes Women's Institute market, and sacks of bog moss to florists and wreath makers. When we created a picnic site in a clearing dominated by bracken, we had to remove up to 15 cms of accumulated bracken leaf-mould to uncover mineral soil where grass would grow; and this we sold as potting compost and soil improver to keen gardeners. But these early ventures soon tailed off, as we became too busy with other work, and also realised that we were in danger of stripping the wood of irreplaceable resources.

If you are going to market timber, you have to be able to get it to a location accessible to a large lorry. Lack of good access is one of the reasons that many woods are neglected. We had our tractor and trailer, and ride improvements were a next priority. Nowadays, especially on Forestry Commission land, rides are constructed with a substantial cambered base of stone and hardcore, and with verges wide enough to allow for stacking of timber, and for the sun and wind to dry the surface, and thereby strengthen it. Foresters are admonished to manage the verges of these wide rides for light-loving herbs and shrubs and associated wildlife such as butterflies, and to keep tall trees well back. But in a small wood such rides take a disproportionately large part of the area. Our rides were typical old-style ones - as narrow as possible, to avoid loss of valuable growing space. We didn't widen them, so that they continued to give the feeling of being inside and part of the woodland, rather than a road slicing through it. We reasoned that the beneficial effects of cutting ride-sides would be provided on a much larger scale by our coppice-cutting rotation.

In Wilderness Wood, it was only too apparent from the ruts that heavy vehicles had been driven straight across the underlying muds and silts in all weathers. Clearly, extraction had been carried out by contractors who had no long-term stake in the fabric of the wood, unlike employed staff, who could be redirected to other jobs until the rides were dry. To ensure year-round, all-weather access we urgently needed to repair and harden parts of our ride network. The well-drained and firm sections, underlain by rocky siltstone, remain unsurfaced to this day, but the stretches on mudstone and clay were impassable. Hardcore is expensive if you have to buy it, but also expensive to dispose of, and a "Free tip for clean hardcore" sign on the roadside soon produced results. We gratefully welcomed a farming neighbour with the remains of a piggery in his trailer, and the massive concrete blocks disappeared without trace into the deep ruts of the West Ride, transforming it into one of the firmest stretches in the wood. This approach was made illegal by the Waste Licensing Regulations of 1994, which turned a service useful to both parties into a costly, bureaucratic process. Over the years the tracks have swallowed countless cubic metres of hardcore, but it's like painting the Forth Bridge – just when you think it's finished, an exceptional storm erodes a gully, or the underlying hydrology mysteriously alters, and a previously well-drained section transforms into a quagmire.

Even before we bought the wood, our leanings towards self-sufficiency had brought us into contact with like-minded souls. From my office in Lewes, our friend Don Pynches was running an organisation called "Working Weekends on Organic Farms," which matched people wanting active weekends with smallholders who would give board and lodging in return for work. Started in Sussex in 1971, it now operates in about 100 countries and has been re-named as "World Wide Opportunities on Organic Farms." WWOOF was very much in the spirit of the times, and of Lewes in particular, and although we never used WOOFers, we fondly imagined that we too would find numerous volunteers only too happy to participate in our exciting venture. One couple helped us clear birch saplings which blocked a ride, in exchange for our double-digging raised beds on their unforgiving Weald Clay smallholding. A friend from university days helped fence and plant the streamside Christmas tree plantation, in return for the promise of Christmas trees to come. Emlyn and his family became regulars at the wood (his small and slight sons were renowned for the meals that they devoured to replenish their energies), and the path that they hacked through the Top Plantation to the western boundary was known as "Emlyn's Path", until obliterated by the Great Storm. And Anne's parents came down from Surrey at weekends to support their eccentric offspring by entertaining grandchildren on chilly picnics, and helping with bonfires. Sadly, no feature is named in their memory.

In our naivety, we assumed our enthusiasm would be shared by any who expressed an interest in our venture. We were quickly made aware of the real world when the village schoolmaster, at the end of a Saturday morning spreading fertiliser around little Christmas trees, asked what the hourly rate was. I had assumed that his enthusiasm stemmed from the desire to address his spreading waistline, or to share a pint at midday. Equally, a soft fruit farmer we met at the pub failed to jump at the free opportunity to try out his new flail hedge-cutter, and, quite rightly, quoted an appropriate hourly rate. We quickly learned that most work would have to be paid for.

One potentially useful set of helpers was the British Trust for Conservation Volunteers, a charity which still trains those interested in rural work. At that time the BTCV would organise weekend labour for suitable tasks, and all we had to do was to pay their transport and provide accommodation. That first spring, a dozen or so twenty-somethings arrived to sleep on the Village Hall floor and help us clear a hollow by the West Ride of scrub, dig out accumulated silt, and line it with heavy-duty polythene. Although this pond-restoration task was completed satisfactorily, it was immediately apparent that people with desk jobs lacked the muscle tone and stamina that we had by then built up. Furthermore, we had to pay a daily rate for the trained chainsaw operator to cut the scrub. Like most relative beginners, his output was low, and I concluded that paying a professional would be more cost-effective.

Our experiences at Balneath a few years earlier had cured us of any delusions that the local public would share our enthusiasm for opening our wood in a commercial way. We were only too aware of the alarm that would be spread by any mention of day trippers, and that the easiest way to fill any village hall, apart from the annual panto, is to start a group opposing development. Once local people had seen that we were not a front for a large housing or theme-park developer, we could gradually reveal our hand. In the meantime, we would discreetly draw up an overall plan to guide us through the next couple of decades.

We had looked at so many woods in the preceding years. In most of them I had mentally worked out how they might be developed to accommodate our ideas. At last we were on our very own patch, and with a blank sheet of paper in hand entitled "Proposed layout"! Now was the time to convince Anne that my two years in Montana, and the schemes for clients in the succeeding years, had not been wasted. Would my experience and insight lead me to a plan which would respect our ideals, conserve the best elements of the site, be attractive to our public, and, very importantly, be practical and economic in every sense? Lay hardcore or concrete, and you start to spend lots of money. Get them in the wrong place, and your mistakes sit there, reminding you of your foolishness and lack of foresight.

The design of any project, be it shopping mall or woodland park, depends not only the intended uses, but also on the management proposed. In other words, what sort of use, and who will run it? In a rural setting, the form and location of natural features have to be central to the planning process if the project is to fit into the site and make best use of it. My master's dissertation had covered design principles for recreation areas in US forests and parks, principles originally conceived when the Civilian Conservation Corps was put to work in the 1930's as part of Roosevelt's New Deal. They still guide matters such as access, site protection, and density of development for picnic sites, campsites, and viewpoints. I now had to make a thorough site appreciation, and get a feel for the spirit of the place. What would draw people to the site? How could you create appropriate car parking without cars dominating? If the demand for access began to exceed designed capacity, could the design accommodate extensions? An early lesson I had learnt in Montana was that layout must be devised on site, and then added to a map, rather than designed on paper and imposed on the ground. And all has to appear as if no planning has taken place, a process not far removed from the landscape design principles of Repton and Capability Brown.

We were secretly envisaging an enterprise with day visitors, school parties, perhaps a small campsite, and manufacture and sale of wood products, managed and supervised by ourselves living on site. Our layout needed access onto the Main Road with good sightlines, and, at its heart, a focal zone with car and coach parking, sales area, workshop, visitor building, and our house. We devised an outline layout for these major elements of infrastructure. The wood didn't have any particular focal point, so we would have to create one. We were very conscious that there was no open space in the wood, and its creation would be at the expense of trees and our wallet, for diggers and hardcore or grass did not come cheap. Many British hate the felling of any tree, but as a forester I had few qualms about felling plantation trees, especially in a wood with little natural history interest. Over the years I had planted thousands elsewhere, and, contrary to common misconceptions, the woodland area in England has increased greatly in our lifetime.

We aligned the planned entrance road in a gentle S-bend through the pines and beech of the Top Plantation, sweeping down at a steady one in ten slope to a 20-metre-square yard, with a spur off to the little picnic spot that we dreamed might become our house site. Workshop and visitor building would be around the yard, and beyond it small parking areas secreted among the trees, to limit their visual impact and give welcome summer shade. The sinuous bend of the entrance road would make sure that none of our planned developments would be seen from the highway, give a sense of exploration, and slow down vehicles.

Our concept included building a house and living on the spot. The house location would have to be convenient for us to manage visitors, as well as hidden from those who did not want to see it. Some people talk of the "good vibrations" of a location, and the ability to divine a safe and convenient place to settle would have had distinct evolutionary advantages. After only a few visits we knew where this would be - the place where we sat with the girls for our picnics and lunchtime fire, just at the edge of the Top Plantation, where the ground fell away to the south. The growing pines sheltered us from the Main Road and cold north winds, and there would be a view southwards once we had felled some coppice. This spot was about 100 metres into the wood – away from the traffic, but not too far for an entrance track.

It was always our intention to have school visits, so access by 56-seater coaches would be essential. Fortunately, the specification for coaches would be met by an entrance for timber lorries. Our existing tiny entrance in the north-east corner spewed straight onto the Main Road between high banks in other ownerships, with dangerously limited sightlines, and one could barely emerge safely with a baby buggy, let alone a car or larger vehicle. So there was no objection, even from the Highways Department, when in December we sought permission to create a new entrance for timber extraction in the centre of our northern boundary. I felled a six-metre-wide road alignment and the yard area, and cut the resulting timber into fencing lengths and firewood. Bonfires dealt with the tops. Once Peter, the excavator driver, had carefully spread the thin topsoil among the trees on either side, in came lorry-loads of hardcore, principally bricks from Grants Hill House in Uckfield, the last place Lord Lucan had been seen alive. We didn't notice any bones with the rubble! While Peter was on site, we got him to smooth off the knee-deep ruts in the West Ride, and to create a "by-pass" that moved the ride from where we hoped one day to make our garden. He also scraped the soil off a small car park below the site we had earmarked for a children's play area.

Within days of our new entrance being formed, we were in trouble with Joy, who drove a small herd of dairy cattle morning and evening along the Main Road – a very effective form of traffic calming. Where previously constrained by a roadside hedge, the cows could now wander as their curiosity took them, and although not accustomed to foraging in a pinewood, some clearly thought it worth investigating. I hurriedly strung some baler twine where the hedge had been, which served until we had time to erect a pole barrier across the new entrance road.

We resented driving even the twelve miles from Lewes, and longed to spend weekends at the wood. A farm is usually sold with all sorts of useful buildings, but Wilderness Wood was a typical woodland in having not even a tin shack. Over the coming years we would have to devote a good deal of effort and finance to creating shelter, but our first one typified our cautious attitude to spending money. For a few pounds we acquired an ancient four-metre-long caravan, which we installed on the spur track that would be the drive to our house. Although we quickly camouflaged it with a coat of mud-brown paint, it wasn't long before we were treated to a visit by the Enforcement Officer from the District Council, presumably tipped off by a suspicious walker. Fortunately he was easily persuaded that the caravan was the tool-store and wet-weather shelter for our woodland work, and therefore didn't need planning permission.

The caravan became our base for exploration, picnics, work-days and weekends, and the primitive log seats and barbecue in the mud in front of it were our first real colonisation. It came equipped with a small and leaky solid fuel stove, which we stuffed with firewood to take off the late winter chill. Brought up on "wild" camping, the girls fortunately weren't worried about using the pit latrine hidden in the pines (there should be several trees there showing particularly good growth!) A water butt collected rainwater from the roof; it was normally restricted to washing or to kettles for tea, although Anne did surreptitiously filter out the pine needles and offer it to thirsty schoolchildren on an early school visit. Lack of exposure to "dirt" is now thought to contribute to all sorts of allergies, and we were clearly ahead of our time.

Our first construction was a small lean-to of poles, built against the bottom of two conveniently located young pines on the west side of the yard, with sides of split poles and a shingled roof (tiles of split chestnut or oak). At first it was a tiny work shelter, soon superseded by the "Barn", as will be described in Chapter 6. Then it became a place to dry out firewood. Needless to say, three decades later this "temporary" structure was still in use, although we had to replace the pine trunks when they rotted at the base. It is only brick and stone buildings that have any chance of showing distant generations how we lived, and Nature reclaims most wooden structures if we turn our backs.

Looking back at the end of that first year, we had certainly begun to make the wood our own – we had cut coppice, planted trees, cleared rides, established an over-night base, and created a brand new entrance road and yard. These works would permanently determine how we further developed and used the wood, so we proceeded with caution, using our own resources as far as possible. With hindsight we should not have taken all incoming traffic past the Barn visitor building. As numbers increased, a conflict would develop between arriving cars and people on foot. Elsewhere, by spreading out the early elements of our development, we tried to leave enough space for a reasonable degree of flexibility. The touring camping site never materialised, and further car parks would in due course be required; but with the entrance track and yard we had, for better or for worse, set the seal on the future layout.

However, we could not do all that lay ahead by ourselves, and would come to rely increasingly on others to help us achieve the dream. No man is an island, let alone in a wood at the edge of a village.

THE VILLAGE AND
ITS WOOD

L and ownership brings many and varied responsibilities, which no doubt vary according to the customs of the locality. When we took over, several villagers told us how they had been taking advantage of an absentee landlord and the lack of fences to collect leaf-mould for their gardens and moss for hanging baskets, or cut bean-poles. Just a couple of weeks after the auction, I was exploring the wood when I heard the sound of a chainsaw. The man with the saw introduced himself as the owner of next door Tinkers Park, from which we had heard the hoots and whistles of traction engines a few weeks earlier. He was cutting up two-year-dead coppice wood as fuel for his steam engines, and assured me he did this with the previous owner's agreement. Taken aback, as there had been no mention of this in the sales particulars, I asked what other wood he thought he could lay claim to, and the gentleman proceeded to walk round the wood, pointing to scattered poles, some easily six years old. We intended using all such "waste" pieces as firewood ourselves, and needless to say our neighbour was none too pleased to hear that any such arrangement was now void. He stumped off, doubtless muttering about townies with no knowledge of country ways taking over the countryside: perhaps with some justification.

At about the same time, a small builder who lived across the Main Road invited us in for a coffee and to bend our ear. He wondered if we could do something about our fast-growing pines, which increasingly shaded his house in winter. In exchange, he revealed that we could make at least £4,000 out of a couple who had just moved into a cottage on the corner of Wilderness Lane, and whose septic tank drained onto the north-west corner of the wood. The right of drainage had apparently been limited to the previous occupants, and he informed us that an alternative arrangement would cost that sum. He knew this because he had built the soakaway on our land, and in the process had almost melted his digger bucket when he accidentally cut the village electricity main cable buried in the wood. It was not clear whether the estimate included the cost of another new bucket, and we did not probe. A couple of days later, just as dusk was falling, a police car stopped at our west entrance where I was loading firewood into the back of the car. I thought he might be apprehending me for theft, but it turned out to be the local bobby, whose parents had moved into the cottage with the soakaway, and were worried sick about the drainage predicament. We said we'd sort it out, and soon had amicably agreed a legal continuation of the arrangement, for a token sum and the lawyer's fee. The alternative solution was the sort that got landowners a bad name, even though we could have done with money to buy equipment.

The English are by nature reserved, but at the same time curious about any new neighbour. When I was a student in Montana, a newcomer would receive a welcome pack put together by voluntary groups, which would include information about all the churches, clubs and cultural groups in the town, as well as tokens from local businesses, and this would be delivered personally by some kind soul within days of arrival. In 1980's rural Sussex no such system operated, so we had to make our own efforts to get to know the community and, we hoped, be accepted before misapprehensions or negative rumours could circulate. A visit to the New Inn elicited from Dawn, the landlord's sister: "So you're the gentleman who's bought Wilderness Wood", which gave me the chance to introduce myself to her and the handful of lunchtime drinkers. Dawn had been at the auction a couple of weeks earlier, and I recognised the face. One of the drinkers introduced himself as the chairman of the Parish Council, and this seemed a God-given opportunity to explain who we were, and our plans. He invited us to say a few words at their next monthly meeting in the Village Hall. It was hard to tell at the time whether we made a good impression, but at least the councillors could see that, if we did have horns and a forked tail, they had been surgically removed or were well concealed.

It seemed Hadlow Down was giving us a cautious welcome, possibly because we confirmed at that meeting that we were happy for villagers to continue walking in the wood. Our closest neighbour at Old Boot Cottage in the north-east corner of the wood introduced himself as editor of the Parish Magazine, and invited us to contribute a monthly article. Inevitably villagers would have a keen interest in the wood, and we were on tenterhooks to present our true selves and gradually reveal our hopes to make Hadlow Down our home, forestalling any false conclusions that we might be money-grasping land speculators. The Balneath saga had taught us the importance of good public relations, and we jumped at this opportunity for free, positive publicity, although our enthusiasm for writing did wane after a couple of years.

When we told our Lewes friends that we had bought a wood in Hadlow Down, we found few had even heard of the village. Those that had would know it for the annual traction engine rally next door at Tinkers Park, or its only pub, the New Inn. This had been rebuilt after the original pub had burnt down in 1890, in red brick and stone gothic style, not unlike railway stations of that period. By 1980 it had been in the ownership of the Standen family for 68 years, and the present incumbent, Gerald, had run it for his sister

Dawn since the death of her husband. When we had first seen the inn several years earlier, it was far from clear that it was open; there was no pub sign, and the building appeared to be a victim of Dr. Beeching's cuts. Our initial reaction that bleak day was to fear the "PH" on our Ordnance Survey map was like the Python parrot, but to our surprise we found a warm welcome, which was repeated when we re-appeared as new landowners. One Sunday morning during that first December, I was map-making at the wood and called in at the New Inn for a beer, to warm myself, and to enquire whether there was a taxi service in the village to take me to the bus stop four miles away. Gerald replied that there was no taxi, but that, if I presented myself at the back door at four o'clock, he would run me there himself. Not only did this publican put himself out on a Sunday afternoon, but he steadfastly refused any payment for his troubles.

The New Inn

The Parish Magazine had recently published the results of a survey of residents' views of how the village might be improved - in the same issue announcing that Hadlow Down would not be entering the Best Kept Village competition. Several respondents had commented that the New Inn did not cater for a wide range of clientele. No carpet, chairs, food, wine, or ice, and decor that did not appear to have been refreshed since Gerald had come back from the RAF. An apocryphal story had it that a public health inspector had complained of a piece of the ceiling falling into his beer. As the pumps did not work, barrels stood on the bar, and therefore the pub was listed in the Good Beer Guide, despite lack of other amenities such as a ladies loo. One freezing winter's day, a customer complained the bitter was too cold. Pointing to the bar on which the barrel stood, I remarked "Don't complain; it's at room temperature". A landlord with no sense of humour might have taken this the wrong way, but by this time Gerald and I had each other's measure.

Pub hours were never enforced too strictly, and, if open, Dawn or Auntie Kit had the midday shift. At lunchtime or after "tea", the honest sons of the soil called in for refreshment and in winter to warm up in front of the blazing fire. From them you could find the name of a chimney sweep or ferreter, or be advised who could move a caravan, cut a hedge, or might be interested in a bit of coppice work for cash in the pocket. Fortunately for us, the surrounding area was dominated by poor land, with small farmers who struggled to make a living and were happy to lend each other a hand; unlike richer farming counties such as Oxfordshire, with its large estates and agri-business. Despite our inevitably middle-class accents, our neighbours didn't appear surprised at seeing us work the land with our own hands.

Set astride the ancient boundary between the parishes of Buxted and Mayfield, the parish of Hadlow Down is a relatively recent creation, and few of the village buildings are more than 150 years old. In the days when roads were little more than sunken muddy tracks, our wood must have been relatively remote, and rightly deserved the name Wilderness. Yet now it was right up against a village, with houses scattered along its boundaries of Wilderness Lane and the Main Road. Surprisingly, there were no public rights of way through the wood, but, with entrance tracks at opposite corners, plus other less obvious points of entry through gaps in hedges, the wood was a popular place for locals to walk or play. Early on we met Helen and her brood of three youngsters, the smallest still in his baby buggy. We were up for the weekend, and discovered the absence of coffee in our provisions. I can go without many luxuries, but freshly-brewed strong coffee is not one of them. Helen, who had been in catering, fully understood, and was back later that Saturday afternoon with enough for several pots. She lived in a cottage on Wilderness Lane and had created a path from it through the bluebells, which naturally became known as "Helen's Path".

Many of our first encounters were with dog-walkers, accustomed to taking advantage of a handy, unsupervised exercise area. We had many a friendly chat with Joyce, walking her dog Barnie. Her late husband had run a small bakery in the days when the village had several shops, and had spent evenings badger-watching in the wood, enticing them to suitable photo-opportunities with Maltesers. One day soon after we had moved in, Anne was conducting a group of small schoolchildren along Emlyn's Path when suddenly she and the teacher spied four large Alsatians bounding towards the group. "Freeze!" was Anne's instruction, and, when they had rushed past, the teacher drolly remarked he didn't realise wolves existed in England. These belonged to Alsatian breeder and owner of the riding stables opposite. When requested to keep them on a lead or exercise them on her own land, she retorted she had horses there. "And I have children on *my* land".

More to our liking was Christina, who would visit almost daily with her Scottie, Charlie, sometimes more often than she had planned. Charlie was wont to roam, and on a calm evening we knew he was abroad when dulcet cries of "Charlieeeeee" wafted up from the depths of the wood. One evening we found Christina sitting in her car at 11pm at our Wilderness Lane entrance, awaiting his return. An indomitable spinster in her eighties, Christina on one occasion tripped in our drive and split her scalp, so we summoned an ambulance. Muttering about the unnecessary fuss, she discharged herself from hospital the next day, to make sure Charlie had his afternoon walk. We were clearly not the only independent spirits in Hadlow Down!

These encounters made us realise just how much we had to learn. The wood had clearly been enjoyed as a local amenity, perhaps from time immemorial, and we had no intention of going down in history as the first owners to exclude others. We were keen to build up goodwill, and also reasoned that each sympathetic local was an honorary warden who would keep an eye open for any problems such as fire, vandalism or dumping. When later we had added a tea-room, dog walkers would sometimes buy a coffee, but the main benefit to us was non-monetary, in the form of their support and unpaid vigilance. They even reported to us there were "men with guns" early one morning, and we were in a quandary whether we should announce when our deer-stalkers might be present. As experienced stalkers they would never put the public at risk, but could have done without the disturbance. As well as the good public relations it achieved, allowing free admission to villagers did qualify us for a small annual management grant from the Forestry Commission.

Some Hadlow Downers would in due course show their appreciation and support by buying a season ticket, even though they had free admission as villagers. Others were less generous. A lady who drove in several mornings a week and made off down the track pursuing a couple of Labradors, objected to being asked if she would like to buy a season ticket, then costing the princely sum of £12. "I thought local people were allowed in free." We established that she lived in the next village of Five Ashes. "In that case, you're not local." "You can't discriminate like that."

"I can, I'm the owner." "Well, you won't be seeing me again". *"Tant pis"*, thought I. It was, however, a lesson that there were all sorts of people out there, and we should have to get along with them if we were to prosper and stay in business.

Being in the centre of the village, walkers were not the only locals to take advantage of the opportunities offered by the wood. Children must have played there for generations, as demonstrated by grotesquely enlarged initials carved in the bark of the Big Beech. Mirroring the camp-building we would later organise for visiting parties, local children made dens deep in the wood, and we were delighted that they should be exercising in the open air and not stuck in front of a TV. Jo and Kate were less happy, resenting the presence of others in "their" wood, and naturally upset when they found their secret dens had been discovered. As a child I had roamed free and made campfires with other lads and, on one infamous occasion, even tried to hit passing cars by rolling chalk boulders onto the road below a vertiginous slope. Children have little sense of danger and its consequences. So when, one windy March evening, I discovered two youngsters with a campfire close to dry bracken, rather than reading the riot act it seemed appropriate to make clear the dangers of lighting a fire where the flames could so easily spread.

The play equipment on the village playing field had been demolished on safety grounds, so our rudimentary adventure playground would become popular, not just with the under-tens for whom it was designed, but also as a place to "hang out" for young teenagers. We accepted this, as the village, along with many communities, lacked amenities for that age–group; although in due course we imposed a 6pm curfew when rowdiness and foul language threatened to disturb the peace of a summer's evening for both ourselves and near neighbours. Every landowner has to accept a fair share of minor vandalism. We sadly had to ban one young lad for a week or two after we found him disconsolately sitting across the top of the climbing net, hacking through the top rope with his penknife. Thoughtlessness, or vandalism, neither we nor he could decide.

In due course we would have a small souvenir shop, and from time to time noticed that local children were helping themselves to the pocket money toys or cookies on display. One of our own offspring had briefly shown similar tendencies when we still lived in Lewes, so we realised that this did not presage a local crime wave; but had to make a rule that unaccompanied children were not allowed in the shop. This became increasingly an oxymoron, as parents were ever more fearful of letting their children out of sight. The modern parent, we thought, was far too protective and risk-averse. The mother of two of Jo's friends didn't like the idea of her girls playing in our wood on the grounds that they might meet unsavoury characters; to which I retorted that the only dirty old man they were likely to meet was me! Another near neighbour refused to let her daughter sleep out in her garden after an incident the previous day in Cheshire, 250 miles away, on the grounds that a rapist was about. More sensible parents let their children roam in the comparative safety of our wood, where the biggest danger was running into a tree or falling over a stump.

Woods must always have been a convenient place to dump rubbish, and our early explorations unearthed a Victorian rubbish tip with a rich vein of bottles. It would have been so easy to back a truck into the entrance and dump the odd sofa or 'fridge, but we were fortunate to be spared a single incident of fly-tipping; presumably a higher level of surveillance was assumed than was actually the case. When recycling became fashionable, the District Council sited collection bins in the car parks of compliant supermarkets and pubs. The New Inn could not boast a car park, so in Hadlow Down the Wilderness Wood entrance was an obvious location for such a facility, with good access for both private cars and the large vehicle that periodically emptied the bottles into its maw with a resounding crash. We received no rent or even thanks, but gained goodwill and a free outlet for our extremely limited quantities of recyclable "trade waste".

Villages throughout Europe have been losing their shops for decades. By the time we arrived, Hadlow Down had only a small village store next to the pub, a tea-room opposite, and a tiny place selling nothing in particular which soon closed down with nobody noticing. The village store closed soon after the Post Office removed its franchise, at much the same time that the tea-room briefly reopened and closed down again: to general consternation, particularly of the elderly, as the village had lost two places for people to meet and chat. We made a site available at the wood's entrance for a Portakabin-based shop, complete with Post Office licence. The enterprise might have thrived had its owner had his heart in it, but a small store selling only convenience food will not survive, especially if it does not stock what customers want. Delicatessen and local produce sales can be the salvation of village stores, but ours somehow did not want to be saved, and closed within months, its site becoming a useful extra car-park for the wood. Perhaps at some future date there may be scope for a shop in combination with the wood's other functions.

Once we had moved to the wood, it wasn't long before we were approached to help with village organisations and events. With a business open seven days a week, and not a natural joiner, I managed to avoid these advances, but Anne was soon roped in to help with school, church and parish council. Inevitably we met the same people running many activities; folk who could be relied on to do the catering, circulate posters, put out and restack the chairs, and all the tedious tasks associated with any event. Such people were termed "village-minded" by a redoubtable spinster, and chair of the village hall committee, who first made us conscious that there were those living in the village solely because they could have a nice house with a large garden from which to commute. Not only did they not participate, they failed to patronise pub, shop or wood. One such couple visited the wood and we asked how far they had travelled. Much to our surprise, we learned they were from Hadlow Down and had lived there ten years. Perhaps we were the first people in the village they had spoken to.

The girls needed no persuading to join in the village variety show each autumn, be it ballet, singing, or can-can, along with other pupils from St Mark's School. For several years we hosted the school PTA summer barbecue in the picnic area, which had the advantages of a sheltered location, adjacent play area, space to dance and ample parking. Such is the quietness of the village that some anonymous curmudgeon saw fit to complain about the band's sleep-destroying noise at the dissolute hour of 9.30 on a Saturday evening.

Land ownership affords the freedom to indulge one's whims, and it is a privilege to allow the same to others. In 1984 we were approached by a Hadlow Downer who was by then resident at a local retirement home, and wished to plant some fifteen trees to commemorate people he had admired in the village. A nice gesture, as fewer than half at that stage had departed to the arboretum in the sky. We therefore established the Grove, and it harbours the fastest-growing trees in the wood, namely four coast redwoods. Growing at a metre a year, they soon dwarfed and suppressed the slower-growing walnut and Atlas cedars that we were persuaded to plant as well. Our other mistake was to plant the trees only three metres apart, giving inadequate space for them all to grow to maturity

It did not take us long to appreciate our good fortunate that Wilderness Wood was located in a village such as Hadlow Down. Our neighbours appeared, for the most-part, aware of the needs of a working countryside, and we sensed that our proposals would be more readily accepted than in some prettier village, where the ethos would be to preserve the status quo. It seemed, too, that we could contribute something to the community, so embarked on our plans with high expectations.

A HOUSE IS CONCEIVED

Most people with any experience of the planning process express utter amazement that we ever got permission to build a house in the wood. Looking back, we share their surprise and bless our good fortune, for it was part of the dream to build a dwelling to our own design and to live on the spot.

Housing is in great demand and expensive in rural Sussex, as the scenery is lovely, and London within easy commuting range. The High Weald Area of Outstanding Natural Beauty had been designated a few years earlier. Wilderness Wood was definitely two miles within it, and outside the Hadlow Down official "village envelope" for development. There was a strong presumption against new houses in the countryside unless absolutely necessary for agriculture or forestry, and past experience of farm-workers' cottages sold off with a few acres, and later extended for yuppy use, had jaundiced local planning officers against even the most genuine-sounding of planning applications.

But we had formulated a plan that, with luck and a following wind, would lay the foundations for getting planning permission for a house. At Balneath we had naively laid our cards on the table, but were viewed as suspect strangers. Our strategy this time was first to get known in the village as amiable and well-meaning eccentrics, and to demonstrate that we would use appropriate good design.

It took us a couple of years to get to know and be known by the village, and also to imbibe a feel of the wood. Finding a location in our 24 hectares that would be agreeable to the authorities was crucial, but we had the luxury of selecting a spot that also felt right to us. Our early picnics had gravitated to the southern edge of the pine and beech Top Plantation, where the coppice-covered land started falling away. Get rid of some of the coppice, and there must be a lovely view southwards.

We already had an entrance road into the Top Plantation and a yard for forestry purposes, so there could be no objections to a house on access grounds. It is a truism in English culture that something matters less if you can't see it, and this applies as much to a rural building as to fornication. Our road frontage was bordered by a hedge and a dense plantation, and any structure more than 50 metres into the wood would be totally hidden from the road. The deliberate curve of the entrance drive obscured any clear view of the yard, and after a season's leaf-fall, the drive was just another inconspicuous woodland entrance, with its simple pole gate and padlock to deter unwelcome vehicles. We next had to build up a case for living on the spot, and in a manner that few could object to on aesthetic grounds. Time to show our style and start building!

Our first structures had been a caravan and a lean-to shelter, but before long we needed a proper workshop and a larger store. Small agricultural and forestry buildings were exempt from planning control, so we could erect our first "proper" building without bothering the Planning Department. It would have been very simple to put up a prefabricated concrete farm building, but that would have done nothing for the appearance of the village, or our own credentials. We intended that this building would show both planners and public that we were going to do things well. It was always our ambition to use the site's resources as far as possible, not so much from a determination to live the pre-industrial life, but to demonstrate how our forbears used what was at hand, before the days of cheap transport and factory-made components. A traditional barn would be an ideal teaching resource, and an attractive and interesting building for future visitors. We wanted an iconic building which would be their first port of call, and would set the tone for everything else we did. In keeping with our penchant for thrift and self-sufficiency, we would do as much as we could by the sweat of our brow.

Visits to the Weald and Downland Museum north of Chichester, to see re-erected old timber-framed buildings, together with a little reading of basic books on timber buildings, had inspired us to have a go at constructing a simple timber-framed barn. We engaged an architect friend to draw up the plans, based on design principles used in the Weald from Medieval times to the early nineteenth century: a prefabricated oak frame, divided into three bays and held together with mortice and tenon joints.

While we were searching for our long-term wood, we had bought a share in a small one near Tunbridge Wells. This had a good supply of suitable medium-sized oaks much in need of thinning, and we had no trouble getting a Forestry Commission felling licence to secure the trees we needed for our barn. These I felled, and dragged to the wood's entrance with our small Zetor tractor. That tractor was without doubt unroadworthy, without rear lights, indicators and much else. At that time countless similar wrecks slunk around the back lanes, enabling a low-capital rural economy to survive. Legal or otherwise, the biggest risk was that the battery or starter motor would be "liberated" when the tractor was unattended. So I drove the 15 miles early one Saturday morning, extracted the twenty logs to the wood's entrance, and retreated back to Hadlow Down that same day, glancing over my shoulder periodically, as there was of course no rear mirror. To lend a hand, and rescue me in the event of a breakdown, Anne's dad followed in his old Citroen. A few days later a timber lorry with built-in crane loaded the logs, and within an hour they lay neatly piled beside the yard at Wilderness Wood, ready for preparation.

The timbers of the frame would originally have been squared up from tree trunks with axe and adze. We cheated. Using a simple mill I had read about in a Canadian manual, and constructed by Ben, our resourceful Lewes blacksmith, I squared up each log with a chainsaw. The saw was clamped to an inverted metal U section, which slid along a length of softwood joist nailed to the log. Once the first slab had been removed, you simply rotated the log and nailed the joist to the flat surface, and so on around all four sides.

Progress with this system is slow, noisy and boring, not to mention the hazards of two-stroke fumes and dust. Perhaps my poor hearing and tickly chest date from that time. A more satisfying process was removing the worst of the chainsaw marks with an adze. This tool is similar to a planting hoe, but with a chisel-sharp edge; you stand on the beam swinging it towards your feet, taking off small chunks with a satisfying split-clunk. In the interests of toe conservation, I thought it wise to don steel-toe-capped boots rather than my usual sandals.

It was not necessary to delve in dusty barns to find out how they were built. A wealth of practical information on design and construction, including detailed joints, was available in various craft publications. Of the joints illustrated, perhaps the most satisfying was the intricate "tie beam lap dovetail" at the top of a main post, where the post, tie beam, wall plate and principal rafter all meet, and are held in place by gravity and a single oak peg. Our barn dimensions were determined by the length of the beams we could cut from our trees. Three bays would give us a total length of 11 metres. Tie beams linking front and rear walls gave us a comfortable span of four and a half metres, and the resulting building would be a useful size for a variety of purposes.

The tiebeam of the lap dovetail joint is lowered
by our tripod crane (out of sight)

Fortuitously, Raymond, the carpenter son of the village
storekeeper, was at that time restoring an eighteenth-century
timber barn on the Downs, so was already familiar with traditional
jointing techniques. He quickly tidied up my rough chainsaw
mortices, and soon we were laying out complete bays in the yard.
With the precise dimensions confirmed, Brian, a builder who
specialised in groundworks because his vertigo precluded ladder-
work, could build the brick footings.

Anybody who saw the film in which the hero seeks refuge in
an Amish community where they raise a barn in a single day, will
appreciate how quickly a timber frame can rise, given sufficient
manpower, and homely women with baskets of cookies and ginger
beer. We had none of these, but somehow heaved each bay vertical,
and used a pole tripod and light block and tackle to lower the tie

beams into place. A photo shows a couple of centimetres of snow on the beams as, perched on ladders, Raymond and I nudge a rafter home with the sledgehammer. No wonder the building trade is in the same accident league as mining and forestry, and our barn folly might easily have been my memorial.

With the walls up, raising the roof was a simple matter of fixing the principal rafters to wall plates and ridge-board, and nailing common rafters in between. These latter were, true to the intended rustic look, simply cleft chestnut rails, normally used for post-and-rail fencing; they gave an "interesting" wavy profile, onto which we nailed battens of half-round chestnut. To shed the rain, we then made and nailed on about four thousand oak and chestnut "shingles." Shingles are among the oldest forms of roofing, particularly common in well-wooded parts of the world such as the Alps and North America. I learned how to make them from a book produced by a teacher in the Appalachians, who had his pupils record the rural techniques of their grandparents. Along with spinning wool and making soap from tallow and wood ash, they described the technique for shingle making. Roundels of timber 12–18 inches long are cleft into slices with a "froe" and mallet. A froe is a long metal wedge with a wooden handle at one end, and Ben the blacksmith quickly forged us one from an old car-spring. Chestnut and oak are ideal for shingles because they cleave well and their heartwood is naturally rot-resistant; though it subsequently turned out they were not durable enough for our humid woodland conditions, exacerbated by the coating of leaves and pollen from surrounding trees. We had expected them to see out our tenure, but twenty-five years later I was again up on the roof replacing them all, helped by George, an architectural student and part-time ranger at the wood.

So now we had the skeleton of a building – impressive timber frame, attractive and unusual roof, and beaten earth floor. To keep out the worst of the weather we nailed weatherboarding, milled from our own pine trees, to the back and the southern end, and began to make use of it as our workshop, store, and wet-weather shelter. Rustic yet functional, our barn should be a convincing demonstration that we intended to do things properly.

The Barn as workshop

To reinforce authenticity, we in due course clad the front and north walls with traditional wattle and daub; wattle woven from hazel rods that we cut from a neighbour's wood, as we had little in our own, and daub concocted from a mixture of earth, lime, chopped straw and fresh cow muck. We didn't get round to this until the girls were at the village school, and invited Kate's class to assist.

Each child started with rubber gloves and a trowel, but, needless to say, bare hands were soon applying this smelly slurry direct. We learned from Kate that one boy insisted on being fed his breakfast next day because his hands still smelt so bad, despite several washes. A photo and article in the Brighton Argus newspaper provoked an angry phone-call that all the children would succumb to typhoid or similar. Fortunately, a GP friend was prepared to inform our caller that cow muck was a traditional wound treatment, though I doubt whether his Royal College would have backed his claim had he been challenged. It was another lesson in unintended consequences from publicity, and how to deal with any fallout.

With the barn up, it was now time to embark on our plans for the house we so dearly desired. Metaphorically, a house resembles a living thing. It is composed of dust, and to dust it returns. In the meantime it lives, shelters its parasitical lodgers, hosts diseases of all sorts, and eventually decays. With good genes, soundly constructed of wholesome ingredients, and well cared-for, its life may extend far beyond our human three-score years and ten. The analogy will be even more apt if and when "designer babies" become a reality, for it is possible to design a house in any style, and for us this was a welcome freedom.

Had we set about house-raising ten or more years earlier, our baby would have been modern in the extreme, with floor-to-ceiling windows, abundant stainless steel, and the latest technology we could afford. But Ronan Point had spectacularly collapsed in 1968, and with it the architectural dreams of a brave new world. Modernism had literally fallen from fashion, and even we were more influenced by the zeitgeist than we might care to admit. A friend suggested an underground house, cut into the hillside – an early "Grand Design"; and today we would certainly build an "eco-house." But by 1982 the cult of neo-vernacular was waxing strong, and even supermarkets were sprouting clock-towers. The Balneath

Wood saga had confirmed the inherent conservatism of the rural middle classes; if we were to stand any chance of getting consent, our dwelling would have to appear as though it had always been there. Despite there being a variety of house styles in the vicinity, from Medieval to modern, "traditional rural" would clearly be least offensive. We toured East Sussex and Kent, photographing appropriate houses of the type we envisioned. They had in common tiled roofs, a brick ground floor, and a first floor of white-painted weatherboards on a timber frame. Weatherboarding suited us well, for a forester wants to use as much timber as possible, and to have it on show. In many cases, the roof continued down at the rear as a "catslide", to give a larger ground floor.

By this time we were discussing designs with Nick, an architect friend who had recently built himself a house a few miles away. He was enthusiastic about the design efficiencies of the traditional barn shape, partly on the grounds that roofs are cheap to construct compared with walls. His house had catslides front and rear, apart from a barn-door-sized window in the middle of the south side. Our house was devised on similar lines: orientated precisely east-west to make maximum use of the sunny southerly aspect, with large windows to the south to capture the sun's warmth, and a catslide and small windows on the north side. The interior echoed Wealden house layouts from Medieval times, with a central hall open from floor to roof ridge, living quarters on either side, and bridges linking across the central space. It only lacked an open fire in the middle with smoke finding its way through the roof, and minstrels in the gallery!

Architectural plans and sketches were drawn up. We knew the District Council planning officers would not support our application. Our site fell outside the zone prescribed for development, and they were unwilling even to visit the site to see its merits or hear our case. With many planning appeals as an expert witness under my belt,

I knew that they would have to be out-manoeuvred. At Balneath, we had omitted cultivating locals or the planning committee. This time we believed the village to be on our side, and this left only the committee. So, when submitting the application in October 1982, we also wrote to each councillor, outlining our dream and explaining why we needed to live on the spot. With the children tucked up in bed, Anne spent a whole evening drafting and re-drafting the letter in the attic office of our Lewes house. When I complained that she was taking a very long time, she retorted that "This letter may be worth £25,000" – the value of a building plot at the time. Our planning application was accompanied by a carefully worded statement of intent, which read: "We intend to manage Wilderness Wood as a family business, making full use of its potential for timber and wood production, its conservation interest and its educational value.... If managed in this intensive and intricate way, and with conversion of material produced into more valuable items, direct sales to the public and educational visits by the public, the woodland will provide the livelihood for a family and employment also for several part-time workers". This public declaration was an accurate version of what we were actually hoping and intending – although, apart from in an educational context, it deliberately avoided mention of the visitors we were hoping to attract.

Three days later, at a carefully chosen time in the evening, we 'phoned each councillor to ask if he or she had any queries that needed clarification. In most cases, they thanked us for the trouble we were taking to explain what was a complex and novel proposal. Our tactic at this point came from observing my father, who for years had been a town and district councillor in Lewes. We knew that part of a councillor's job was to be available to his constituents, and had noticed Dad was most amenable after recharging the batteries with supper and first drink of the evening.

Those chats at the New Inn now paid off. Early on, one local drinker, Geoff, had asked me to guess what he might do for a living, and, when I suggested used car salesman, he had fortunately thought "What a wag!" It turned out that in his spare time he was Leader of the council, and he spoke vigorously in our support, together with another councillor we had met socially two years previously, who was independent in both thought and political allegiance, and liked our application. The two of them convinced the rest of the committee to visit the site, despite the officers' protestations.

Working woods in February seldom resemble a picture postcard, and ours was no exception, with its mud, piles of semi-processed wood, and flapping polythene on the half-finished barn. Wishing to show we would be a thoroughly respectable addition to this Tory-led district, we tidied the place as best we could, and had tea and biscuits at the ready to ward off the day's chill. The committee properly and politely refused both tea and offers of further information, and we lurked in the caravan, willing them to award appropriate Brownie points for our lovely proto-barn.

Consultations with authorities such as the Nature Conservancy and Forestry Commission had produced sympathetic, but non-committal, replies. The County Highways Department could raise no objections, as we had our new access road, but the County Estates Department gave our application the thumbs-down, on the basis that 24 hectares of woodland would not produce an adequate income for a family. They could not foresee the commitment we were willing to make, or perhaps were unable to imagine someone voluntarily choosing such an arduous lifestyle. Years later, representatives of the County Council brought a Spanish delegation of rural planners to visit the wood, proudly showing us off as a shining example of rural diversification. When I sardonically pointed out to the assembled experts that we had received no encouragement from their hosts, the councillors lamely explained that they hadn't appreciated what we intended.

Anne attended the final planning committee meeting a few weeks later, while I completed a tree-planting scheme for a client in a nearby village. It was the men on the committee who were carried away by our proposal. Geoff suggested every village needed a couple of genuine eccentrics, and an elderly bloke mused that every time he drove through Hadlow Down he wondered if anything took place there, and now was their chance to make something happen. A lady councillor complained it was their sex that was normally accused of being emotional, and the men should listen rationally to the planning arguments.

Anne sped the ten miles to where I was exhaustedly planting the last few trees on that bleak March afternoon. Today, a mobile 'phone call would relay the amazing news that emotion had carried the day. We had been given full approval, subject to a "Section 52 Agreement" limiting occupancy of the house to someone engaged in, or retired from, forestry or agriculture, and preventing ownership of the house being separated from the land of Wilderness Wood. They weren't just tears of sweat that streaked my face. At best, we had expected to be made to live in a caravan for some years to show our commitment; at worst, a fifty percent chance of approval on appeal. Never people to go overboard, it is unlikely we had more than a celebratory pint of Harveys that evening, and my mother said something like "That's nice, dear", just as she had when I 'phoned to say I had passed my degree exam, eighteen years earlier.

With permission to build a home in the wood, we could now nail our colours to the mast, and definitely make Wilderness Wood our future. Until this moment our wood had been little more than a rather time-consuming hobby. Our patience and careful planning had paid off, combined with not a little luck, and we could embark on the next stage of our lives.

OUR HOUSE : GESTATION, CONFINEMENT AND BIRTH

O ne of the phrases from school French that stuck in my mind was *"On a fait bâtir une maison"*, which translates as "One had a house built". This conjures up in the mind some businessman of the Belle Epoque consulting an architect about a plot by the Seine, on which he wanted to erect a symbol of his wealth and married state. A builder would be appointed, and at periodic intervals Monsieur et Madame would visit, accompanied by the architect, to view progress and discuss the arrangements.

In contrast, our process was to be a "self-build", and we would do as much of the work as time and abilities permitted. Knocking three derelict cottages into one ten years earlier, helped by a small builder, had given us a taste for the work and a passing knowledge of the building process. It was therefore with relief that we heard that Mr. Gander, our Lewes builder, was prepared to come out of retirement and act as clerk of works. He found the necessary tradesmen - brickie, carpenter, plumber, etc. - and agreed payment rates on our behalf. Most work was on a day rate against realistic estimates.

Exact siting of the house was a balance of several factors. Too far north, and the ground would require excessive excavation.

Too far south, and we would lose the side protection of the plantation. We compromised in the case of one fine young beech, moving the house two metres southwards in order to retain it. During our time it trebled in diameter to 40 centimetres, but will probably not be commercially harvestable until at least 2050 - assuming its leaves in the roof gutters do not condemn it prematurely.

Once details had been agreed with the Building Inspector, we set about the ground works in July 1983, with a large digger lifting the thin topsoil from the house footprint and spreading it over the area of our future garden. Kate, by then a five-year-old tomboy, relished being allowed to sit in the cab while Peter, who had previously built the drive and Barn footings, effortlessly swung half tonnes of soil about. In no time, the site was level and foundation trenches dug, and, when checked with a surveyor's level, found to be correct within a couple of centimetres. Peter could have scraped the skin off a rice pudding with that machine.

With digger on site, it made sense to install the septic tank and drainage. We had coppiced an area below the house site that spring to create a small field, and Peter dug out the stumps and installed the soak-away for the septic tank, in the form of a long french drain zig-zagging down the slope. The field was extended when we cleared the lower paddock a few years later, and eventually provided enough grazing for three ewes and their offspring. With the dry, dusty conditions of that July, we wondered if grass would ever grow in the unpromising and compacted ground. Peter located water, electricity and telephone in a single trench alongside our drive from the Main Road. Although many roots were cut quite close to pine trees, none blew over, despite warnings against this practice in the arboricultural guides of the day. Either we were lucky, or the trees hadn't read the British Standard. Peter also cleared the ground for a vegetable garden and small orchard.

In the United States, a significant proportion of the population lives in mobile homes. Apart from wealthy retirees who migrate between Canada in the summer and the desert South-west in the winter, many are too poor to afford normal houses, and live in varying degrees of comfort or squalor in trailer (caravan) parks, earning the unfair sobriquet of "trailer trash". When that September we sold our beloved Lewes home of ten years and moved into a caravan, the thought that the Yarrow family might be joining the semi-homeless never crossed our minds; which is not to say that it didn't occur to Anne's parents, who lived at the smarter end of Woking in Surrey. For us it was purely a money-saving and practical expedient that would enable us to live on site while the house was built. Caravan dwelling with no foreseeable end would have been entirely different, and we often marvelled how a nearby family, whose children became close friends of ours, maintained their serene optimism living thus in their parents' garden.

An advert in the local free newspaper had found us a nine-metre-long mobile home, and this was delivered by low-loader at the end of August. To assist its manhandling from the drive to its pitch behind the Barn, the two weighty night-storage heaters came out, and with much sweating, grunting and expletives the cumbersome box on its tiny, useless wheels was slotted between the pines. Within a few hours, electrics, water, septic tank and telephone had been connected, and we could use the cupboard-sized WC rather than suffering the back-door trot of our grandparents' generation.

We pulled our old four-metre 'van into position at right angles to the bigger one, and connected the two with a rough and ready porch built of slab-wood and roofed with corrugated plastic. In this porch, which enabled us to move between the two units in the dry, we installed a large antiquated gas stove, bought for £10 complete with gas bottle. Since that time we have observed caravanners taking their own washing machines to French campsites, but we thought ourselves pretty damned clever by rigging one up beside the cooker. The space also gave us somewhere for the inevitable muddy wellies and wet clothes.

What excitement we felt, as we arrived at our new home! By third world standards our accommodation was almost palatial, but moving from a house to something only a fifth of its floor area took some downsizing. I had built a pair of bunk beds for the girls in our Lewes house, and these shoe-horned into their end bedroom once the legs had been shortened by a few centimetres to fit under the roof. Otherwise, all our furniture went into storage on a friend's farm. Mobile homes come equipped with built-in furniture, and we tried to ignore the fading coverings and the faint smell of a cheap 1960's American motel.

Visiting friends and relations remarked how seamlessly we had fitted into our new habitat, but it was never clear whether they thought we were reverting to form, or commendably flexible and uncomplaining. The two-and-a-half-metre-square "lounge" was comfortable enough, with its faux-flame electric fire, put-you-up sofa and pull-out table, and we managed to find space to extract honey with the old tin centrifuge that we had brought from Lewes along with the five hives. True to her mother's long-term commitment to the Women's Institute, Anne even made a batch of marmalade, and continued to bake the weekly bread. An essential modification was converting the minute second bedroom to a primitive shower, to sluice off the grime and sweat of a day's woodland or building work. This installation became known as "Joanna's pleasurable puddle", as she would plug the outlet and happily sit in one of the warmer spots of our new home.

Fortunately the winter of 1983/4 had hardly a frost, and only one brief snowfall. But even a mild winter tested the minimal insulation of the caravans. When Anne found sodden clothes at the back of the girls' cupboard, we realised we had to do something about the condensation streaming down the walls. We had already bought fibreglass wool to insulate the house, but this wouldn't be needed until well into the next spring. Wrapped round the caravan, it more than quadrupled the insulation. We encased the whole package in a black plastic sheet normally used for covering silage heaps, cut holes around the windows, and tied it around with baler twine. From a distance our home resembled a black pudding, and was known affectionately as "the black slug". Next summer, the glass wool went into the house walls, the sheeting was cut into strips to cover our firewood piles, and the binder twine had a second life tying up pea-sticks and bean-poles. From the start we practiced the four R's mantra of Reduce, Re-use, Repair, Recycle; even though it had yet to be coined.

The smaller caravan became our bedroom and office. It had a tiny solid fuel stove, designed for coal. We stuffed it with wood at bedtime and, as it was on my side of the bed, I was deputed to stoking every two to three hours. Men need to get up in the night in any case, as Anne pointed out (and not always to go home, as the old joke relates). Installing an electric fire would have seemed extravagant when we had all that free wood, and against our principles of renewable energy. To conserve heat, perhaps we should have made another black slug, but then, who knows? The two might have started breeding, and Hadlow Down would have been overtaken by a plague of tree-chomping monsters. Clearly, our imaginations needed controlling.

The school autumn term had just started when we moved in. Jo was a self-confident nine-year-old, but five-year-old Kate's first day apprehension is clear in a photograph we still treasure. St. Mark's primary school is a few minutes' walk away at the other end of the village, and at that time had only 28 pupils in its two classes, so that our two were a welcome addition. They both thrived in its care, and later went on to the local comprehensive, university, and post-graduate studies. Unlike many in our position who might have educated their children privately, we both felt private education was, and continues to be, socially divisive and inegalitarian. I had gone to a back-street primary in Lewes with forty in a class, yet had emerged relatively intact. There was little comparison between my 1950's experience and St Mark's, apart from both being church schools. Kennedy had implored his people to ask not what America could give to them, but what they could give to America. Perhaps what the Yarrows could give wasn't always welcome, for early that winter both girls contracted chicken pox, and the caravan became a daytime isolation unit both for them and a couple of friends who had also come out in spots. Possibly our girls' attendance helped the school to stay open, and during our thirty years in the village it achieved a designation as "outstanding" in all fields, with a waiting list for admissions.

Neither of us could type. In Lewes a part-time secretary had come in two or three times a week to help run my consultancy, Chris Yarrow and Associates, and bash out letters and reports on a portable typewriter. We soon found a Hadlow Down neighbour who was glad to fill this role, and had no innate objection to our primitive office accommodation. Little did my small stable of clients realise the office circumstances, as meetings were held at their offices or on their land. The services offered to small businesses by a county town compared with a tiny village became all too apparent that first autumn. Where were the copy-shop, the fax machine, plan printer and report-binder we had so conveniently visited a few minutes' walk away in Lewes? Fortunately Geoff, our supporter in the planning process, had his own consultancy next to the village school, and we many times combined picking up the kids with use of his photocopier or fax. For other services, we had to get the car out and make for the nearest town.

When not advising clients, I would work in the wood or on the house. As newcomers, we were something of a curiosity that winter, perhaps to be pitied. The rector's wife expressed concern for our well-being, and, because of my absence from church, her husband may have had grounds for concern for my soul. Both were unfounded. However, outdoor work in a wood or on a building site is hard and dirty. It was therefore only to be expected that, after we had served a resident with bags of logs one Saturday afternoon clad in old and dirty clothes, he should express surprise when we met at a drinks party two hours later, garbed in lounge suit and party frock. We had even managed to clean our finger-nails.

Outdoor living induces both a healthy appetite and a full night's sleep, so more than once we were awakened by the arrival of a builder's lorry. One morning we woke to see a pile of newly-baked insulation blocks steaming in the morning chill, as they were unloaded a couple of metres from our bed. More frequently, it would be the jolly trio of brickies arriving from Lewes, and, as we were putting the kettle on, how about some teas, one with no sugar?

We sourced many of the building materials ourselves. As far as possible we bought second-hand, to reduce our environmental impact, and because we were committed to building as traditionally as possible, and old products often simply looked nicer. The bricks were hand-made, and had formed an estate wall. They were thinner than modern ones, and immediately humanised the scale of the house. To keep down costs, Anne and I would distribute building materials around the site in what we hoped would be the right proportions. Anne somehow never mastered a barrow-load on the springy, wet scaffold-boards that criss-crossed our muddy site; a warning of the poor drainage that would always make gardening here a real challenge.

The brickwork soon reached the tops of the downstairs windows and door frames. Above this level our house was to be timber-frame, and so it was time to call for David the carpenter. Unless one goes in for off-site prefabrication, timber building entails much measuring, cutting, fitting and nailing. David was a dour Scot, single, and towards the end of his working life.

He was undoubtedly a hard worker, but a man set in his ways, who found it difficult to work with others or to take instructions. He consequently worked without a trainee or mate, and progress was sure, but slow. Our design had a timber-framed first floor and large roof with two attic rooms, all of which needed cladding with plywood for rigidity. But by the time that two-thirds of the heavy roof rafters had been added, rising to tree-top level, no plywood had yet been applied, despite my entreaties. Imagine our horror, when, after a November gale that had shaken our caravan all night, we noticed the whole top of the house gently leaning out of vertical. Time to show who was the customer, if not the expert carpenter! With a cable fastened to the house framework, and Gerald's winch hooked to the base of a tree, I took up the strain, and, stroke by stroke on the lever, pulled the frame back upright, each nailed joint groaning in disapproval. A quick survey with a builder's level indicated no great harm had been done, and for the rest of that day David and I nailed on dozens of plywood sheets to give the structure the rigidity it was lacking. A chastened carpenter thereafter was more ready to do jobs when requested.

Traditional house-building is a slow and costly process, with few significant innovations in the last 200 years. If you buy a TV, you don't expect a team of electricians assembling the wires, transistors and screen on your lounge floor. It comes prefabricated, as do most consumer durables. In contrast, house assembly is so drawn out that you eagerly look forward to notable stages in the process. One such milestone was when the roof was made watertight. The brickies returned to thrust the two chimneys though the rafters, and it was time to summon the roofers.

It may have been a mild winter that year, but there was rain in plenty, and our exceedingly level concrete ground floor was covered with five centimetres of water, dammed in by the four external door sills. A roofer's first task is to cover the rafters with a waterproof membrane, held down by battens onto which the tiles will be fixed. The whole house becomes suddenly darker, with a new-found feeling of enclosure. For us, the chance to pump out the ground floor and start the process of drying the interior was a real milestone. The next one was when the glass went into the window frames, and the house began to feel snug. The final milestone was when walls and ceilings were plastered, covering bricks, blocks and plasterboard in a smooth and unifying coat, like icing on the Christmas cake.

We sourced our roof tiles from an abandoned quarry against the Downs near Henfield, which held assorted piles of bricks, masonry and other reclaimed building materials, presided over by a well-built fellow whose appearance and habitation suggested his ancestors had not long settled in one place. We had chosen these tiles because they were hand-made and slightly curved, which would give a texture to the roof, unlike modern flat machine-made ones. Mr. Gander informed us that these "Coverwells" had been made at nearby Horam, and were reckoned to be top quality, unlikely to defoliate in frost, or break easily. We were not pleased when we saw tiles sailing through the air, discarded because of a chipped corner; and yet the same tiler minutes later would be cutting the side off a perfectly good one in order make it fit. They were working to a fixed price. Time was money, and putting aside a chipped tile for later use took time. No wonder skips are full of valuable building materials destined for landfill.

With the roof on, flooring could begin. We were using pitch pine floorboards recovered from demolished offices at Brighton railway station, and both of us spent many hours pulling out nails. The boards were then stacked in our home-made dehumidifier to suck out some of the moisture absorbed whilst they were awaiting use. Once sanded and sealed, the inevitable gaps and nail holes lent a rustic charm, but David couldn't for the life of him understand why we wanted to use second-hand wood. We had given up on arguing our recycling ethics with him, though I suspect his Scottishness may secretly have approved. Internal walls and ceilings were clad with plasterboard, and much of this was nailed in place well into the night by Slavik, the Polish odd-jobber; but we were the only ones disturbed by his hammering, in our caravan just twenty metres away.

We were never tempted to use plastic for our first-floor weatherboards. Manufactured from fossil fuel, and ultimately destined for landfill, they would have gone against virtually every principle we possessed. Ours were new planed hemlock planks from British Columbia, pressure-treated to permanently protect from rot and woodworm, with three coats of micro-porous paint. This only needed a scrub with a brush and water before recoating ten years later.

Midsummer had arrived, and Jo was impatient to move into her own bedroom. In the absence of stairs, she used the ladder to gain access to the room she had claimed. Luckily she wasn't given to sleep-walking, but we were relieved when joiners installed the custom-made staircase, and we could all move safely between floors.

After almost exactly a year of caravan life, our house was ready, almost certainly the first human habitation on the site. As we moved furniture and possessions from our friends' granary and Anne's parents' spare room, and spread them around our expansive creation, we pondered how little space and how few possessions we had needed in the previous twelve months, and what forces lead us to mortgage ourselves in order to accommodate them and acquire yet more.

By organising the house-building project ourselves, we probably saved a third of the cost that a builder would have charged. Fortunately we both enjoyed the building process, and were young and fit enough to immerse ourselves into every aspect. Our experience of house conversion in Lewes, and frequent camping holidays, were no doubt a good preparation for twelve months of comparative discomfort. "Incredibly lucky" was how Anne's mother termed our new state, as we sipped a celebratory glass of

Champagne's finest that September. Undoubtedly there would be the worries and responsibilities that come with any property ownership, but we felt fully up to them. Who else had the good fortune to live in such amazing circumstances, and masters of their destiny? It was now time to see if we measured up to the challenges we had set ourselves.

House-warming invitation,
VE Day 1985

LIVING THE WOODLAND LIFE

Does one ever start a day or week saying "At last it's happened. Now we can really start living"? Life is a continuum, with one week merging into the next, and our memory is punctuated only by major events, such as a holiday, or moving house. In old age we may reflect on times past, but for most of our lives we take such heed of the morrow that we seldom acknowledge or enjoy the now. Sometimes there come moments when one wishes to freeze time, fix it in an all-embracing, multi-sensual experience. As six-year-old Joanna would say, "I'm feeling all smiley inside", a state of contentment achieved so readily by a child.

Was now the time we could really start living? We had happily survived as a family in two caravans, barely an eighth of the area and costing less than one hundredth of our new abode. Would all the effort of the preceding months and years be justified? At least we wouldn't have another winter in such cramped, damp conditions, even though we had told ourselves it was an adventure. We now had our house!

The first impression was of the immense space. Our house's most striking feature was the hall. A large central space, open from ground floor to roof, it was a place everybody had to pass through, and would provide a locus for family events. The first floor landing covered only half the floor area, leaving a large void on the south side, where light streamed down from a clerestory window, and at Christmas our tree could reach up to the roof.

Now that we had cleared some woodland to accommodate the septic tank drainage, the hall and main rooms looked out over one of the best views in the county, across the wood to the Downs fifteen miles away. As we proudly showed friends round, one remarked how the house was unusual in that all its rooms had windows on two sides, which gave a subtle lighting effect. Never ones to spend money unnecessarily, we installed as many of the curtains as possible from the Lewes house, and there some hung until we left almost three decades later. No wonder an estate agent said the property looked "tired"!

No house is perfect, and the shortcomings of ours slowly emerged. Our open-to-the-roof hall allowed all the heat to rise, so that the attic rooms were by far the warmest, and its tiled floor and absence of carpets gave a very hard acoustic, particularly when Kate practiced her trumpet. As we had designed the house, we had only ourselves to blame.

As in houses the world over, our large, bright kitchen became the most-used room. The multi-fuel Rayburn was one of our best investments, for not only did it cook our food, but also gave copious hot water and had spare heat for five radiators. Best of all, its fuel was largely free, for we were able to use unsaleable off-cuts of wood, supplemented by twigs and branches gleaned on every woodland walk. Its chimney gave a gentle background heat to the rooms above, obviating any need for additional heating.

Most centrally-heated homes have automated controls so that one can set the boiler to come on before teatime. With a wood-fired boiler, we had traded convenience for self-reliance and minimal use of fossil fuels. Keeping it fired up 24 hours a day can become a chore, and a certain degree of forethought and discipline is required. In warm weather the fire was let out, and we cooked on a gas stove fuelled by bottled gas, but used so little that a 27 kilo bottle lasted three years. To save immersion-heater electricity, we would get a tank-full of hot water by burning two or three cardboard boxes. After we had recycled bottles, paper and cans, the only contents of the dustbin were the inevitable plastic packaging, which we were unwilling to burn on account of the resulting poisonous fumes.

The energy and water used by two identical families can vary two-fold, depending on lifestyle. We tried to build responsible resource conservation into everything, whether by having ninety-second showers, saving vegetable rinsing water for the garden, or turning off lights when not in a room. Woe betide any office staff who filled the kettle when only one cup was needed! We argued that a simple small saving made several times a day added up to a massive saving over a lifetime. I was probably very difficult to work for. However, it must have sown some seeds, for Joanna made sustainable living her life's work.

Previous generations accepted lower levels of comfort, and our childhood homes had been no exception. Unfortunately, our deliberate low energy use resulted in room temperatures that did not measure up to modern expectations. When we built the house in 1983, a 100-millimetre thickness of glass fibre insulation in walls and roof was standard, but we soon cursed ourselves for not installing more. Because of our frugality, visitors found our temperatures bracing, and one baby-sitting friend would bring an extra rug as well as her portable TV. Some years later we slid 20 millimetres of polyurethane board under the weatherboards, and insulated the cavity walls. Even so, our secretaries would still find it too cold when sitting at their desks, and we probably broke office and factory temperature regulations.

The house was noticeably warmer when the winter sun shone, for all the major windows faced south, and we had cleared most of the trees on that side. In the architect's jargon, it was designed for "passive solar gain". In order to make the most of the sun, after a few years we built on a basic conservatory, and many a bright winter's day was enjoyed there, despite our decision not to heat it artificially. Overhead, the summertime luxuriance of a Black Hamburg vine precluded the need for expensive blinds, and gave us up to forty bunches of juicy grapes each August. Meanwhile, warm air flooded into the house through the connecting door and windows.

The house design facilitated the indoor-outdoor life, with its copious welly store outside the back door. Grubby clothes had hooks in the utility area, fondly known as the de-mudding zone, and the hot tank was located in a drying room, so that rain-soaked jeans could be made re-usable overnight. The washing line in the orchard, combined with the drying room, allowed us to avoid that energy glutton, the tumble drier.

Soon after we moved in I bought Anne a reclining garden seat, jokingly remarking to the garden centre salesman that it was for the wife's relaxation on her two free days a year. "As much as that?" he remarked. And how right he was! Fortunately Anne enjoys "pottering" rather than just sitting, with the result that she is as badly un-read as me, but we enjoy plentiful home-grown fruit and veg. Our inherently infertile soil did have one advantage, in that rank weeds such as nettles and docks grew with polite restraint unless they got their feet into the nutrients of the compost heap or chicken run. Even though the topsoil from the house footprint had been spread over the vegetable patch, it was still barely a spit deep. Any depth or fertility would have to be imported. As we took our spades out of the shed, we reflected we were almost certainly the first people ever to have cultivated this land. The minimal depth of soil became really apparent when we came to excavate the pits for planting our small orchard, and our cankered apple and plum trees would always sulk morosely, with their roots in the untilled siltstone rock.

I concentrated on creating a family-sized vegetable garden, and left Anne to occupy herself with women's things like flowerbeds; although I was prepared to establish a lawn. We had read about the raised bed system, and dumped soil from the paths onto the vegetable beds, covering the paths with weed-and slug-discouraging woodchip. The plots would be rotated on a five-year cycle, with hens occupying one bay. Each winter we dismantled and re-erected the netting that kept the chickens from helping elsewhere in the veg. patch, deep-dug their vacated plot, and planted with the potatoes and leeks that benefitted from their cloacal emissions. To maintain their supply of green food, the hens had access to the adjacent orchard.

My lawn was not an unqualified success, having been hurriedly levelled, and formed from poor soil, heavily compacted and laced with an assortment of subsoil and tree roots. As the soil shrank and the roots decayed, the lawn's surface became increasingly uneven. Matters were made worse by moles, attracted to the best earthworm population in the wood, in turn drawn in by our applying lime to sweeten the sour soil. Stony areas, undiggable by moles, retaliated by growing a fine coat of moss, which announced the two week dry spell we call the English summer by turning brown. To Anne's delight and my shame, daisies and buttercups thrived. Our lawn would win no prizes.

Living in the wood gave freedoms we had previously only dreamed of. We could simply barrow woody garden waste into the nearest plantation, rather than disposal by noxious bonfire or expensive trip to the council tip, and leaf-mould was there for the taking in any woodland depression. A country walk began at the garden gate, as did rough shooting; rabbits, grey squirrels and pigeons gave me sport, a sense of being useful, and free meat when I aimed straight. Wild country was just over the garden fence.

Surrounded by our own land, there were no pacts to negotiate with any mean-spirited neighbour. Around the house we thinned out pines and beech to let in evening light, and kept coppice on a short rotation to preserve the view to the south. We started with six self-sown birch trees on the lawn, gradually reduced to one as their crowns grew and shade increased. On the rare day that it was too hot to sit in the full sun, the birches gave dappled shade, and we enjoyed the inevitable breeze created by the tall house and hilltop location. G and T time would find us admiring one of our greatest assets, the priceless view of evening sun on Firle Beacon. This happy hour was accentuated by the stillness that descended when the last visitors had left, and the doorbell no longer rang. On these occasions I might take myself off to admire the view from two thousand feet in a microlight I shared with a friend, which was hangered in a field two minutes by bike from the house.

Anne's dad said he'd never come across a home where work was so intermingled with daily life. He'd obviously never lived with a farmer! As our woodland venture took shape, along with the mud that came through the front door on our shoes came a never-ending flow of administrative demands. In the kitchen, hall and living room, as well as the office, concepts were discussed, policies formulated, and work plans made. Our home was the bridge from which the good ship Wilderness Wood was steered. Inevitably we became more deskbound than we or the public might have imagined. In the early days our self-sufficiency meant that we ourselves attended to all the paperwork and ever-increasing 'phone-calls. As the business grew, we gradually expanded the part-time secretarial help that had initially been engaged in our caravan days to type my consultancy reports. Although Anne and I espoused self-reliance, we grew increasingly uneasy at trends to eliminate service jobs in the name of cost-cutting. Professionals such as solicitors and doctors are nowadays expected to do their own typing, and highly paid executives to make their own travel arrangements, where previously they would have had a PA or secretary to allow them to get on with the task for which they had been so expensively trained.

It was a rare day indeed when no staff came into the house, and the absence of a separate office entrance led to an inevitable loss of privacy. Eventually we might have up to five of us crammed into our two little office rooms on a wet day, typing consultancy reports, answering the 'phone, dealing with Wilderness Wood paperwork, or sorting out orders and deliveries.

With the unpredictable pattern of visitors to the wood and the changing seasons, few days were identical. We preferred to do the brain-work in the first part of the day, and the rude mechanical tasks afterwards, as mental reserves are harder to assemble when the muscles ache. To live our chosen lifestyle we needed to stay reasonably fit. It was not just the heavy work associated with forestry that required stamina, but the everyday tasks such as sweeping the yard or gardening. There were plenty of opportunities for "useful" exercise, and we would often set off on a walk equipped with swaphook to cut back vegetation from the rides, or take the axe to the wood-pile, so local gym clubs advertised to us in vain. Anne tells how she caught herself wondering what a middle-aged Cambridge graduate was doing in filthy clothes, chucking logs from a Land Rover onto a customer's drive, or making pea-sticks down in the wood; but reflected that she would far rather be out in the open air, doing something useful, than on a machine in a gym.

There was no journey to work; just five paces across the hall from kitchen to office, and on many days we did not leave the wood. This self-imposed isolation was offset by the constant and welcome stream of visitors and suppliers, such as Chris the log merchant and Bill the hurdle-maker, giving an excuse to stop for a chat and tea-break. Many regular visitors inevitably shared our hopes, concerns and values, and some became real friends.

While the girls were at the village school, one of us might accompany them the quarter-mile along the Main Road, as much to get exercise and swap gossip at the school gate as to ensure their safety. Not for us getting out the car, as we were strong advocates of walking to school. Jo took the message aboard, and would sometimes cycle the five miles to her comprehensive at Crowborough, despite the hill-infested High Weald terrain. By this stage we had an old seven-seat Volvo estate, and, with no school bus, shared the school run once or twice a week. Our two were the only ones who dared complain to our face when we dropped them well short of the school, as we explained that the entrance was congested and they needed the exercise.

With our long working week, the girls had largely to amuse themselves, a task we made more challenging by the absence of a TV. Jo had become an avid reader by the age of six and has had a way with words ever since. Kate, ever practical, sometimes helped on a nearby farm, and was never happier than assisting with lambing, or charging around on their quad bike. Their friends were always welcome at the wood, and when parents came to pick them up they had to be prised from a den, or pretend pony showground in the paddock. On many occasions Anne had to entertain with a cup of tea while waiting for their offspring to re-appear from somewhere in the depths of the wood.

John Seymour's *Self-Sufficiency* had kindled the dream of having a variety of livestock, and we considered both goats and pigs, but initially settled for hens. The free-range system is admirable provided you protect the vegetables from the hens, and their diet of grass, other plants, and insects gave beautiful, deep yellow yolks. Once enjoyed, your own spanking fresh egg can never be matched by the bought alternative. Someone soon donated a cockerel. This handsome beast would announce to all foxes within half a mile that there was a ready meal for the taking, and it wasn't long before dawn squawking heralded a visit to the run. A shout from our bedroom window of "B....r off, Mr Fox" sent it packing. If it returned, it risked a sudden death from my twelve-bore. The hens recycled any food scraps, and the need for bought-in chicken feed declined once we had a café in the Barn. Orange peel, tea leaves, and other items the hens turned up their beaks at, went onto the three-bay compost heap, which was kept sweet with wood ash from the house, and "human wetting agent" when I remembered. Even rabbit bones, mussel and crab shells were thrown on, soon dissolving to release their valuable calcium and phosphorus in the acid compost or soil. We have all experienced clothes moths in woollen items, but few will have observed how quickly a compost heap devours an old sweater. Old wool, or shoddy, was a common soil improver and source of nitrogen in years gone by, and who were we to scorn our forebears' wisdom?

Sweet Chestnut
(catkins and leaf)

We had arrived at the wood with five beehives and their contents. Although it is said that "Bees in a wood never do good", our strain did well in the sunny orchard, especially if good summer weather encouraged them out to reap the abundant chestnut nectar from the billions of flowers that smell to some like old socks. There was a very ready market for their honey, but hives have to be dismantled weekly in summer to prevent swarming. Bees hate the smell of sweat, so the tell-tale of the day's exertions had to be showered off before donning full bee suit, complete with gloves, hat and boots, for a sweltering hour or two before another cool shower to restore freshness. Tired from a day's exertions in the wood, I didn't need such a practical hobby, and the bees went to a couple settling in Pembrokeshire.

Chickens and bees were soon followed by orphan lambs, just as at Lewes; except here they could be kept to maturity in their own new paddock, where Jo and Kate bottle-fed them before and after school. In the early evening, when lambs are always frisky, the girls would encourage them to race up and down, so they and lambs slept well at night. A local farmer persuaded Anne to take on one of his black-and-white horned Jacob ewes, with twin ewe lambs to keep as our little breeding flock. Passing children would point out these "goats" to their parents, so we put up a sign to explain who was what. Inevitably Jo and Kate gave them all names; "Mint" and "Sauce" were rejected as too insensitive, but at the time of the first Iraq invasion a now sophisticated Jo called three males and a female Saddam, George, Tony and Claire.

Jo and Kate with Wiggles and Squiggles

Naturally sheep and lambs in time proved a popular attraction with visitors, but we resisted the temptation of becoming a petting zoo. We used our little flock as a prop to explain how woodland had been cleared to farmland, with sheep and goats used to kill off resprouting tree growth and seedlings. The analogy with the third world still holds good, where browsing is an agent of deforestation and desertification.

In an area of small, friendly farmers, we could transport the ewes to a neighbour's farm for covering by a ram each November. A day's lambing course, and mugging up a smallholding manual, turned Anne into a passable sheep midwife, and we were fortunate that the Jacobs were natural mothers. One of the few remaining small abattoirs was virtually on the doorstep, so the lambs had only a brief final ride in a borrowed trailer. In Lewes days I had not only slaughtered our lambs, but butchered the meat and cured the skins, and "Chopper" still decorates the living room floor after almost 40 years. We had only a small freezer, so much of the lamb was sold as chops and joints to friends. We knew little about finishing our stock, but few complained about the over-fatty cuts as the price was reasonable.

Neither of us had ever wanted the inconvenience of a dog, in spite of the girls' pleas, and we compromised with pet rabbits in moveable hutches in the orchard. After a holiday on Patmos where stray cats took over our villa, we were persuaded to add the kitten "Moss" to our household. Although from a local farm, she unfortunately never showed any interest in the rats that from time to time took up residence under the chicken ark and compost heap. Moss came to a sticky end on the Main Road a few years later. She was rapidly replaced by two brother and sister kittens, "Ratty" and "Puck". We later learned their strikingly different appearance was probably the result of their mother having more than one boyfriend. Fortunately neither showed any interest in the Main Road, but Ratty, the more companionable of the two, often followed us round the wood on an evening walk. He, too, must have felt the wood was a continuum of the home we had made.

The abode we had fashioned for ourselves was integral with our dream for Wilderness Wood. Living in it, our whole life became inextricably woven with the wood and its fortunes. We were no less involved with the wood than a family living on a canal barge working the waterways of Europe, and as a lifestyle it was in many ways as unique. How lucky we were to be able to plan the routes where our vessel might venture!

FORESTRY AND
A STABLEFUL OF
HOBBYHORSES

When Anne and I chose to make Wilderness Wood our
home for over half of our working lives, and set out
to show that, against conventional wisdom, we could
make a small woodland pay, we must have had a foolhardy faith
in ourselves. As a land use and an industry, forestry forms only
a tiny fraction of the British economy, and few of us know that
Britain was once almost totally covered by forest. Currently little
more than a tenth is under trees, and it is one of the least wooded
countries in Europe. Population pressure for food meant our
original wildwood had been largely cleared before Norman times,
and as the centuries rolled on we became increasingly reliant on
imports of food and timber. Our roles as traders and imperialists
cushioned us from the realities of over-population on our small
island, as we outgrew our ability to support ourselves from our
own land. It is reckoned we were net importers of food by Tudor
times, and timber for ships had become a scarce commodity. By
the beginning of the twentieth century, forest cover was down to
five percent, and the First World War U-boat attacks highlighted
Britain's reliance on foreign timber imports.

Britain had become an urban, industrialised nation. Yet at the beginning of that war our remaining woods were still a valuable part of the rural economy, and timber was a costly item. A cubic foot of standing oak timber was worth between five and ten times an agricultural worker's hourly wage. Nowadays, the chap with the chainsaw would only need to work half an hour to buy it. But faced with death duties, the doubling of rural wages during World War One, and the subsequent rural upheaval, landowners had other things on their minds than restocking devastated woodland whose timber had been requisitioned for the war effort. Conversely, the Forestry Commission, formed in 1919, started planting large areas of productive conifers to build up a strategic timber reserve. This, together with significant private afforestation, continued apace until the 'eighties, when economic arguments undermined the enthusiasm. In order not to impinge significantly on food production, most planting took place on the cold, wet and infertile moors and mountainsides of upland Britain, and therefore the great twentieth-century expansion of British forestry hardly registered with the urban population far away in the lowlands. With negligible efforts to educate it otherwise, it is little wonder the British public is woefully ignorant about the crucial role of forests.

By the early 1970's, British forestry was polarised. Professionals like me had been trained to produce large quantities of fast-grown conifers for the pulp and paper mills, and timber for other needs as trees grew bigger. Most grant aid was concentrated on planting bare ground. Meanwhile, the mainly broadleaved woods of the lowlands were increasingly neglected. Poor timber prices, and the long-term investment required to re-establish quality hardwood production in woods devastated by another World War, did not attract landowners who were being subsidised to produce food at all costs. As a result, many lowland woods, especially coppices, were grubbed up for agriculture or planted with fast-growing conifers. With a declining timber supply and rising costs, many small hardwood sawmills closed in the late twentieth century, and it became even more difficult for small woods to sell their output. Today, almost half of broadleaved woodlands, mostly in private ownership, are unmanaged and therefore unproductive.

Sadly, many of the efforts to bring woods back into production in the last three decades have been a waste of time and money, both private and public, and nowhere is this better shown than in the response to the Great Storm of 1987. Our rambles through Sussex woodlands are spoiled by observing the many thousands of planted oaks, ash, cherry and other trees, now irretrievably suppressed by regrowth from stumps and self-sown fast-growing weed species such as birch and willow. The Forestry Commission was supposed to check that the required survival rate was achieved at the end of the grant period of ten years, but generous replanting grants were wasted because there was no mechanism for ensuring that owners subsequently "released" the planted trees by clearing competing ones. The health and economic viability of such woods would have been greatly enhanced by incentives for continued tending and early thinnings, as in some European countries. Collectively, it is little short of incompetence on a massive scale. As a nation we want woods, but can't somehow arrange for them to produce worthwhile timber.

In recent years we have increasingly appreciated forestry's non-timber benefits to our well-being, such as landscape, wildlife, and open space. The widespread objection in 2011 to selling off the nation's forests could not have made this point better. This illustrates a basic paradox. The oxygen, wildlife habitat, beautiful landscapes, recreational opportunities and so on are lumped together by economists as "non-market benefits", derived from "natural capital". These non-monetary benefits to society are estimated to total in excess of one billion pounds a year, but the woodland owner receives no income from them. Education and TV programmes both emphasise the environmental aspects of forests and woods. When we asked visiting schoolchildren

"What are woods for?" they offered oxygen, or wildlife, but seldom timber. We would agree, but then go on to explain that Wilderness Wood was there because it had always produced useful wood and timber. Despite the widespread use of plastics and other raw materials, wood is still an integral part of our daily life. Solid wood in houses or furniture may last decades, but every disposable piece of paper and cardboard is also wood-based. Each of us uses an average of one tonne of wood a year – a solid lump one metre high, wide and deep - and British forests meet only about 15 percent of our needs.

With so little woodland left, we British had lost whatever forestry tradition we once had, and, unlike my French or German counterparts who had a respected position in society, as a forester I met with the typical reaction of "You cut down trees." Few people were aware of the complexity of factors that go into the long-term management of a forest, and forestry should not be confused with exploitative logging of virgin forests. At a forestry meeting I heard the comment "Forestry isn't rocket science. No, it's more complicated". Unlike established professions such as medicine or architecture, anybody can call themselves a forester, and I have lost count of the examples of poor practices, such as trees planted in dense shade, or an inappropriate mixture of species, which result from amateur advice. The difference between a professional forester and a man with a chainsaw or planting spade is similar to that between an architect and a bricklayer. However skilled a craftsman, without plans and direction his efforts risk misapplication. In the case of woods and forests, trees planted on the wrong soil do not thrive, and it is all too easy to harvest at a faster or slower rate than the timber is growing. When we bought Wilderness Wood, the streamside poplars had been planted on too infertile a soil, and most of the coppices had been cut in the previous five years. Wrong species, and scant regard for continuity of output!

The art of forestry concerns itself with management of the resource over very long time scales. The superb beech and oak forests of northern France are managed on plans drawn up early in the nineteenth century, with regeneration periods measured in decades. The worst influence on forests is rapid change, be it government grants or taxes, ownership, or management objectives. As a professional adviser to others, I could do no more than recommend the best solutions for a client's land, usually for a regrettably brief period. Purchasing Wilderness Wood provided me with the opportunity to "do my own thing", without the vagaries of a client who might alter tack, or change forestry adviser. Now we had the opportunity to control a wood, and to influence its direction for a considerable time.

I had studied forestry at the University College of North Wales for four years from 1960. This course was tailored to provide officers for our state forest service, and those of the dominions and remaining colonies. Indeed, our professor had been principal at the forest institute at Dehra Dun in India until 1947, and his swearing in Hindi, as we climbed a Snowdonian hillside, reduced a fellow student from Bhopal to giggles. Like medicine, forestry is an applied science, and we had to imbibe copious amounts of botany and zoology, along with a working knowledge of geology, soil science, surveying, and engineering, before we were permitted to study the art of forestry. Not only did we tour the ancient forests of Dean and the New Forest, but also visited private estates and many of the new upland forests, and a year's study of classic continental silvicultural systems culminated in a tour of wonderful forests in north-east France, where we feasted regally as guests of the *Eaux et Forêts*, the state forest service.

In the 1960's, forestry training in Britain unashamedly emphasised the production of industrial quantities of timber, more or less to the exclusion of other benefits. Although the Forestry Commission had designated several "Forest Parks", its recreation provision was half-hearted, and the Commission employed not a single landscape architect or recreation planner to humanise its spartan campsites and car parks. With an eye to possible employment opportunities, my degree dissertation was a survey of the public's concept of amenity in British forestry, followed by two wonderful years working for a Masters in Forest Recreation at the University of Montana, USA. Here, I studied the American philosophy and practice of providing for recreation on their public lands, and how this might be applied to British conditions. And, of course, how to ride a horse Western style, and fish for wild river trout! How would I be welcome back in 'sixties Swinging England?

I perhaps exaggerate when I say that, on my return to Britain in 1966, to the landed classes countryside recreation meant huntin', shootin' and fishin', and they were blissfully unaware of the growing demand for rural access by a largely urban population. Recreation for the masses was measured in terms of numbers of football pitches and swimming pools per thousand people, and planning for recreation in the countryside was still in its infancy. At conferences on rural recreation, land agents unashamedly showed their distaste for the urban hordes, who they imagined would wreck "their" countryside by drowning birdsong with transistor radios, and leaving a trail of open gates and plastic rubbish. The planning system was of little help. Whilst farming and forestry could be practised with almost no constraints, other equally justified uses of the countryside, such as the creation of fishing lakes and camping sites, required planning permission, which might be obtained with great difficulty.

From the late 'sixties I railed at foresters at all levels for not seizing the opportunity to capitalise on their amazing land assets, or even admitting that they might owe their fellow countrymen a right to share the land. Many exemplified G W Bush's alleged quip that the French had no word for entrepreneur, and hid their lack of imagination or enthusiasm behind polite inertia. As I write, a national newspaper at last has a section-length promotion for the recreational opportunities on Forestry Commission land,

featuring modern holiday cabins. Such self-confidence in its
role as a recreation provider is a total sea change from forty years
ago, and it is difficult to cast one's mind back to that time, when
a feasibility study from a major firm of accountants identified
a demand for thousands of holiday cabins on their estate. By
all accounts that study was shelved. They lacked the vision to
implement what could have been a major source of revenue to
subsidise the loss-making growing of trees, and built only a very
small number. Convinced we could show the way, a friend and I
in 1969 conceived a scheme to create a self-catering holiday village
in open woodland on Speyside in the Scottish Highlands, partly to
advertise our recreation planning skills, and also to show that such
developments could be built in a way that assisted rural economies
without detracting from the landscape. That development in part
enabled us to proceed with Wilderness Wood a decade later.

A fundamental distinction between the USA and Britain is that,
over there, the vaste public lands of the National Forests, National
Parks and Wilderness Areas are managed by Federal services on
behalf of the people. Access, in one form or another, is a citizen's
right. In Montana, for example, all water is open to fishing
access, even on private land. Similar rights exist throughout
most of the Nordic states. Other than access to the foreshore
of our "sceptr'd isle", we English have no general tradition of
access to our countryside as a right. It took the mass trespass
on Kinder Scout in 1932 to sow the seeds of our national park
system, but even in 2011 the government was intending to sell
off what little public forest the citizens owned. In access terms,
in England and Wales we are little more than serfs, with huge
swathes of land owned by descendents of the Norman Conquest
and beneficiaries of the Dissolution of the Monasteries; apart from
Forestry Commission land, the amount of publicly-owned land
available for recreation is derisory.

By 1980, the concept of "multiple use" had become common parlance among foresters. This idea, that land can serve more than a single purpose, may be applied to all sorts of situation. Thus, a reservoir could accommodate fishing, sailing and bird-watching, rather than just provide drinking water, although the objections from managers were often fierce, and provision initially grudging and half-hearted at the field level. The Ministry of Agriculture was giving farmers grants to build irrigation ponds, but would countenance no financial support for anything but the single purpose of water storage for food production. Against similar unsympathetic views by many foresters at that time, Anne and I wanted to show how Wilderness Wood could produce a number of benefits. We would welcome the public to our small woodland, and hoped to show how little impact such access would have on the woodland and its production of timber.

The British distaste for commerce is especially prevalent in the countryside. We like to have a quaint landscape, despite our insistence on the cheapest possible food. A fruit farmer client of ours on the Kent/Sussex border had met huge local opposition when he proposed to diversify by flooding some bottom-land for a trout fishing lake. The objection to this quietest of sports was that it would be commercialisation of the countryside - as if fruit-growing was somehow non-commercial! Even when we were well established at Wilderness Wood, our attempts to provide for low-key, tasteful activities such as a wedding reception in a woodland grove would sometimes be met with similar prejudices. Allied to distaste for filthy lucre is the British disdain for overt happiness in others. A TV programme lamenting how sailing boats on Lake Windermere detracted from the landscape of Wordsworth failed to mention the pleasure this activity gave to countless amateur sailors, and how, for most of the year, there would be hardly a boat in sight. Many of us take an adversarial stance, and are often hypocrites in the process. The NIMBY reacting to a country park proposal ignores the impact of his own leisure or tourism travel, or that the foreign lake by which he spreads his towel is near somebody's home. *We* are on our holiday; *they* are tourists. Anne and I were very conscious that public opinion could easily turn against us, and to avoid opposition, would follow the principle of getting on with things incrementally and unobtrusively.

By seeking to work, rather than benignly neglect, an ancient wood in a beautiful location, we were entering a lion's den of ignorance and prejudice. There is no truly "natural" landscape in Britain, as just about everywhere has been influenced by man over thousands of years. Wilderness Wood was no exception. Its coppices, of an introduced species cut to the ground every few years, were just as unnatural as the pine plantations, and the underlying soils had been degraded by centuries of tree harvesting. The wood was perhaps not as modified by man as a field of wheat, but hardly natural. And yet here we were in an "Area of Outstanding *Natural* Beauty". The drafters of the 1949 Act that enabled this designation had probably not read Dudley Stamp's *Making of the English Landscape*, or were guilty of sloppy use of language. The combination of ignorance and romanticism undermines formation of rational forest policy, and has been the subject of many a rant at anyone foolish enough to lend me an ear on such matters, probably black-balling me from any forestry advisory committee.

Chauvinism is rife in modern British woodland circles. Many wish to keep at bay all species that didn't manage to re-invade Britain after the last Ice Age, before the land bridge with continental Europe was lost about eight thousand years ago. Had that geological catastrophe been delayed a few millennia, species such as Norway spruce, European larch and sycamore would now have the same citizenship rights as common oak and goat willow. This accident of geology has permitted zealots to rail against species brought over the Channel in Roman times and later. The blight of invaders such as grey squirrels and rhododendron has been repeatedly trotted out as a reason for excluding ALL non-native species, particularly with reference to trees; not because they are causing a problem, but simply because the countryside should be as "natural" as possible, and therefore only "native" trees allowed. For some bizarre reason, the number of different insects that plague a tree is almost the sole criterion by which it is judged. In many cases native trees do support a greater range than exotics. On the other hand, Southern beech from Chile has a greater variety than our native beech, and a dense stand of Norway spruce has a greater biomass of invertebrates, such as mites and spiders, than an oak wood. The sycamore occurs throughout Europe, and is thought to have been introduced to Britain by the Romans. It is well naturalised and seeds prolifically, but many assume that, because seedlings are common in their flower beds, they risk its taking over whole woods. Any casual woodland visit would show that this seldom happens. Nonetheless, woods owned by conservation organisations are ethnically cleansed at great expense. Sycamore is condemned because of its small range of 43 insect species, compared with over 400 on oak, whilst the derisory six on yew, and two on box (both natives), are conveniently forgotten. But, like spruce, sycamore supports vast *numbers* of insects, as anyone knows who has parked his car under its deluge of aphid honeydew. The huge biomass is a valuable base to the food chain, just as plankton in the sea.

Adherence to the concept of nativeness and local provenance bears little examination when it emerges that a species thought to occur naturally, such as elm, is found to have been introduced by mankind, or that tree pollen is blown here regularly from Scandinavia. This means that half of a "native" birch seedling's genes may have come across the sea last year. We would have been embarrassed trying to justify the "natives only" argument to the diverse classes of schoolchildren who visited the wood, and were appalled when a brain-washed student of arboriculture turned down our offer of a summer job upon discovering that she would be working in a wood that harboured "alien conifers".

Many woodlands, enriched with more productive non-native tree species with support from taxpayers' money, are now categorised as Plantations on Ancient Woodland Sites (PAWS), and, despite being not yet ready to harvest profitably, are having non-native elements liquidated in the hope that pristine English ecosystems will somehow re-establish themselves. A few years ago such actions would have resulted in prosecution as illegal felling, and not in the national interest. Now, the resulting woods, like those deliberately planted with similar "natural" objectives, are usually becoming impenetrable wastes of squirrel-damaged scrub, for our successors to harvest as expensively-established firewood. Our historical investigations had confirmed that Wilderness Wood was an ancient woodland site. Thousands of years ago it may have been an oak forest, but now it was clothed in sweet chestnut, a tree introduced two thousand years ago. Our wood was technically a PAWS, but we had no intention of ridding it of non-native but productive trees. Unlike most native broadleaved trees, at least the sweet chestnut was well suited to the difficult growing conditions.

The removal of conifers has severely undermined the viability of our timber-processing industry. Not only has new planting steeply declined in the last thirty years, but virtually all has been of broadleaved trees, whose productivity is usually one third that of conifers. Sawmillers will soon suffer a severe reduction in timber supply, as the impact on forestry of conservation interests takes effect. Can Britain really afford to allow this greenest of productive industries to fade away?

Although foresters had been practising conservation and sustainable land use long before they became the buzz-words of today, they agreed to follow the strictures of the UK Woodland Assurance Standard (UKWAS). This was a code established in 1999 by representatives of the forestry industry in response to criticism that commercial forestry was not as environmentally beneficial as it might be. Under the Standard, veteran trees are retained, dead wood is left for insects and fungi, rides widened for herbs and shrubs, chemical use is minimised, and so on. All these add to the complications of running an enterprise, but have been willingly embraced despite minimal, or no, financial incentives. There is a danger that the status quo becomes sacrosanct, and change is always seen as wrong. At one stage the local Forestry Commission officer tried to discourage us from using limestone chips on a footpath because it would alter the acidity of adjacent soil. He could not claim our unnaturally acid soil held any special interest, and dropped the request when challenged. Meeker souls might have complied. Many years ago I heard the mantra that "Standards are for the boring and the conscienceless". One could now add "and for box-ticking bureaucrats". At Wilderness Wood we did not need the UKWAS to tell us not to extract after heavy rain, to avoid silting streams. These were *our* rides; rutting them would only mean expensive repairs later, and muddy stream water was soil lost to the wood. Foresters are by nature accommodating types with no strong lobby, and I sometimes upset conservation groups by suggesting that, to balance matters, it would be nice to see some wooded nature reserves modified in the interest of timber production. A response was that my suggestion was "unhelpful".

A new influence from the early 1990's was the emergence of forest certification. When this was first mooted in Britain, I attended a seminar to hear a representative of the Forestry Stewardship Council outline the scheme's scope and requirements. Certification was initially for the protection of tropical rainforests, and included measures to prevent deforestation, and for the protection of indigenous people, and the environment generally. The speaker agreed that the various UK Forestry Acts by and large achieved adequate protection in Britain, and that our forestry was among the best regulated in the world. I asked what changes would be necessary to the woodland management as practiced by the professional foresters round that table. "Virtually nothing", came the reply. By this time I had the bit well between my teeth, and suggested that the whole process of form-filling, inspections, monitoring and re-inspections would achieve nothing more than jobs for people with third class degrees in environmental science, and add yet further financial and administrative burdens to an already moribund rural industry. As to the speaker's suggestion that the western world should set an example, I retorted that it had so far achieved little success with human rights, so why should it with forest certification?

It was argued (erroneously!) that timber from certified woods would have a marketing edge over non-certified, and that the public would know that the product came from "sustainable sources". The Forestry Commission, large estates, and those managed by the big forestry management companies could absorb the costs, and in due course became "certified". At a stroke of a pen, timber from trees planted decades earlier became retrospectively kosher, as though all previous sins were forgiven. While about half of the whole British woodland area is now certified, few small woods have joined the club, finding the scheme unnecessary, expensive and irksome. It includes regular inspections by authorised agents, the regular monitoring of insects, birds and the like, and all the associated form-filling. Certification does mean that large timber purchasers can avoid the worst aspects of forest exploitation, but the general public has little knowledge of, or interest in, certified wood, and we virtually never lost a sale because Wilderness Wood was not certified. We did once lose an order for chestnut poles to an outer London Borough whose officials would buy only from certified sources; my suggestion that they ensure their eventual purchase arrived by horse and cart was received with stony incomprehension. Had we believed the world would be a better place if we jumped through the hoops, we might have complied. But we did not, and remained proudly uncertified.

In summary, when we took on Wilderness Wood it was a relic of millennia of land use. It had evolved to meet each generation's needs for raw materials, and was not "natural", but greatly modified. As in previous ages, it would now have to be managed to meet new requirements, in an era when its physical products such as wood were of low value. We embarked on the challenge with the great advantage of specialist training, and our proposals were tempered by a broad understanding of a small wood's place in the English countryside. By the time we bought the wood, Anne and I were already trying to live in ways that minimised our footprint, informed by both upbringing and education. The principles of our lifestyle melded closely with traditional forestry, which is measured in decades or even centuries, planting and nurturing trees for generations as yet unborn,.

All around us were countless neglected and unproductive woods, and we had no intention of adding Wilderness Wood to their number. We were no charity, and had even less intention of spending large sums on practicing management systems such as coppicing purely for historical reasons or claimed wildlife benefits. Our challenge would be to grow wood and timber that produced an income in today's market; to do our small bit in reducing reliance on imported timber; and, most importantly, to find ways of cashing in on those non-market benefits the public enjoyed.

WE DID IT OUR WAY

There ant no place like Sussex
Until ye goos above
For Sussex will be Sussex
And Sussex wun't be druv.

W Victor Cook, 1914

A s a forestry consultant, I would often be asked to advise on the "right" way to manage a woodland. But it's not that simple – it all depends on the aims of the owners and managers, whether they be small landowners like us, or a state forest holding. I found pinning down the client's priorities could be more difficult than making a prescription for their wood. Often owners, particularly if new to forestry, were very vague about what they wanted from their woodland: did they want income, privacy, a wildlife refuge, a legacy of timber for grandchildren, or what? We obviously had to go through the same process ourselves.

Our intention was to open the wood for a range of countryside activities, including picnicking visitors and school visits, but, whatever else we might do, harvesting of useful, wood-based products would be a *sine qua non*. To us, making the best use of land was a moral imperative in an increasingly crowded world, and we intended to make it clear to our visitors that Wilderness Wood was a productive woodland, and not just a park, nature reserve or tourist attraction that happened to have trees. We would strive never to lose sight of this long-term objective of timber production, despite changing fashions of national forestry policy. We believed that other activities could subsidise this if necessary, and that, by showing production was not significantly compromised by public use, the wood might become an exemplar of responsible land management in the outstanding environment in which we had the privilege of living and working.

Even before we had bought the wood, we had begun to consolidate our fuzzy ideas into a short, sensible list. Once Wilderness Wood was in our ownership we again debated our priorities, and quickly settled on the framework of management. In due course these broad aims would be publicly displayed in the Barn and in our teachers' pack. In summary we set out to:

- Maintain the holding as a *working* wood, with production of useful timber and wood as fundamental, while also providing a wide range of other services within the concept of "multiple use." Other uses and developments must be compatible with timber production.

- Build a financially-sound business, with income from on-site sales of wood and wood products, and from visitors, at the same time as giving worthwhile rural employment. We would avoid as far as possible becoming reliant on grants or other subsidies.

- Maintain and enhance the resource base of the wood, and be an exemplar of first-class silviculture, whose guiding principles include the sustained good health and conservation value of the ecosystem.

- Give people the opportunity to enjoy and learn about the wood.

These objectives translated into practical woodland management policies. We would:

- Increase the overall size of trees and the volume of standing timber by letting selected trees grow older.

- Reduce the area of coppice by a third, to provide a wider range of woodland types.

- Convert part of the coppices to high forest (big trees) by "storing" the coppice.

- Convert most of the even-aged plantations to uneven-aged, or "continuous cover", forest (CCF); extend this into adjoining coppice by planting; and take stored coppice into the CCF system.

- Plant timber-producing trees best suited to the site conditions, irrespective of country of origin, and encourage appropriate self-sown trees. We had no objection to introducing new tree species provided they would grow well and had a reasonable expectation of being useful when harvested.

- When thinning, favour the trees whose retention would enhance both the visual and economic value of the woodland. Straight-stemmed trees of any species would be retained, as they would have a prospect of producing useful timber, and trees of poor growth or form would be put to whatever use was most appropriate.

- Identify, protect and enhance areas of wildlife habitat for their own sake as well as to demonstrate aspects of forest ecology

These seven policies would bring many benefits: diversified products, thereby spreading risk and increasing flexibility; more varied habitats; interesting management challenges; and, above all, a more varied and attractive landscape. One of our intentions was to encourage visitors, and we knew that the public prefers to see large trees, and abhors sudden change or the appearance of artificiality. Wilderness Wood was already fully stocked with trees, and only a rich fool would fell large areas in order to effect change in species for its own sake. At purchase, our wood had limited visual appeal. The coppices were little more than an assembly of thousands of bean-poles, and the young plantations were very obviously planted - monotonous straight lines of even-aged trees barely thicker than your leg, whose limited beauty was often masked by a fuzz of dead lower branches and shoulder-high bracken. Our silviculture would subtly change the composition of the stands, gradually converting these plantations to uneven-aged forest.

We decided we would continue to manage the wood through a legal agreement with the Forestry Commission, to meet their overall objectives of sound management. When we bought the wood it was "dedicated", that is, covenanted with the Forestry Commission for growing timber and other woodland products. As new owners of the wood, we had to re-dedicate it soon after purchase. The pre-existing plan of operations was available, with its map of compartment boundaries. I re-drew compartment and sub-compartment boundaries more in keeping with the physical characteristics and tree composition of the various parts of the wood, notated on the larger-scale map that I surveyed that first autumn. We agreed a five-year plan of cutting, planting and so on, and, apart from the occasional visit, the District Officer left us alone. Once we had an agreed plan of operations we did not have to apply for a separate felling licence for every activity and, more importantly, the likelihood of the local authority imposing a Tree Preservation Order was almost nil. The Commission submitted each five-year revision to various bodies for consultation, and over the years to our knowledge there was no objection on planning, landscape, or other grounds. In due course Woodland Grant Schemes (WGS) succeeded Dedication Schemes, and, although the emphasis was still on planting, management for wildlife and other objectives took on a greater emphasis, and was officially incorporated into the various grants which ensued.

Although we were clear in our own heads what our guiding principles would be, it was many years before we got round to committing them to paper. A written list would have helped our staff to understand what lay behind our sometimes bizarre approach to business management. Our operational approach would be to:

1. Use the wood's assets to their best advantage, and as profitably and sustainably as we could manage.

2. Make the best use of harvested wood. Every heterogeneous material has a hierarchy of value in its constituent parts, be it a side of beef or a tree. A butcher does not sell the best cuts as mince; nor would we sell planking timber for fuel. Selecting the best use for every piece of wood would be crucial to financial success.

3. Sell direct to the public by building up a retail trade, thereby cutting out the middleman.

4. Add value by simple manufacturing. Wilderness Wood was too small to provide a living from selling raw materials, growing perhaps only 50 tonnes of softwood and 90 tonnes of hardwood each year. And, if we wanted to increase the overall size of our trees, we

could not harvest as much as this in the short term. It would be impossible to compete on price with third-world labour, but we could sell on local provenance, on service, and the lovely setting.

5. Try to waste nothing in all areas of the business, from bagging up off-cuts for barbecue fuel to feeding tea-room waste to the chickens. Every action should mirror the conservation principles we set for our daily living. We would minimise fuel use, turning off equipment if left standing, and lights when we left the room. Deliveries were combined with school runs or shopping, and staff were paid to take small items in their own car if the customer was near their home. Dropped nails were picked up; bent ones straightened; and offcuts stored, awaiting conversion to small products such as welly-pullers or "log-roll" edging. If we did waste anything, it was perhaps our own time.

6. Buy or rent equipment to work the wood as efficiently as its small size would permit. We had no desire to become a historical theme park and turn our backs on the modern world, felling trees by axe and hauling out by horsepower.

7. Minimise the use of chemicals. It did not need pesticide regulations to persuade us, for they were expensive, and spraying was one of the most unpopular tasks in the forest year. On the other hand, there was no way we would join the growing band of back-to-the-land dropouts by eschewing artificial fertilisers or trace elements, just because they weren't "natural".

8. Use suppliers and bought-in products consistent with our ethics and objectives. We would attempt to

support local, small and responsible businesses, and, while avoiding the temptation to become a garden centre, would buy in a small range of locally-made wood products to supplement our own.

9. Make our welcome as inclusive as possible, and try not to discriminate by price. We aimed to offer value for money, whether reasonably priced poles and pea-sticks, children's activities, or cups of tea.

10. Explain to people what we were doing. We set out to be educational, even evangelical: helping people to understand that wood is a renewable resource that we all use, and pointing out that Wilderness Wood was producing wood and timber as well as being a beautiful and enjoyable place with lots of wildlife. We would connect people with the natural environment by promoting what later was called "green" living.

All around us woods were being neglected, and many new ones were destined to become little more than scrub. Growing trees without producing timber implied the rest of the world owed us a living, but in the post-colonial period this concept was indefensible. The concept of multiple use, far from being the proverbial streetwalker, all things to all men at a price, would enable us to run a business with a range of complementary activities which we hoped would act as a showpiece for enlightened land use. We knew traditional forestry on this scale could barely break even, and we looked to recreation to subsidise it, with our visitors as our principle market for wood products. And, if we could make the woodland into a place of beauty, our factory floor could also be our greatest asset.

We were drawing on many years' personal experience in the fields of countryside recreation and forestry. Others had dabbled in diversifying woodlands, but we intended to do it whole-heartedly. We were not part of a larger organisation, answerable to distant committees, and sudden over-riding changes of policy. We could, and would, do it our way.

Using break and froe to cleave a chestnut pole

HOW WE MANAGED OUR WOOD: COPPICING

My forestry degree had dismissed coppicing as a historic relic, with just two lectures on the subject. Now it would loom large in our work, if only because about two thirds of the wood was coppice. Coppicing, as a form of exploitation, probably goes back to the earliest times that woodlands were deliberately managed. The system relies on the ability of most broadleaves trees to re-sprout when cut. If cut near ground level the stump or "stool" lives on, fed by the roots below, which are often as extensive as the branches above. In the place of a single trunk, the coppiced stool sprouts a number of stems, depending on the stool's size and age, and these may grow up to two metres in the first year. As the years go by, the weaker stems die in the shade of the more vigorous ones. When the remaining stems are big enough to use, they are cut again – and so on until the stool dies, perhaps hundreds of years old.

The advantages of the coppice system are manifold. Firstly, no replanting is required and the young growth need only be protected from browsing by domestic stock or deer. Secondly, in the days before chainsaws and machinery, poles that could be easily cut and moved by hand had a distinct benefit. They could be harvested at the size needed, and no further sawing was required, whereas larger timber had to be cut into beams and planks. Thirdly, by varying the length of the rotation (the period between cuttings), the woodsman could determine the size of material he produced. Thus, a maker of walking-sticks, thatching spars and tool handles might harvest after only four years. On the other hand, a man requiring rafters and beams for a building would require re-growth from areas left for twenty years or more.

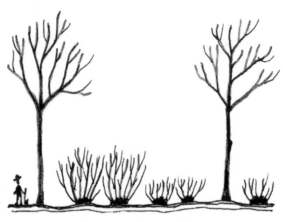

Coppice with standards

The classic coppice system from Tudor times was "coppice-with-standards" – that is, coppice with a scattering of tall "proper" trees, usually oak. The coppice would be cut at intervals for firewood, charcoal, fencing, and all the innumerable other uses of small wood in those days, and the oaks were felled after 150 years or more for buildings and ship-building. The standards were usually retained as the property of the landowner. The right to cut coppice might be retained within a family, paying rent to the landowner, father and son cutting an area divided into fifteen or so equal-sized "cants", the term used for a single area cut in one season.

Each species had different uses. Flexible hazel rods were ideal for hurdle-making and woven fencing, the wattle of wattle and daub walling, and thatching spars. Springy ash would meet the needs of wheelwrights and tool-makers, whereas dense hornbeam made mill cogs. The bark of oak poles was needed by tanneries. But, in the days before fossil fuels, the vast bulk of coppiced wood was used as firewood or charcoal. Its bloomery sites suggested that Wilderness Wood was already a coppiced woodland in Roman times, providing charcoal for its iron kilns. Any species would do as fuelwood, but by the nineteenth century sweet chestnut was being extensively planted in the Weald to provide hop-poles for the flourishing hop industry. Anne's historical rummaging had unearthed a tithe map of 1870 showing the field south-west of Wilderness Wood as a hop-garden, presumably using Wilderness Wood poles to hold up the hops, and Wilderness Wood charcoal as fuel to dry them in the oast-house of Wilderness Farm. The many oasts which dot the local landscape bear witness to the former importance of hop-growing, and it was a happy coincidence that both hops and chestnut grow well in Kent and Sussex. Hop-growing required as many as 3,600 poles per acre of hops, and it is reckoned that up to 60,000 acres of coppice were needed to serve the industry.

With the decline of country crafts and the replacement of wood by materials such as plastic, and above all by fossil fuels, the demand for and value of coppice declined. Sweet chestnut kept its value better than other species. The hop industry had sadly declined from its peak in the 1870's to near extinction by the millennium, despite the resurgence of real ale, but chestnut was still in demand in the early 1980's for chestnut pale fencing, which is made from thin pales or spiles of split chestnut bound with several strands of wire. However, soon after we moved to Wilderness Wood the chestnut market also was struck by a blow from which it never recovered. Cheap plastic and metal alternatives were already taking over from pale fencing as temporary barriers on construction sites, and then the devastation of the 1987 Great Storm flooded the market with material free to those who would take it. In the 1950's the right to cut an acre of good chestnut coppice might sell for six to eight weeks' wages. Nowadays, one is lucky to sell it for one week's pay, which barely covers the administrative costs over a fifteen year cycle.

During the 1970's an estimated three-quarters of an acre of coppice was being grubbed up for farming each day in East Sussex, England's most wooded county, and other woods were converted to plantations of faster-growing conifers. Small and scattered, often with appalling access, the remaining woods and copses gradually lost their role in the economy, with ever fewer men wanting the hard life of coppice and forest work. In La Fontaine's fable *La Mort et le Bûcheron*, the woodcutter prays for death to release him from his bitter life. To avoid this mindset, we would have to earn more than the basic woodcutter, and hoped to do this by processing the raw material into higher-value products. Apart from chainsaw replacing axe and billhook, and the tractor instead of horse transport, coppice work had barely become more productive since tracks based on woven coppice sticks were laid across Sedgemoor 5,000 years ago. Coppicing was still a highly labour-intensive system, but woodsmen now expected to earn enough for cars and holidays, and, in these days of international free trade, we would be in competition with far-eastern wage rates. As I tried to formulate a plan, I had an O M G moment, wondering what we had taken on. Were we pitting ourselves against the onward march of progress like dreaming romantics, or could we find the elusive answer where others had failed?

In our rambles we had observed countless coppices that had not been cut for decades, made worse by an influx of species such as willow and alder which are useless to a modern coppice worker, who specialises in hazel or chestnut. Neglect a coppice, and the trees grow year by year until the weight of the stems proves too much and the stools blow over, while others decay, or die back from lack of light. Restoring a neglected coppice is an expensive business, as the first cut may yield little usable material apart from firewood, and so the work may need to be subsidised. Fortunately, most of Wilderness Wood had been cut in the last few years and its trees were sweet chestnut, a species which still had a market. Many coppices had been replanted with chestnut for its fast, straight growth and natural rot-resistance. Durable heartwood is laid down after only three years' growth, compared with its close relation, oak, where you have to wait ten to fifteen years. With chestnut, only the outer centimetre rots readily, leaving a strong, durable heartwood core. It is therefore first class for fencing and garden constructions. In addition, it cleaves readily, and the woodsman, equipped with hammer and froe, axe and wedges, can quickly split fence posts and rails, pales, or even shingles, as we had done for our Barn. Cleaving is much faster than hand-sawing, of fundamental importance in the days before mechanisation. Grown to timber size and sawn for planks or beams, chestnut is virtually indistinguishable from oak.

Within a few months of buying the wood, I had evolved a strategy for the management of the coppices. Reluctant to have so many eggs in such a shaky basket, we decided to reduce the area by about a third. Some of the coppiced ground would be sacrificed to other uses – our sheep paddock and Christmas tree plantation. We would bring two-thirds of the remaining coppices back into a regular 15-20 year rotation, and start by cutting about half a hectare a year - so that we would eventually have a regular supply of material suitable for products such as fencing and rustic poles. It seemed that our predecessors had "farmed to quit", and instead of a range of different age classes, most of the coppice we inherited had been cut in the previous five years. There was consequently little of harvestable size. Therefore, in the early years we would coppice only relatively small areas. To re-establish an even distribution of cants, we would have to cut into the extensive areas of three- to five-year-old coppice. We chose an area suitable for making bean-poles and pea-sticks, plant stakes, and firewood, for which we already had a limited market. As an owner keen to make a start, I really put my back into felling and processing those first few dozen stools, and found aching limbs better than any sleeping draught. I reasoned that if I, a largely desk-bound 39-year-old, could make bean-poles profitably, so could younger, fitter souls.

The remaining third we would gradually convert to "high forest" by a system known as "storing", which is a relatively quick way of obtaining large trees. Storing is the process of thinning out stems on a stool, leaving a few to grow on and concentrating the growth into these stems. The process can be repeated a number of times until one stem is left. My rationale was twofold. Firstly, we wanted more large trees for visual reasons. Secondly, the demand for coppice products was declining inexorably, whereas there would always be a market for hardwood timber (timber from broadleaved trees), that could be sawn into planks for sale or our own use.

Because it is all manual work, and therefore costly, the actual process of coppicing has to be meticulously thought out. We had to evolve a system that wasted as little time as possible, but made the best use of every stick cut. Each worker has his own favourite working system, and if he is to stay in business it will be an efficient one. Observe an experienced coppice worker, and you may notice his steady pace, his neat piles of produce, the cheerful fire blazing not far away. Study more closely, especially if you have tried some of the work yourself, and you will see not a wasted movement. The curved end of his billhook acts as an extension of his arm, so that he lifts the next pole without having to bend so far. He will have felled each pole so that lop and top can be chucked the minimum distance onto the fire, or to form a mat for the extraction route he has planned. In short, he has worked out the whole process to minimise his time and effort

Our yearly half hectare cut would yield about 3,000 stems to fell, trim, cross-cut, stack, load, transport and unload, all by hand. As our product range developed, we found that the most valuable coppice material was straight lengths of chestnut two to three metres long, for rustic poles and for making trellises and rose arches. Shorter, stout, chestnut poles would be fencing material, and the thinner ones cross-pieces for rustic work and furniture. At the base of each chestnut stem, we would look out for a curved piece to form the back leg of a garden seat or the top of a rose arch. Each kind would be thrown onto its pile, for extraction later. All the bent pieces, and non-chestnut species, were stacked at rideside as 1.3 metre cordwood lengths, to be covered with polythene sheeting and cut the following winter into firewood. Birch tops were thrown onto their own piles, to be converted into bundles of pea-sticks.

Our Wilderness Wood business model meant that every season brought different tasks, from cutting and extracting coppice, tending Christmas trees and making garden products, to maintaining trails and teaching school groups. We realised early on that we needed year-round, permanent staff. Each had to become a jack-of-all-trades, and we fondly hoped the constant challenge and variety of work would make the job interesting. The downside was that no-one became really fast and proficient at more than a few tasks, and coppicing was an operation that we might better have contracted out to a real expert. It was undoubtedly unrealistic to expect we could achieve an expert's level of productivity after just a season or two. Productivity included details like remembering to take sufficient fuel, tea and lunchbox, to avoid trips back to the workshop. Such trips meant little relaxation unless the permitted thirty minutes' break became fifty, and my suggestion that a proportional drop in pay might be fair was understandably unpopular.

Because of multi-tasking, it was seldom possible to devote full days or weeks to coppice work, and piece-work was difficult to apply. Only when we took on casual labour could we pay per pole felled, trimmed and stacked. The target was seventy poles a day, each one cut to length and stacked.

Coppice must be cut in the winter, between November and March. This would have fitted into the traditional farming year, but there are other, more compelling, reasons. Tree leaves used to be valued as animal fodder, but these days they just increase the weight of material to be manhandled. Secondly, manual woodland work is best done outside the heat of summer, especially now one is encased in protective clothing, and dying of heatstroke a real risk. But, most importantly, if you have the health of the stools at heart you cut when the nutrient-rich sap of the tree is stored away in the roots for winter. The sweet sap that oozes from birches cut in late winter, sprouting lurid slime moulds that even Anne could not begin to identify, is a reminder of how much of the tree's energy is lost in the stems and leaves of a summer cut. For us, coppicing had to compete with the ever-busier Christmas season, as well as firewooding and tree planting (replacement Christmas trees, at the very least), and the end of March always seemed to gallop towards us all too quickly.

The subject of fires can generate a lot of heat. By its nature, coppice produces a substantial amount of small branches, and in times past every last twig would have been carefully bundled into faggots for firing ovens. Nowadays, this lop and top is waste material which can trip you as you work, so the temptation is to get rid of it. Add the chance to put down chainsaw or billhook and straighten your back, never mind warming your backside, and a bonfire becomes irresistible. However, mindful that every minute spent tending a fire is a minute lost to actual production, we needed to minimise the use of fires. Their downsides also include scorching nearby stools; loss of nutrients gone up in smoke or washed away in the next downpour; and the loss of habitat for ground-nesting birds, mammals and fungi. Finally, a fire can all too easily get out of control in the dry, windy conditions of early spring, and we well remember the time we were torn between running to call the fire brigade, and staying to put out the flames that were blowing frighteningly fast through the dry leaves. After that we never had a fire without a fire-beater to hand; and in later days a mobile 'phone, though a good deal of the wood had no signal.

I compromised with our woodsman Andrew and his crew that only half of the lop and top should be cremated, but there was always a temptation for unsupervised youngsters to have a bonfire every day, as they were employed by the hour, rather than on piece-rate. Few teenagers these days have lit a fire in the grate at home, or belonged to the Scouts, so effective fire-lighting was a skill we had to teach each trainee. All too often their supply of dry paper would run out under a pile of damp sticks, or they would smother their struggling fire under a huge pile of branches. The centre would burn out, leaving a hollow core inside a mound of charred and steaming boughs, which I would unceremoniously haul off to get to the remains of the fire. "Never put branches on the fire above the height of the flames" became the mantra by which they learned their fire-craft. I also stipulated that any fire should be lit at the beginning of the day, so that the inevitable first half-hour of almost constant supervision would be justified by several hours of efficient burning, when whole branch-lengths could be thrown on without wasting time in cutting them up. Better one big fire every three days than a small one daily. By not feeding the fire for the last couple of hours, and giving it plenty of time to burn down, there was less risk of it spreading when left. If a new fire were needed the next day, a few shovelfuls of embers from the previous one would speed its creation, without recourse to paper, let alone the used car tyres favoured by the old-timers.

Poles down in the wood were worth little, and we needed them in the yard for sale or processing. Extraction could take place at any time ground conditions permitted until June, when the growing shoots on the coppice stools become too vulnerable. The ground was likely to be driest in spring and early summer, but we tried to avoid running over bluebell areas between March and June. Their leaves would already be pushing up under the carpet of dead leaves by February. In practice, we rarely managed to get the poles off in time. In past times, apart from being slippery to walk on, it is unlikely that woodsmen would have bothered to avoid the bluebells, and crushing once every fifteen years or so probably does little harm. But bluebells were for us an important visitor attraction, and people would not appreciate seeing them squashed, especially when we were asking them to keep off!

Coppicing in full swing

Our productivity was hampered by hand-loading every single coppice pole, as we could not justify a tractor-mounted crane that would be underused for much of the year. We did, however, acquire an old builder's dumper. This proved to be the ideal tool for us, with the double advantages of excellent manoeuvrability and fast unloading. You simply tipped up the bucket and out fell the contents! It was also invaluable when we needed to transport soil and roots from areas we were clearing for car parking. Our first dumper was hand-started, but had the vice of back-firing, which on one occasion broke Tim's hand. Tim was my consultancy assistant, and spent any spare time earning his pay in the wood as our foreman. We quickly upgraded to one with an electric starter, and thereafter suffered only flat batteries. The engine of this elderly vehicle smoked embarrassingly as it chugged past our visitors, and did little to endorse our green credentials. The bucket took material such as cordwood and fencing material up to two and a half metres long. For longer poles we had to use our tractor-hauled trailer, but beginners often got bogged down, usually astride a coppice stool. Each spring we reserved a pile of poles for the local Working Horse Trust, whose horses and volunteers came to extract a few tonnes of material in front of admiring crowds.

The ideal cant shape would be square rather than long and narrow, in order to minimise the length of boundary. Boundaries cause overshadowing by the older surrounding crop, depressing the new growth. Also, regrowth is vulnerable to depredations by deer, which naturally like to stay close to cover; so the bigger the cant, the better the growth and less the damage. A square-shaped half-hectare would have 70-metre sides, but our little wood seldom had suitable areas that large, so often two cants would be cut. How often we regretted cutting a small area, when we saw shoots browsed off by deer in June!

Within a few weeks of buying the wood we realised that there was great variety in the quality of coppice growth, from average to down-right awful, and we concluded that this was largely a factor of soil, and age of stools. I greatly envied the far better coppice woodland on the north side of the village, shown as farmland on early nineteenth century maps, and presumably on soil whose nutrients had been replenished by farming practices. Our massive stools, up to two metres across, were far older, and many were ailing. We knew that long-term coppicing deletes soil fertility, as every last twig was taken out of the wood over the centuries, and unlike farmland, no liming or fertilising took place to restore nutrients.

By far the worst coppice was on the central spur below Owl Wood, and I assumed this was why Scots pines had been planted here twenty years earlier. After planting, the understocked and slow-growing coppice would have provided little competition for the pines. Sadly, the limited records from the previous agents gave no clues on this point. The recession of the early 'nineties meant that Tim and I had very little consulting work, so had time to carry out a proper forester-style enumeration of coppice throughout the wood. This involved one-hundredth-hectare sample plots, in which we recorded the species, number of stools, number of stems, their diameters, height at ten years and current height. From this we were able to determine the productivity of each area, but this elaborate exercise in all honesty only confirmed what my now-trained eyes told me. The poorer coppice tended to be short and crooked, with fewer stems per stool. The stools were less densely spaced, and the intervening land was filled with self-sown birch and willow.

In the early days we considered these as wasted spaces, for a chestnut worker had no use for these other species, which were therefore dismissed as "weeds". Where gaps between the stools were greater than five metres, we planted chestnut transplants in protective tree shelters, or "layered" poles from a neighbouring tree. To layer, you partially cut through a chestnut stem, bend it over and peg it down, throwing soil over the stem where it touches the ground, to encourage rooting. Both planting and layering proved initially successful in establishing new young trees, but these soon became swamped by the vigorous growth of the surrounding coppice. Good, established chestnut coppice will grow over two metres in the first year after cutting, and in the hot summer of 1989 it grew by double this. Unlike the established stools, with massive root systems occupying all available soil, the poor little transplants' roots are barely larger than a handspan, so after three years they were still less than a metre tall, and over-topped by adjacent coppice. For the new trees to succeed, you must re-coppice the surrounding trees after five years to put all trees on a similar footing; but we had no market for so much small material, so we let them grow on. Sadly, most transplants and layers therefore died in the shade, our efforts marked by forlorn, empty tree shelters. After the first few years we ceased gapping up, and accepted the birch and willow as freely-given firewood when we next coppiced.

In order to diversify the wood, and to produce larger trees quickly, we commenced storing about half a hectare of ground at the southern edge of the wood, with relatively good soil and drainage, and some of the best growth we had. The trees had been last coppiced in 1969, and after twelve years were already eleven metres tall. I marked with a blob of paint the best three stems per stool for retention. These were always the straightest, preferably chosen so that their crowns would each have similar space in the canopy in which to spread; and ideally at the edge of the stool so that, as they grew, they would develop their own roots, rather than being perched on top of a decaying stool. The unmarked stems were felled by two young woodsmen. Excluding my time spent on marking and supervision, the labour cost of that first thinning was £550, but the material emerging was worth some £1,200 retail (1981 prices). We made an acceptable profit, provided we ignored our retail overheads, and had the expectation that profits would increase at each thinning, as the size and quality of material improved. A woodsman's skill and judgment are crucial, especially when he has to be left unsupervised for days at a time. Imagine my frustration on finding that large bonfires had been built close to remaining stems, scorching the sides facing the fires to a height of five metres. Unlike humans, whose blood conducts away heat, a tree's bark quickly gets hot, and the underlying cambium is killed. That part of the stem dies, a wound opens to the air, and rot enters the tree. If the wound does manage to grow over, there will be an area of discoloured wood or the trunk will become hollow, and useless for anything but firewood. And these were the BEST trees!

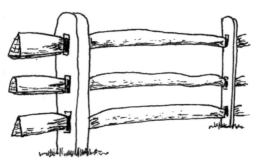

Traditional cleft rail fencing

The area we first thinned in this way became known as "the stored area", and we repeated the thinning again at six to seven year intervals, each time leaving the best stems. In the latter three thinnings, the material was sold standing to Bill, a specialist maker of the traditional Wealden post and cleft rail fencing. In some cases he could get over fifteen rails from a single stem, each worth to us 75 pence; and Bill was doing all the work, leaving us a small amount of firewood as a bonus. Lately, Andrew was able to convert the sizeable stems to high quality planks for use in garden and other furniture. By the time we sold the wood this area looked like a well-established and mature woodland, with trunks up to 40 centimetres diameter and 23 metres high; and yet the stems were only 44 years old.

Within the trunk, larger diameter chestnut often has cracks around the annual rings, known as "ring shake": thought to be partly genetic and partly due to soil conditions. None of those felled exhibited this fault, giving us hope for the future. One advantage of storing is that it can be done at any time of the year, because the additional sap from the roots goes to the remaining stems, and the stool seems not to suffer. All-year storing permits the "supermarket shelf" approach to supplying orders, rather than relying on large stocks in the yard. The main disadvantage of summer-felled timber is the high sap content. Combined with rapid drying on long, hot days, this can cause cracking, especially if the poles are peeled, and we found it advisable to leave summer-cut produce for as long as possible in a cool, shady place with the bark on before using it.

Walking around coppices, including our own, I have noticed in recent years increasing numbers of chestnut crowns dying back, and bark peeling off near the base of stems. Individual stems, whole stools, and in some unfortunate cases up to a quarter hectare, may be affected. The problem is caused by a fungus-like organism, *Phytopthora*, related to potato blight. Encouraged by wet conditions, this root disease is killing chestnut coppices all over south-east England, and there is no cure. It can probably be spread by deer, so disinfecting our boots and keeping the public out is no solution. We harvested dead and dying material, but informed advice has little to offer to stop its spread.

Woodland management evolves with human needs. It is generally considered that the intense cropping of the coppice system degraded forest soils, leading to longer cycles and poorer material, together with declining vigour of individual stools, which owners have been reluctant to grub up and replace. From being the predominant woodland management system, coppicing had generally become a historic relic by the time our stewardship started. Fortunately, rot-resistant sweet chestnut still found a market for fencing and other outdoor products, although with a diminishing band of coppice craftsmen willing to work it. Demand for traditional products such as pales has declined, and bulk markets such as pulp and fuel chips are hard to meet at a profit, as coppice does not lend itself to mechanisation. Coppicing can suit part-time or hobby woodsmen because of its modest equipment needs, provided they can find outlets for its products. We managed to build up on-site sales at the luxury end of the market so successfully that we had to supplement our production with bought-in chestnut poles from other local woods, providing welcome cash-in-hand for the small remaining band of lone workers.

Even the best-laid plans sometimes fall foul of Nature, and a strong wind from the south-east in December 2013 threw over some of our best stored stems. There may be a maximum height we can allow our trees to reach on our thin soils, before they become prone to windblow. But with climate change and an onslaught of *Phytophthora*, even Wilderness Wood may have to change its direction again, and windblow may be the least of its problems.

GROWING BIG TREES

"**W**hy are the trees so amazingly straight?" a visitor once asked me as we walked round the Top Plantation, and I suddenly realised that much of a forester's work is simply not understood. I had to explain that, without the forester's intervention, woods produced large numbers of poorly-shaped trees, not the tall, fat, straight trunks that would fetch a good price at the sawmill. And as well as being valuable for timber, at Wilderness Wood we wanted big trees to make the place more attractive. My own undergraduate survey in 1964, and much other research, confirmed that people like large trees more than smaller ones. In Wilderness Wood our sole tall tree, the Big Beech on the eastern boundary, stood at 35 metres, and there were a few middle-sized oaks and beech in the hedgerows on the south and west boundaries. Elsewhere the coppices and young plantations were unimpressively short.

Most of our plantations had been created around 1960, as confirmed by the records we were given at purchase, and by a friend in the village who had actually helped plant them for the firm managing the wood. They had been established according to standard forestry practice of the time, by planting small trees at regular, close spacing of about two metres: mostly conifers, plus lines of beech in the Top Plantation. They would have been weeded for three or four years, and failures replaced, and then left to their own devices for twelve to fifteen years or so, until the forester made his way through the brambles and bracken to see how his client's trees were growing. If he was lucky, someone had brashed them, or cut off the lower dead branches, so that he could pass easily between the trees.

When we bought the wood our twenty-year-old plantations had reached nine metres in height, but had scope to grow to 25 metres over the next half century. However, I would need to intervene by carefully felling poor trees and giving more light and space to the better ones; otherwise they would grow tall and spindly, and many would fall over before they had reached a useful size. This process of "thinning" concentrates the yearly increment of wood on the trees that will have most value. Depending on the growth-rate, we could expect to thin every five years or so. Under the conventional plantation system, this intermittent harvest would be repeated until trees reached the "final crop" size, at an age of about 60 years for the pines, and 120 for the beech. These remaining trees would all be felled, and the site re-planted, in a system known as "clear-cutting".

Left alone, trees grow as tall as they can. They have evolved to reach upwards to the light, competing with their neighbours, and suppressing less vigorous specimens. The most successful occupy the highest levels in the forest canopy; other species have evolved to tolerate the partial shade of the lower levels, and gaps caused by dead trees, fire and so on. Such forests are known as "high forest", as opposed to ones where people do not allow trees to reach their ultimate height, such as coppices. High forest, whether of natural or plantation origin, is the way by which most woods and forests are now managed in order to grow large trees and produce the timber we use in such vast quantities. The discipline by which a forester manages such woods and forests is called "silviculture", of which there are several types, depending on the circumstances. With my own wood at last, I could now practise my own brand of silvics, as they called it in Montana.

When we first ventured among the twenty-year-old trees of Ant and Owl Woods and the Top Plantation, I could immediately see that thinning was needed soon. Although every fourth row had been removed four year earlier, crowns were touching, heavily-branched "wolf" trees threatened to suppress their better neighbours, and thin, drawn-up "whips" were likely to snap under the next heavy snow, or blow around, damaging their neighbours. A French forester once told me us that "thinning is a noble task", meaning that immediate profit is seldom the main objective. This is the absolute opposite of exploitative fellings, when a timber merchant is allowed to "take what you like", with an inevitable decline of the wood's value. A forester usually leaves the best trees to grow on, for the good of the forest, and the benefit of those who follow. In France, where there is a tradition of excellent silviculture, even the top brass of the State forest service expect to get out regularly to mark a thinning. It is where all a forester's skills come together, as he takes account of the needs of different species, the soil, the exposure to winds or frosts, and how the stand of trees will have developed in five or ten years time at the next thinning. He must also bear in mind markets, present and future. Does he favour the faster-growing trees, or perhaps the ones that may improve the soil but are less marketable? Does he stick to the objectives laid down decades earlier, or does he bend to the latest fashion? Get two or three foresters together, and they always generate a vigorous yet respectful argument on how to mark a thinning! In our case there was no-one to argue, and I was able to get on and clear out poor specimens as I saw fit, with these early removals being processed for low-value firewood for our own use or for sale.

From those first student field trips into young spruce plantations and clear-fell areas on Snowdonian hillsides, I had a gut feeling that there must be a better way to organise forests. Unless I altered matters, our little plantations in Wilderness Wood would perpetuate the shortcomings of the clear-cut/replant system. When a large area of trees is felled, "forest conditions" are lost: the water table rises, and the ground is exposed to full sunlight, resulting in rampant growth of weeds such as bracken and brambles which swamp the replanted trees, requiring expensive weeding. Out in the open, the newly planted trees grow coarse, heavy branches, and have wide annual rings, yielding poor timber until competition with neighbours slows down their growth rate. For over half the life of the plantation, thinnings yield lower grade wood, fit only for firewood, pulp or woodchip, and harvested at little or no profit. Not least of the objections is that the general public does not like the sudden change to the landscape caused by clear felling. Since the days of Capability Brown, they have preferred the romantic image of bucolic wildness, as depicted in the art of Claude and Poussin, with the natural world minimally influenced by Man.

So, from the 1980's, a few British foresters began to consider other ways of managing and re-establishing trees. One such alternative is known as Continuous Cover Forestry, or CCF. This has formed a major role in Continental silviculture for many years, and at Bangor I learned all about the mysteries of *Wagner's Blendersaumschlag*, French systems of *Uniform Shelterwood*, and the intricacies of *Single Tree Selection*. These, and other variations of CCF, have a common theme: the woods are composed of a variety of tree ages and sizes, and are never clear-felled. Where possible, natural regeneration is used, and one works with Nature, rather than against it.

CCF has many advantages over the clear-cut system. Firstly, trees are always present, and visual changes are minimal; it creates an attractive mixture of tree sizes and a wider range of niches for wildlife, with far less habitat disturbance. The uneven tree heights give the trees greater stability in windy conditions, and older trees can seed regeneration, sheltering it from drought and wind. In terms of production it has been calculated that, in well-established CCF forests, 85 percent of the timber comes out as the more valuable sawlog sizes, with better ring-widths and fewer knots, compared with only 50 percent in the conventional clear-fell system. Finally, CCF is more flexible than even-aged systems, where the product size range is limited, and you must never delay a thinning.

If CCF is so good, why it is not more widely practiced? Why were my plantations just one age group? The simple answer is that it is inevitably more complicated than clear-cut systems. For a professional silviculturalist, it is the equivalent of cuisine as opposed to catering, and, if one has the time and inclination, something to embrace with enthusiasm. Sadly, many forests are still at the level of the factory canteen, churning out stodge at the lowest possible price. Although inherently flexible, the system requires a long-term policy commitment, otherwise efforts to manage the stand structure will be misunderstood or wasted. It takes decades to achieve an ideal range of tree sizes, with their numbers in the right proportions to ensure a continuous supply of high-value large trees. It is relatively easy to detect if an even-aged plantation is under- or over-stocked, whereas a wide area of CCF forest must be sampled to determine if trees of different sizes are present in the right proportions: skilled, painstaking work, requiring good record-keeping, and the process must be repeated every few years to monitor progress. There are other drawbacks: trees to be harvested are scattered through the forest, and it's difficult to use large machinery. It creates large uniform areas, without the open spaces associated with clear-felling, with little room for light-loving flora and fauna.

Despite its drawbacks, and perhaps because I didn't mind going my own way, I was resolved to convert a significant proportion of our plantations to CCF. But where should we start? Being right in the public eye, the pines of the Top Plantation between the Main Road and our new yard were an obvious candidate. Few in 1981 had attempted a conversion such as this, so Anne and I visited Lord Bradford's Devon estate, where he and his forester Phil Hutt had pioneered a system which came to be known as the Bradford-Hutt Plan. Put simply, in an established plantation they felled a ninth of the area every six years, by dividing the area into 18-metre squares and, within each, felling a six-metre by six-metre plot. In each felled plot they planted about nine trees. After 54 years, they would have nine different sizes of tree evenly spread throughout the wood. A line of trees was felled at eighteen-metre intervals for access, and, at each intervention, remaining trees from the original planting were thinned in the normal way. Having laid out the grid, it was said you could leave it all to the bloke with the chainsaw, who would be able to locate and replant each new plot, and thin the intervening trees with little supervision. We were entranced!

The rather dour Forestry Commission District Officer from Uckfield did not like the idea of felling prematurely the number of trees the Bradford Plan entailed and, although he couldn't stop us, refused to sanction a replanting grant. Heaven know what he would have said if he had been around to witness the excesses of PAWS restoration! Undaunted, by the spring of 1981 we had cleared and planted 24 plots in the Top Plantation with western red cedar (Thuja) and European larch, and carried out a thinning of the surrounding trees. Each transplant was protected against rabbits by a plastic tree shelter. Thuja was perfect. It suited the peaty soil and thrived in the partial shade. What is more, it could be easily propagated in the small leafmould nursery bed we had created. To supply ourselves with trees, we simply tore 15-centimetre tips of foliage from a neighbour's hedge, dipped the stalks in rooting compound, and stuck them in the ground, watering occasionally in hot weather. Presto! Nine months later we had well-rooted cuttings at a fraction of the cost of bought-in stock, and, with no delay between lifting and planting, the little trees were in perfect condition to plant out.

In my enthusiasm to get started, I gave insufficient consideration to the selection of species. The larch hated our wood: wrong soil, and nothing like enough light. It faded into oblivion, suffocated in the over-enthusiastic embrace of resurgent bracken. Not learning from a fundamental mistake, the following winter we "beat up" (replanted) the failures, only for them to die again within a few weeks. How had I so easily forgotten those lessons from Prof. Mobbs on the correct selection of trees? Next year in the Owl and Ant Wood plantations we used southern beech and European beech in our "Bradford plots", but neither thrived in the poor soils. Was that distant thunder, or Mobbs turning in his grave again? Having specialised in recreation planning, I had been away too long from practical silviculture; as a trained forester, I was offering my critics a pair of cobbler's shoes.

Six years later it was time to clear and plant the next set of squares, each on the north side of the first, so that the new trees would benefit from side light from the space to the south. The system allows one to vary the species composition, and we wanted to get away from the taint of monoculture by employing a wider palette of trees. This time we planted Douglas fir, which I believed would suit the site. I was right, for it grew vigorously, except that it tended to become spindly with insufficient side-light.

The classic CCF of Europe aims to rely on natural regeneration, that is, trees that grow naturally from seeds of the older trees nearby. Sadly, few British foresters have much experience with natural regeneration, and tend to look on it as a problem, possibly because it is so often of unwanted species, such as birch, aspen and willow. Even when useful saplings establish themselves at no cost, they like to thin out the dense regrowth into straight lines!

Getting your replacement seedlings naturally depends on having shade-bearing trees of timber value already present as mature trees, and many parts of mainland Europe are blessed with a wide range of such natives, including silver fir and spruce. Beech and hornbeam are our only native timber trees sufficiently tolerant of shade, but neither is really suited to many sites, including ours. Shade-bearing holly grows at the wood with enthusiasm, and adds to its diversity, but is too small and slow-growing to be a useful timber tree. We therefore have to rely on other countries to supply us with species suited to the shadier conditions of the lower canopies, and are fortunate that the Pacific Northwest of America can furnish us with trees that flourish in our similar cool, maritime climate. Hence the shade-bearing Thuja, the western hemlock (Tsuga), and the citrus-scented Douglas, with fantastically strong timber much sought after by the sawmiller, which all grow happily at Wilderness Wood. Hemlock regenerates so readily that some estates consider it a weed, because British sawmills do not like it, unlike their Canadian counterparts. However, we would be delighted if it regenerated, along with the Scots, Thuja and Douglas. We found pine seedlings taking root over a hundred metres from their parent trees, and Anne often noticed them on her fungus hunts in October, but most had gone by the following spring. Our "nat. regen," as foresters term them, suffered from deer and rabbit browsing, a much greater problem than on the Continent, where wildlife is better controlled. We undoubtedly could have done more to encourage regeneration by scarifying the ground to provide a good seedbed, and then protecting the young plants from browsing.

Our second round of plots was barely established when our plans were knocked sideways by the Great Storm of October 1987, and we devote a separate chapter to this horror. It is said that when one door closes, another opens, and the storm forced us to reassess our efforts to embrace CCF. The greatest devastation was in the hilltop Top Plantation, right in the public eye. We would obviously have to retain every worthwhile tree, and fortunately there were plenty of surviving pine and beech between the house and Main Road, and next to the play area and picnic site. The core of the plantation was almost a blank slate, apart from our six-metre plots of young Thuja. Before the storm we had concluded that such small plots were over-shaded by surrounding trees, so decided that in future each 18-metre grid square would be divided into four plots of nine metres square, and each with a different species. We extended the existing six-metre-square Thuja plots with the same species. To their north, a square of Douglas fir; to their east, a square of beech; and, above the beech, a square of Norway spruce. The storm tore out the middle of Owl Wood, and here we replanted with pure Douglas, mimicking natural stands of a single species which can occur in nature after a storm or fire.

Douglas Fir   Thuja
(western red cedar)

Our continuous cover plantations became foci for extending the areas of high forest into adjacent coppice. To blur the outlines of Owl Wood and Ant Wood, we established clumps of Douglas and Thuja around their peripheries. These clumps were about twenty metres across, separated by similar sized areas of coppice, which we stored. Clumps and stored coppice now form a significant element of the CCF area, and soften the edges where it adjoins the coppice.

Without doubt our rejuvenated plantations at Wilderness Wood became the most attractive parts of the wood, to both people and wildlife. Overhead, the wide-spreading crowns of the pines feed huge amounts of energy to their orange-hued trunks, enabling them to grow generous amounts of high-value timber on these, the most valuable trees. The crowns provide roosts for owls and perches for hawks. Below, the young generations stretch skywards, devoting their energies to gaining height, and making do with thin, light branches which create only small knots in the straight, close-grained timber that typifies the trees of multi-storey woodlands. As well as providing nesting and roosting sites, the thickets of Thuja provide concealment for deer, and children playing hide-and-seek. Young trees are sheltered from extremes of sun and frost; seedlings escape the deer's eye. Our fellings are so light and scattered that a year later we have to search hard for stumps to remind ourselves where individual trees were cut. If we find that difficult, how inconspicuous must our harvesting be to our visitors and neighbours!

We were able to harvest a whole range of material from our CCF areas. From the earliest days, prunings from the lower crowns of Thuja and Douglas fir supplied foliage for sale at Christmas, and branches for children's shelter-building. High pruning with an extendable pruning saw was a therapeutic job that I reserved for myself. At the end of a pruning session you can really see the impact, revealing lovely, straight trunks, and knowing they will grow on to provide fine, knot-free timber. In 2007, planks from the pines provided the frame and weatherboard cladding for our Barn extension. Early thinnings of both Douglas and Thuja were sold as tepee poles for over £20 each. We supplied twenty-centimetre diameter trunks for a log cabin, and no doubt this could be a lucrative market in future. The continuous cover system pays little heed to how old a tree is, but in 2010 we built an extension to the converted mill that Anne and I moved into, using wood milled from trees we had planted only 22 years earlier. People commonly believe you only plant trees for future generations. Building our house extension with timber from trees we had planted was one of the most satisfying things I have done.

High-pruning to produce knot-free timber

In 2010 we were delighted and proud to win first prize in the silvicultural class of the Royal Forestry Society's Excellence in Forestry competition. The judges were impressed with the intensity of management and profitable multiple use, but what pleased us especially was the full-colour photo in the Society's magazine of an area of our CCF, and the judges' reference to our pioneering place in this field. Recognition by one's peers can be the ultimate accolade, and it is said that winning an Oscar extends an actor's lifespan by four years. Will I now live to exceed my mother's extraordinary span of 102?

THE GREAT STORM

nne had been tossing and turning with a feverish cold, listening with increasing alarm to the creaks and groans of our timber-framed house. Nearby trees screamed as the wind tore up the valley; gates crashed against their posts, and the night sky lit up as if by lightning as power cables of the National Grid shorted four miles to the south. It was the night of Thursday 16th October 1987, a date indelibly etched on the mind of every landowner and forester in south-east England. That night, between one and five am, a near-hurricane-force wind swept in off the Channel, with the eye of the storm making landfall near Worthing. Lifting garden sheds into the air, turning over caravans, taking roofs off houses, and felling countless trees, the storm headed north-eastwards across Sussex and Kent. Crossing the Thames Estuary, it swept unimpeded across the flat East Anglian landscape, slipping once more onto salt water, whence it had gained its power.

The impact of the Great Storm was likened to the effects of atomic war. Communications were severed, power in all forms ceased, and citizens had to fall back on their own resources, a novel experience for many. You might think that a family living by the tenets of self-sufficiency would take it in its stride. Perhaps we did, and the worst storm in 300 years had surprisingly little impact on our long-term direction for the wood.

Unable to stand it any longer, Anne woke her snoring husband with an elbow in the ribs and "The sheep are out. They're in the garden." I stumbled downstairs in the darkness. Flashes in the sky lit up the silver trunks of the six-metre-high birches in the orchard, their tops bent horizontal, and leaves and small branches whistled by. But the overarching impression was of warmth. Barefoot, with only a dressing gown for cover, it felt like standing by the downheater of a large store. We later learned that the temperature had risen seven degrees centigrade in one hour, a common feature of the sort of tropical storm we were experiencing.

The three sheep must have been relieved to see me, as they willingly trotted back to the familiarity of the orchard, forsaking the forbidden delights of the vegetable garden. The gate was still on its wire hinges, and only needed another piece of baler twine to keep the woollies in, so with some relief I returned to a fretting wife upstairs.

By three am, the house began to voice new sounds. With mains power gone, torchlight investigation revealed that the east wall of the house, a few feet from our bed-head, was flexing away by as much as a centimetre as each gust passed. We shall never know how much more wind it would have taken to suck away the whole east side of the house, but I volubly cursed the carpenter for leaving out the wall ties which should have reinforced this point. We checked the children's rooms, found them fast asleep, returned to bed and exhaustedly joined them in sleep ourselves, as the storm subsided into a gale.

We awoke at 7.20 with the 'phone in the office ringing insistently. Bleary-eyed, I heard Dave, our trainee woodsman, stating that there were trees blown down across the road, and he wouldn't be in on time. I raised my eyes to the window and saw light. This was not the normal early morning glimmer descending down the gap between house and trees, but bright light shining unimpeded from the west, where a vista of clear sky smiled across a sea of fallen pines and beech. "Hell, so have we. See if you can get in."

The events of the night came flooding back. No, it hadn't been a cheese-induced nightmare. On all sides, our world had changed. Broadleaved trees, yesterday still in full leaf, were now bare. Where once there were dense crowns, now broken limbs pointed to the sky across ragged gaps. The beech and Scots pine plantation that we had recently so carefully thinned was now a mass of leaning trunks, like dominos waiting for the signal to topple. Everywhere the ground lay hidden beneath a shambles of snapped limbs, fallen trunks and foliage. To the south, through salt-stained windows, the distant view to the Downs had suddenly expanded. Our coppice and pines had fallen in groups, revealing vistas of the Blackboys ridge two miles away. It, too, had a new jagged profile, where yesterday woods and lines of trees had stood, and beyond it on the skyline we could now see Wilmington Hill, of Long Man fame. A bright sun shone from an almost clear sky, as if to say "Have a lovely day".

Turning on the battery radio, we began to learn how widespread and devastating the "hurricane" had been. All schools in the county were closed. Travel was impossible, with railway lines and roads blocked by fallen trees. There was no electricity across the Southeast. Perhaps a premonition had induced me to lay the telephone cable in a trench from the road to the house, and so we still had contact with the outside world. We 'phoned to reassure both sets of grandparents. My parents in Lewes, 14 miles upwind, had lost a few slates from the roof and were more concerned for their elderly neighbours than for us or themselves. Anne's parents, who had a London *pied-à-terre* by Tower Bridge, wondered why on earth we were calling them at eight am to tell them we were all right. "Why shouldn't you be?" They were quite unaware of the storm that had passed by their treeless enclave of dockland redevelopment in the preceding hours.

No through trail. Kate shows her toy dog the Storm damage

As Anne always says, a forester needs to do a survey before he can act. We needed to make a tour of our domain to see the extent of the damage, but it was difficult to walk a few metres, let alone all round the wood. The crucial hundred metres to the Main Road involved clambering over or under dozens of trees blocking the drive. From the woodland entrance, we could see the road stretching away on the other side of Wilderness Lane, 150 metres to the west. But between lay a carpet of our 20-year-old pines, neatly laid down with their tips just touching the hedge on the far side of the carriageway. They had fallen in formation at 3.20 that morning. We could pinpoint the time by learning later of a lorry that had passed by on its way to Manchester at 3.15 am; the driver had turned back after encountering a fallen oak at the west end of the village, only to find our pines were now blocking his way out of the devastated South-east.

The storm had blown from the south-west, and when my friend Dick took me for a flight over the Weald of Sussex and Kent in his

Our wood at purchase. Central Ride, looking over
a sea of young coppice to west boundary trees

Anne's dad contemplates a tree three times his age.
The Big Beech on the east boundary was our tallest tree

Jo in the foxgloves, 1981

Four-year-old Kate explores the bluebells

Looking down the entrance road alignment
through 20-year-old pines

More or less the same view, 25 years later.
Note the increased size of trees

Newly-laid spur road to site of the house, 1982

The same view, with house

Our first family lunch in the house was in the larder,
with Anne's parents. Note the primitive pole seat

A view to die for. Looking from our house over
the wood towards the South Downs

A 1950s postcard of the Main Road, before our
Top Plantation was established

West of our entrance after the Great Storm, October 1987.
The fallen tree tops had reached the far pavement

Sixty years after the postcard, with storm-blown
trees now replaced

Hidden away in the Top Plantation prior to the Storm, the play area became visible from the Main Road

The storm-damaged Top Plantation 20 years later, under conversion to continuous cover. Note the surviving pine on left, and the chestnut and birch among the planted Thuja and Douglas fir

A villager and dog on the East Ride. Recently-planted trees extend continuous cover across the ride from Ant Wood

Mike coppicing. He pushes the pole over before completing the cut

I measure a 22-year-old Douglas fir in the continuous
cover area *(Photo Country Living/Cris Barnett)*

Walkers on the trail in the stored coppice.
At purchase, these stems were only wrist-thick

A young visitor is fascinated by a fly agaric

Sarah's Streamside Hut is a walker's destination
at the bottom of the wood

Walkers enjoying springtime in the bluebells,
on an area coppiced the previous winter

Reserving and decorating a cut-your-own Christmas tree

The Yard at Christmas

Well into the staff Christmas dinner

We proudly pose with one
of our Christmas trees
(Photo Country Living/
Cris Barnett)

The Duke of Cornwall's
Award, 1993

light aircraft a couple of weeks later, we could see the pale faces of upturned root-plates starkly lit up by the low November afternoon sunshine. Their trunks and crowns all pointed pathetically to the Thames Estuary. Not all trees had succumbed. The worst gusts had laid low swathes about 100 metres wide, within otherwise undamaged woods. These gusts had been measured at 104 mph, at nearby Herstmonceux. Little wonder that trees were wrenched from the ground, particularly after such a wet autumn. Trees whose roots held fast snapped like matches or lost whole limbs, and the truncated crowns of many massive oaks and beech still bear witness to that night.

The wisdom of installing a wood-fired Rayburn became obvious. Unlike thousands of other households that day, tea and porridge made their way to the breakfast table as usual, and we could look forward to a hot shower when work was done. Anne, feeling the combined effects of heavy cold and lack of sleep, set about the relatively gentle task of washing salt from the windows, blown inland from the Channel 27 miles away, to cheer up the lightless house. Dave, who had called two hours earlier, had managed to walk across the fields to avoid the tree-blocked Main Road, and was ready for work. But where to start?

It is a requirement in English law that a landowner must prevent his livestock and plants from trespassing onto the Queen's Highway. Our sheep had obligingly returned to the fold when bidden. The fallen trees had no such intention, and the Queen, or at least her loyal representatives aka the County Highways Department, would clearly like us to exercise our obligation to right our wrong, even if it wasn't our fault. We had a couple of chainsaws, and fuel, matches and paper. All that day and the next, chainsaws buzzed as David and I sliced pine trunks into short lengths, and piled them on our verge. Several villagers came to express their condolences for our loss, and asked how they could help. And help they did. For days they dragged branches to a bonfire in our drive, where we cremated in a crackling, smoky blaze the limbs and foliage of several hundred pines. By dusk on Saturday, the second day, the road was cleared. A lone policeman on his motorbike parked up and came over to where I was piling the last of the logs, to find out how things were. His concern combined with the stress of the previous 36 hours, and he gently touched a shuddering shoulder as eyes swam behind the chainsaw visor.

Eventually we managed to get right round the wood, and the enormity of the damage was revealed. The Top Plantation, on an east-west ridge, had caught the full force of the wind, and had been destroyed except for a few boundary pines and beech, which fortunately included most of the trees screening the house from the road, and the trees around the Barn, workshop and yard. The play area had been located in a secluded glade, but, once fallen trees had been cleared, children now had a clear view of the Main Road. We wondered whether the charm of the place could ever be restored. Lower down the hill, with relief we found the Big Beech still towering over our eastern boundary, although missing a large bough. Gusts had felled the whole centre of Owl Wood, blown out pockets of the nearby Ant Wood, and toppled at random many of the taller coppice stools throughout the holding. Their upturned root-plates revealed the extremely shallow nature of our soil. In many cases, roots had ventured only a few centimetres downwards before turning outwards. Siltstone rock or a high winter water-table had prevented roots from growing downwards for a secure anchorage. No wonder the trees blew over, and contrary to rumours fed by anti-conifer sources, broadleaved trees and conifers were equally susceptible.

Life inched its way back towards normality. For neighbours down the tiny lanes, it was weeks before both electricity and telephones were reconnected. The lucky few snapped up two-stroke generators, but many had to bury the contents of deep freezes. We enjoyed several days of luxuries such as prawns, smoked salmon and ready-to-eat beef wellington, and in return let others cook on the Rayburn or enjoy hot showers. As one village friend ruefully remarked, that first Sunday at church, the Yarrows had no shortage of firewood. I came across a motorist loading the back of his van with our neatly stacked logs, and when asked what he was up to, he suggested he was helping us. "More like helping his bloody self", commented a less than charitable acquaintance at the pub that evening.

The shortage of tree-fellers meant many lanes were not cleared for some time, as the main roads took priority. Children from Wilderness Lane took delight in walking their way to school under a huge Corsican pine which now bridged the road, happy that no car could mow them down. No fuel could be pumped until electricity was reconnected to petrol stations, so we and many others had great difficulty in obtaining fuel for the chainsaws. This, and the shortage of fellers, delayed the clearing up process considerably. We heard tales of stockbrokers and others paying extortionate sums to have their drives cleared so they could get to the City, where the 21st October became Black Monday, as 26% was knocked off the value of the Stock Market in a single day. Some wondered which Apocalyptic horseman would next trot into view.

It was estimated that over ten years' harvest of timber was felled that night in south-east England. Not only was there a shortage of men to salvage what could be saved, there was also a dearth of suitable haulage trucks, and of markets. Britain has a relatively tiny forest industry, especially in the South-east. The region had been losing its sawmills for many years. Bulk users of wood, such as the papermill at Sittingbourne in north Kent, had closed, and markets for industrial quantities of timber were now far away in the North and West. Along with other forest managers, I spent countless hours on the telephone trying to locate workers, hauliers and markets, the task made slightly easier by the Forest Windblow Action Committee, set up by the Forestry Commission to collate information on markets, contractors and so on. In late January, the House of Commons Standing Committee on Agriculture paid a visit to five affected sites in East Sussex, including Wilderness Wood. Needless to say it was behind schedule when its coach eventually came down the drive. They had no time to get out, and Anne had to address them briefly in the coach before they drove on to the next site. We'll never know what impression they gained at Wilderness Wood. One Sunday lunchtime that spring, a young man came over to us in a pub garden some miles away. He was one of the civil servants on the Committee's visit, clearly with a good memory for faces; but, with diplomatic discretion, revealed nothing about Anne's impact on the affairs of State.

Our MP had listened carefully to our problems, and forwarded our representations to the Forestry Minister. I had stressed the cost of getting timber to distant places such as Devon, and the precipitous fall in prices, leaving growers seriously out of pocket. Sadly, the grant for replanting storm-damaged woods was much less for conifers than for broadleaved trees, reflecting the government policy for de-coniferisation that is still in place. We had drawn our MP's attention to the fact that our soils, like many others in his constituency, were not fertile enough for successful broadleaves, but the Minister stood by the policy of the day, and we had to take our losses on the chin.

We were fortunate that we had our own small labour force, and could get on with the job of clearing up straight away. Elsewhere, contractors worked where they could get the most money, servicing well-heeled golf clubs once the immediate utility clearance work had finished; small estates without their own men would have to wait. We needed to hurry if we were to salvage timber from the wreckage. It would deteriorate rapidly, especially in rising spring temperatures. Pines would soon get "blue stain" – a fungal discolouration that reduces the value of the timber. Also, the timber would dry out fast, and, as much is sold by weight, we needed to get the logs to market as soon as possible.

At that time we had just two woodland workers: Paul, our young woodsman, was barely older than Dave, the trainee from agricultural college. For lads still in their teens bent on a career in forestry, this must have seemed a golden chance to prove themselves by putting their chainsaw training into practice, and they set about the challenge with relish. The first task was to pull fallen and hung-up trees off the shambles, and for this we bought a winch for the tractor. Once each trunk was safely on the ground, we snedded (cut off) the branches flush with the trunk, and cut it into the lengths required by the market. These were winched into rough piles, later to be stacked at the woodland entrance to await the timber lorry.

The team was supplemented by Charlie, one of the old school of small woodland contractors. Charlie had a beard, and his broad girth was held in place by a wide leather belt. His gentle Sussex burr was as slow as his old Fordson tractor, which was never known to get out of second gear. This was equipped with a Highland Bear, a big hydraulic arm and grab that lifted timber onto an antique trailer, specially made from an old lorry chassis. The trailer cunningly took its traction from the tractor's PTO via a car gearbox. Despite carrying a load of several tonnes, under Charlie's command this rig was seldom bogged down. As if by instinct he knew the best route to take, and would often prepare soft ground with a mat of branches. In his hands the Bear edged logs into place and lifted several at a time with such delicacy one felt that, had they been eggs, none would be broken. Nothing would hurry Charlie. When asked how long a job would take he might reply "It'll take as long as it needs, but not much longer". Should things occasionally go wrong he'd say "Never mind; we'll see it through", and whenever he stopped for his thermos of tea, all the nipples on the Fordson and the Bear would be likewise refreshed with grease. It was rumoured he used as much grease as diesel.

Before replanting the plantations, we had first to remove the debris of broken wood, branches and foliage that covered the ground to a metre's depth. Once the sawlogs had been stacked by the entrance and huge quantities of smaller or broken pieces had been carted to stacks for later use as firewood, off came the trailer, and the Bear would lift the branches and carry them to piles, soon to be massive bonfires. In those days blokes like Charlie would assist the burn with a couple or three old car tyres, to get a good, hot blaze. Not for him paper, twigs and loss-making "fart-arsing around" that were the norm when health, safety and clean air became the preoccupations of the workplace. He had worked all his life in the woods and knew how to look after himself and the men who were with him. No Risk Assessment was needed, nor, we suspect, would he have signed one, let alone written it. Generous to his friends, he courteously respected those with book knowledge. Sadly, he died in 2008, at the relatively young age of 63. His funeral service, in the packed-to-overflowing chapel of Eastbourne crematorium, was held up for half an hour while the timber tug, carrying, not thirty tons of trunks, but just his coffin, negotiated the packed car park. Charlie would have loved the chaos his final journey had caused. Sussex-minded to the core, he "wun't be druv."

The weeks rolled by, and no lorries came to collect the piles of sawlogs. As April turned into May, ominous cracks began to appear at the ends of the logs, and I might be seen of an evening, hose in hand, spraying the stacks. It is normal practice to get pine off site within six weeks of harvesting, to avoid pine-shoot beetle breeding under the bark. We had verbal contracts with a couple of distant sawmillers, the nearer one in East Anglia. It is not only children who can use pester power, and the fruit of my constant 'phone calls was the sudden arrival of a vast timber tug early one morning, returning for several further loads. In the end, the money from the timber, together with the value of the firewood stacks, just about covered the harvesting costs. This was far better than it might have been, but a great loss overall. We estimated the future timber value foregone to be in the region of £50,000, irrespective of damage to the appearance of the wood on which our business so heavily relied. I had to bite my tongue when a well-meaning friend said how sorry she had been to hear of our storm damage, but at least they were "only conifers". What, I thought, would she have made of a suggestion that, had she lost her pension pot, it would not have been so bad if it had been with a foreign company?

The following autumn saw the windblown sites cleared of debris. Six years earlier we had started converting the 20-year-old plantations to an uneven-aged continuous-cover mixture, by felling plots and replanting the spaces with a variety of species. Now we were faced with an immensely larger replanting task, and my long-term plans had to be suddenly refigured; several decades of restructuring would have to be achieved in one, or at most two, planting seasons.

That first spring, a number of people offered to help us re-plant. As well as the village school planting an oak and a couple of lime trees on the road frontage, a local women's group donated a cherry tree which still adorns the entrance. Along the Main Road, some dozens of trees were planted by a working party of our Friends of Wilderness Wood; the replanting here included a good proportion of ash trees, as this was the only soil in the wood rich enough to sustain this demanding species.

With several thousand trees to plant in the Top Plantation alone, we had to do it as efficiently as possible. One of the problems of planting in ground previously dominated by pine trees is the deep accumulation of undecayed needles, too indigestible for the few earthworms to pull into the soil. Unless planted into mineral soil, young tree roots dry out in summer droughts, and the tree dies. To overcome this, one can turn the soil over with a spade and plant into the mixed material, a process known as "pit planting". This is slow and laborious, and we would be lucky to plant 250 to 300 trees each per day, a third the number achieved by simple notch planting. I hit on the idea of using a hand-held posthole borer from our local tool hire firm. This two-man device gouged out a hole 20 centimetres across and deep in a few seconds; then it was two small steps sideways, keeping in line, and the correct distance from the previous row, and repeat the process. Hefty work for David and Paul, but at least it did not involve repeated bending, and young men always love working with power tools. It was then a very quick process to notch-plant into the disturbed ground.

The normal practice is to plant at two metre spacing, but this leaves a significant portion of the land unproductive until the trees "close canopy" (their side-branches touch) some years later. The replanting was costing us a lot of money, so we offset this by establishing a cash crop of Norway spruce Christmas trees in the intervening spaces. For every long-term beech, Douglas fir or Thuja, three spruces were planted. With such a potentially valuable crop, there was a big incentive to keep the weeds down, and seldom has a young plantation had such lavish attention. An experiment at killing the resurgent bracken with Roundup spray proved disastrous, with many trees scorched as a result. So, back to manual methods! Only a minute's walk from the house, we spent many a summer evening out with the swaphook before supper, searching for the little trees in the head-high bracken that was flourishing in the peaty soil, or even pulling up brambles by hand. Thank heavens we had planted in straight lines, so we knew where to expect the trees! After a day of meetings, or sitting in the car between tree surveys, getting out and exercising arms and legs can be very satisfying, especially as the results are immediately visible. I had a miniature radio with earphones, and, as I wielded my swaphook, the sound of choral competitions at the Llangollen Eisteddfod brought back student days at a very Welsh university.

As we had so many trees to protect, it was economic to erect a rabbit-proof fence around the Top Plantation, rather than protect each tree with an individual shelter. The problem of rabbits, deer, and other potential pests is discussed in Chapter 14. The spaces close to pine and beech trees left standing after the storm were too shady for Christmas trees and Douglas, and so we planted shade-bearing Thuja. In the open areas, after three years the faster-growing Douglas began to overtake the Norways, so we removed the firs' lower branches, to assist our spruce Christmas trees as well as improve the quality of the Douglas timber crop. Proximity to the yard meant we had a "cut-your-own" area on the doorstep, and over the next few years many happy families climbed over the stile beyond the play area to choose their Christmas tree in what felt like a "real forest." Those Christmas trees probably paid for the whole replanting cost. As forestry thinnings they would be tax-free income, unlike a normal Christmas tree plantation which the taxman classifies as an agricultural crop.

The young beech plants didn't think much of the peaty soil, so we beat up failures with sweet chestnut. Once all the Christmas trees in the pure spruce plots had been harvested, we planted a few coast redwoods to fill in the spaces between the self-sown pine and birch that had managed to establish themselves among the spruces. Within twenty years we had achieved an area of very varied species, height, and trunk diameter, even away from the older pines and beech.

The aftermath of the storm continues to this day. Throughout the South-east, promising young to middle-aged stands of productive trees were destroyed, to be replaced with untended scrub or misguided attempts to plant broadleaved trees on unsuitable sites. The thriving market for sweet chestnut, which might command up to £1,000 an acre, disappeared overnight and never fully recovered, as fallen coppice was suddenly available at little or no cost from landowners glad to have it tidied away in a glutted market. Perhaps the chestnut market was anyway poised to collapse, as new methods of securing building sites and road works took over from the traditional chestnut pale fencing, but the sudden shove precipitated by the storm must have helped.

It was commonplace for conservation spokesmen to praise the storm for opening up woods to the benefit of ground flora and associated wildlife. Unlike us, they did not have standing timber as a significant business asset, and could afford to see that silver lining within the cloud. Throughout south-east England there are, almost three decades on, still woods littered with upturned stumps and the remains of fallen trees that were too expensive for their owners to clear, adding yet another nail to the coffin of the declining small woods economy.

Wilderness Wood was among the few woods that got straight back into the business that had been planned for it. In the weeks after the storm, a rumour came to our ears via that village bulletin board, the New Inn. It was apparently being said in some quarters that the Yarrows were going to build a housing estate on the roadside land conveniently cleared of trees by the wind. In fact, looking back with the perspective of a quarter-century, it's clear that the storm, so traumatic at the time, deflected us little from our long-term plans for the wood. The destruction all around, and the loss of familiar and loved landscapes, at the time struck like a bereavement. We were forcibly taught that the stability and security of our day-to-day surroundings is an illusion. Joanna tells us how, as a thirteen-year-old child, she assumed that the world she woke up to on 16 October 1987 had changed forever. Now, she is amazed at how the woodland has re-grown in just 28 years. The play area was soon secluded by thick forest; the replanted Top Plantation, where for years we had to rescue the little replanted trees from shoulder-high bracken, was again a "deep dark wood", the setting for Gruffalo hunts and fairy gardens. Some Douglas firs have already reached a height of 20 metres, challenging their older pine neighbours. The north side of the house is darkened anew by the conifers of the Top Plantation, which have already supplied many tepee poles, and timber for other uses. We managed to cover the costs of clearance and replanting, but lost hundreds of pine trees that would by now have significant timber value and be ready to harvest. On the other side of the coin, our drastically restructured plantations have a greater variety of species and sizes than would otherwise have been achieved.

Down in the coppices, few clues remain to that stormy night. A lone elderly birch standard couldn't resist the wind; for years its fallen trunk provided an object-lesson in decay, as wood-rotting fungi succeeded one another, but by 2010 the only trace was an indistinct line of spongey wood and bark in the leaf litter. When we cut the horizontal poles from windblown coppiced trees, most of the root-plates tipped back and re-rooted; but in the boggy area near the stream, where the chainsaw has hardly been for decades, a few giant vertical rootplates, with decaying poles still stretched out to the north-east, have become magnets for shelter-building children, oblivious to the destruction that created their play-space. When those rootplates eventually decay, curious mounds of soil will sit beside leaf-filled depressions in the ground. What will archaeologists make of them?

WILDLIFE OR PEST ?

No sooner had we bought the wood than our friends were asking us what lived in it. There is immense interest in natural history, exemplified by the many TV programmes on matters as varied as grizzly bears and the mating habits of the robin, and our friends were no different from the rest of the population in assuming that Wilderness Wood was teeming with wildlife to be observed and cherished. A one-hour TV programme takes hundreds of hours of waiting for just the right moment, and gives a distorted idea of the abundance and general attractiveness of wildlife. It succeeds by being visually stunning and having charismatic presenters. It would be our challenge to harness this public enthusiasm and interest while making do with the resources of an ordinary Sussex woodland and its amateur teachers.

We always intended to put wildlife on a similar footing to the other benefits that Wilderness Wood could provide, and acknowledged its role both as a subject for study or enjoyment, and as a fundamental component of the ecosystem of the wood and beyond. Both of us had studied ecology at university and were therefore reasonably well-placed to assess the varying habitats within the wood, whether the boggy area with its sphagnum moss, or the sunny spot dominated by heather, and home to sunbathing grass snakes and lizards. As we pushed through the dense streamside growth on our initial explorations, we knew we must manage it carefully to provide the right balance of sun, shade and humidity to encourage the variety of moisture-loving liverworts and ferns. However, our searches revealed nothing of great interest or rarity, unlike Balneath Wood which we had so nearly bought, with its immense variety of plants.

Our satisfaction at having nothing special raised eyebrows when I provocatively announced it to a clutch of students studying countryside management at a local college. Why, they argued, we could get more specialist visitors to the wood if it had. I patiently explained that the wood was multi-purpose, and we wished to encourage the general public to visit. Had we rare or precious items, be they orchid or osprey, our visitors would probably have to be excluded or severely restricted. We felt that our role was to explain to our mainly urban public how a typical Wealden woodland ticked, and introduce it to some of the basic concepts of ecology and how they applied to our wood or their lives. I likened it to an introductory art class, needing only a naked model or vase of tulips in the village hall. The budding artists did not need the Louvre or National Gallery, which would be the equivalent of a National Nature Reserve.

Within a few years we were taking school parties round the wood, and would ask the children what animals they thought lived there. There was the inevitable parade of the bears, tigers, and pandas they had seen on TV, but with a little prompting, and reference to favourite story books, they would remember Mole, Rabbit, Owl and the Mouse family, who might be hiding behind or under those trees over there. Many had little idea of the size of these animals, some suggesting a mole was as large as a cat. This was perhaps to be expected if their only experience had been a TV close-up beside a digitally reduced David Bellamy. Once we had shown them the small hole under a molehill, we were able to bring out the one kept in the deep-freeze along with the ice-creams, and they could feel the fur which used to make perfect mud-shedding trousers.

Another frigid resident of the freezer was a metre-long grass-snake, who rested between school visits in an ice-cream carton. He had come to an untimely end under a log rolling from a cordwood pile. Perhaps having seen a programme on cryogenics, one child asked in all seriousness if it would come back to life when it unfroze. We were unable to give a satisfactory answer as to why what might work for embryos did not apply to snakes.

It was obvious that we also failed to give a satisfactory reply to the lady who rushed to the Barn one summer Sunday afternoon, asking us to rescue a toad from the jaws of a grass-snake. We tried to explain that this was the natural order of things, and a snake had as much right to its meal as she had to the barbecue she had just eaten. Some, including daughter Kate, have a fear of all snakes, and it is in open woodland glades that one is most likely to encounter one basking in the sunshine. Such encounters are inevitable when working in young plantations. Woodsman Mike, whilst out weeding the Christmas trees one June day, bent down to pick up a "stick" he thought might be a nuisance when we later came to mow between the trees. Both grass snake and Mike fled on contact, and it was some time before he would return to finish the job, even though he knew the snake was harmless.

Occasionally an unusually attentive group of schoolchildren would excitedly spot a dozing grass-snake in the wan spring sunshine, or even catch a glimpse of a fleeing rabbit or squirrel. But usually it was a matter of spotting clues to the wood's larger inhabitants. When we walk the streets, we are only reminded that an animal has been before us if we see something unpleasant left by a dog. Our forebears must have spent a lot of their time observing such signs, as for them it might have meant the difference between having, or being, a meal. On a recent trip to Nepal, our park ranger guide was able to show us the spore of a female tiger which had crossed our path just hours earlier. To the disappointment of visiting schoolchildren at the wood, if not their teachers, we had no such large footprints to show them, but there were plenty of other signs. Owl pellets not only showed where an owl roosted, but, soaked in water, gave clues to its diet. Aesop was right when he told of the fox and grapes, for we found their droppings often contained pips and skins from the vineyard two fields away. Shallow scrapes with smelly, semi-liquid poo glistening in the sun indicated that a badger had marked its territory; its olfactory power is confirmed when your dog insists on rolling in it for cosmetic reasons.

A discussion with older children about food chains would soon make it clear that all the chains start with plants, converting sunlight into food which is inevitably eaten by something. But those woodland rabbits whose burrows and droppings they have noticed don't have carrots to eat, or even grass, so they eat the trees that we are trying to nurture. Without protection, natural seedlings, and the tops and bark of young planted trees, are devoured by the ubiquitous rabbit.

We used plastic tubes to protect the scattered planting in our storm-damaged Owl and Ant Woods, and were able to reclaim most for later plantings in the continuous cover plots. Where a large number of trees are to be planted, it is more economical to fence around the perimeter. The crucial element of a rabbit fence is wire mesh, which is dug into the ground about five centimetres, and turned outwards fifteen centimetres. When a rabbit spies the tasty-looking trees beyond, it digs down as close to the fence as possible. If all goes to plan, its way is impeded by the horizontal wire mesh, and it gives up with a rabbit curse. No forester is infallible all the time. When we came to replant the Top Plantation after the Great Storm, we found that young trees inside the new fence were being eaten. We had fenced in a couple of rabbits. They were quickly unearthed with the help of a Jack Russell, and this story greatly amused our younger school visitors. It also provided a trick question: do foresters like rabbits? Answer: no, they eat my trees; and yes, they taste great in a pie. Unsurprisingly, there were more who empathised with Peter Rabbit than with Mr. McGregor.

When not hopping through gates left open, rabbits had an uncanny knack of finding where the clearing saw had nicked the wire mesh during summer weeding, or where the wire had rusted and broken. Telltale organic Smarties were the sign, along with nibbled shoots, and we had the painstaking chore of patrolling the perimeter to try and locate the entrance hole. The best time to do this was the morning after snow, when tracks would lead straight to the point of entry. A simple technique, but not much help in August.

The grey squirrel is another woodland resident helping itself to the forester's crop, and much more difficult to control than the rabbit. Walking under the pines on a March morning and noticing the bright orange-brown scales and stripped cores of numerous cones, I would be reminded that the time had arrived for putting out squirrel hoppers. This was the season grey squirrels were at their hungriest, and the poisoned bait would be most attractive. I dreaded finding scattered flakes of green-speckled beech bark, as

Pine cones eaten by squirrels

this would mean their appetite had led to permanent tree damage. When we first surveyed the wood, we noticed that patches of bark on the upper trunks of many pines in Owl and Ant Woods had been removed by squirrels. They are after sap in the sweet-tasting phloem just under the bark, and skip from tree to tree testing each for the best meal. About three years prior to our ownership, there must have been a huge surge in the local population, with the result that about half the trees in Ant Wood had enough damage to wreck any future timber value. Fortunately, careful removal of the worst affected trees over a number of thinning cycles enabled us to produce mature stands of fine trees, though some must have faults hidden deep within them, to be revealed when the sawmiller has his way. Many limbs on the beech trees were ring-barked one summer, when I failed to get out the poison hoppers on time. Once the bark has been chewed off all round a limb, the portion beyond it dies, the wood rots, and without warning the bough comes crashing down, particularly at times of strong winds or heavy snow. In order to keep squirrel numbers in check, I would each March trundle out six specially-designed metal hoppers to different parts of the wood, tie them to trees, fill them with Warfarin-dosed wheat, and conceal them as best I could from human eyes. I inspected them every week or so and kept them topped up with bait. Each mid-August I repeated the journey, and, as I pushed the wheelbarrow of hoppers and spare bait back up the Central Ride, became increasingly aware of advancing years as the weight seemed ever heavier. We could never expect to eliminate this pest, but only keep its numbers down, hoping that the long-promised squirrel contraceptive trials would take away this expensive and time-consuming chore. I was not impressed when the well-funded Woodland Trust suggested in personal correspondence that they could not afford to control this pest in their expensively-planted woodlands, whose young oaks would never reach the dimensions featured in fund-raising brochures.

There seems to be an increasing reluctance to control woodland pests, and one can understand the appeal of a cute, bushy-tailed grey squirrel as it hops onto the garden bird-feeder. In woodlands, squirrels nest in dreys, dense nests of sticks high up in trees. As long as our pines were still thin enough to respond to a heavy jolt at shoulder level, I could usually rouse a squirrel from its home, much to the delight of whichever group I was conducting round the wood. One such fellow never seemed to learn that it was me rather than an earthquake, and would appear on demand every time. Anne suggested we put it on the payroll!

I once upset a group of visiting students by explain that shooting squirrels was inefficient and time-consuming, only justifiable as fun. On the basis that I and many others think of golf as a way of ruining a nice walk, they were asked to be tolerant of different tastes in recreation. Late one summer afternoon, I took a break from my desk to walk round the wood, both for fresh air and because the best fertiliser is the farmer's (or forester's) footprint. It was the season when squirrel and rabbit numbers were building up, so I tucked the twelve-bore under my arm. As I came out of the garden gate, a middle-aged lady exclaimed "I hope you are not going to use that!" I resisted the temptation to reply that my wife had not left me for the milkman, nor the business gone bust, or even that she should not allow her judgement to be unduly influenced by violent TV; but yes, if vermin came within range, it might end up on the dinner table. Did she wish to debate the balance between the Buddhist position and Buffalo Bill, or perhaps between animal rights activists and the realities of rural life? She needed to get home, and I wanted my walk, so that was not the occasion. Thereafter I did try to be more discreet with my gun, even though it offended my sense of honesty. Some time later Father Christmas gave me a high-powered air rifle, and with this I could quietly (and cheaply!) plug away at squirrel dreys without upsetting the peace. At our farewell staff party, Sarah, our long-serving education manager, made a little speech in which she suggested that, when we had moved, I would miss the squirrels; to which I retorted "I usually do!" Sadly, as long as people feed these "tree rats" on their bird-tables, and negligent woodland owners allow them to breed uncontrolled, the future of productive broadleaved trees is greatly compromised, and the return of the native red squirrel a distant dream.

In Sussex even an unobservant motorist is nowadays likely to notice the most splendid visitor to the wood, the fallow deer, as he drives down a country lane, or even on a main road at night. Originally introduced by the Normans, its numbers have grown immensely in the Weald in recent years for a variety of reasons, not least the neglect of woodlands following the 1987 storm, and the reversion of ploughed land to permanent grass for horses and other grazing. Around us almost every wood is connected by "shaws", (narrow strips of valley-side woodland), facilitating easy access across the landscape, and Anne and I see deer on almost every country walk. In the absence of wolves, they no longer have a natural predator, and on average one is killed by a vehicle each day on Ashdown Forest six miles to the north-west.

Apart from causing immense damage to cars, and sometimes fatal accidents, a herd of deer can wreck young arable crops, and eats as much grass per head as sheep. Because they breed in his woods, the woodland owner has a responsibility to his neighbours to keep numbers down, and damage to his own trees is not insignificant. Where numbers are high, their browsing of young regrowth makes it virtually impossible to grow good coppice or obtain natural regeneration of trees, unless the deer are excluded by some means. We found it bizarre that animal rescue organisations would spend hundreds of pounds taking an injured deer to an animal hospital, at the same time as landowners like ourselves were making strenuous efforts to keep their numbers down.

Normally a shy animal, the deer became used to the sight and smell of humans at the wood. They were therefore not deterred from browsing our Christmas trees, or fraying saplings in order to mark their territory. At over £10 a metre for a deer fence, we could not afford to keep them out, and reducing their numbers by culling became a necessity. A father and son, rough diamonds from Gravesend, were soon paying regular visits, arriving well before dawn to install themselves at the bottom of the wood in a shelter or high seat, from which they had a good view over our co-operative neighbour's field. Often they would be at the door by breakfast time on a bleak November morning, smiling contentedly, with a promise of a haunch and venison sausages in return for loan of the dumper to retrieve the carcase. A mature male might weigh forty kilos, even after the guts had been removed where it fell, so dragging it by hand was far from easy. We were therefore surprised when Josef, our Slovak forester, arrived similarly at the door one morning, but with a large back-pack of very fresh venison joints. Deer management is part of any Slovakian forester's training, and in rough country they are often far from any vehicle, so their tradition is to cut the carcase into manageable portions on the spot, leaving bones, head and pelt for the wolves, foxes and carrion feeders.

Each autumn we were given so much top-quality meat that we had to take care not to make dinner guests plough through a venison-based meal three times running. They were less likely to be subjected to a badger stew, something we had enjoyed soon after moving to the wood. The school caretaker had found a badger killed by a car on the verge outside the wood, and asked if we would

like to tan the pelt after he had shown the animal to the school
children. Later that day I carefully stripped off the badger's coat,
to reveal a very solid ten kilos of meat in perfect condition. Not
wanting Brock to have died in vain, we butchered it as one would
a lamb, and found dense, lean meat with a centimetre-thick layer
of fat wrapped across the back like a blanket. With a diet similar
to a wild boar, we expected a pork-like flavour, and were surprised
that it tasted more like mutton. Word soon reverberated around
the village that "those Yarrows" ate badger, and perhaps it was just
as well we had by then moved out of the caravan.

It is not just the larger woodland animals that make a meal of the
forester's trees. As I stepped outside to get some logs one autumn
morning after a windy night, I noticed pine twigs all across the
yard, their green needles contrasting vividly with the brown fallen
beech leaves. After thinning the pine plantation that summer, we
had left piles of unpeeled poles in the yard, waiting to be used
as fencing material. Now we had the dreaded pine shoot beetle,
whose population can soar when pine logs are left around with
their bark on during the early summer months. The beetles burrow
under the bark and lay eggs which hatch into larvae; these later
pupate, and emerge to fly in huge numbers to the small twigs in
the crowns of surrounding pines trees, into which they burrow to
overwinter. Weakened shoots then fall in autumn gales. Not only
does the defoliation weaken the tree, but, next spring, the greatly
increased population of beetles seeks out bark for breeding, and,
failing to find felled logs, turns to the trunks of living trees. With
luck, the attacked trees drown the boring beetles in a dribble of
resin, but an attack by numerous beetles on a weakened tree can
ring-bark it. The tree dies, and provides a large area for more
breeding pairs, and the infestation continues.

For some years thereafter the trees around the yard proclaimed
my negligence with their thin crowns. Never again did we leave

unpeeled logs close to the pines, but made sure pine cordwood was in future stacked down by the western entrance, well away from our valuable trees.

Both commercial farming and forestry alike modify the habitat in order that as much of the sun's energy as possible is harnessed to the crop species, be it wheat or oak trees, and other "weed" plants are discouraged or eliminated. In our acid soils, vigorous bracken was a competitor that had to be cut back around newly-planted trees. Rhododendron was another acid-loving plant that we pulled up or poisoned, as we were only too aware how it could take over a woodland. Felling "weed" trees for which there is no economic use is nowadays frowned on, as food and lodging places for animal species may be lost; but we would remove birch and willow that were competing with more valuable species, especially if we had gone to the trouble of planting them.

Britain has an unusually large number of veteran trees, which are noted for their wealth of fungi and insects, and hole-nesting birds. To make amends for our lack of old trees in our woodland of coppice and young plantations, we put up bird and bat boxes. Perversely, it was not the boxes in the wood that were occupied, so much as those displayed for sale in the yard. Equally perverse was the reluctance of any bird to make its home in the bird boxes in which we had installed cctv cameras, so that our visitors could observe tit chicks being raised.

The wood is of course home to a bewildering myriad of harmless insects and other invertebrates, and Anne and Sarah in time learned enough about them to keep one step ahead of a class of primary schoolchildren on a bug hunt. An easy way to observe one group of insects is via a moth hunt. Each summer a naturalist friend, Simon Curson, would conduct a torch-lit evening walk, having first put out a lamp moth trap, and invite the punters to apply a sticky syrup of sugar and red wine to the trunks of trees.

After hot chocolate in the Barn we would go back out to see what had been attracted to the light or food, and were surprised, not so much by their numbers, as by their bizarre names and Simon's ability to remember them. It must have been a particular type of Victorian clergyman who had come up with names such as Rosy Footman and Setaceous Hebrew Character.

Earlier in the year Simon used to lead a dawn chorus walk, helping bleary-eyed participants to sort out the calls of as many as two dozen different kinds of bird. There were all the usuals, such as wood-pigeons, robins and blackbirds, but also willow warblers, blackcaps, goldcrests, and the challenge of distinguishing the see-saw calls of great tit and coal tit above the raucous crowing of our cockerel back in the orchard. Anne accompanied Simon on the walks, but I, never an early riser, prepared the breakfast. Having perhaps left home before five am, participants were more than ready for the porridge and boiled eggs, straight from the hen coop, which I had ready on cue at seven thirty. However, even a late riser can have a bird presented, as it were, on a plate. One hot summer noon, I was hand-weeding the Christmas trees with a sickle, and accidently cut the head off a pheasant sitting on a clutch of twelve eggs. She had hidden her nest out of sight of birds of prey, and her speckled brown plumage was such good camouflage that I didn't see her, even an arm's length away. We put the eggs under a broody hen, but only three hatched out, and they were killed by the hen. We ate the victim of course, as a dead pheasant is a dead pheasant, shooting season or not. On another occasion I was walking along the West Ride and heard a terrible screaming. Coming round a bend, I spied a sparrowhawk attacking a green woodpecker on the track, feathers flying. The hawk made a hasty retreat but the victim was sadly too injured, so I put it out of its misery. On my return later that evening the corpse was gone: a meal for the returning hawk, or pinched by a fox?

As well as insects and birds, the wood offered flowers to attract and interest our visitors. Each spring was marked by drifts of wood anemones, followed by seas of bluebells in late April and early May. For us they were a crop, in that we were able to invite a mainly elderly market to walk our Bluebell Trail, and follow it up with tea and cakes in the Barn or tea-garden. For many, it provided their first country outing of the year. There were already spring walks through the lusher bluebells of the hornbeam coppices down on the Weald Clay, but we could offer ours in the surroundings of an actively coppiced woodland. Our trail led through the better areas, with pole-mounted signs themed on bluebell facts and folklore. We never knew whether any little boys were inspired to stick feathers on their arrows using glue from the sticky bulbs, as I might have done as a nine-year-old follower of *Just William*.

Our bluebells were by no means ubiquitous, with quite abrupt boundaries. They were absent or very scattered where coppice stem growth was poorest, so both flower and tree seemed to be limited by soil quality. Their great variability may have been accentuated by a ground fire which, according to Gerald at the New Inn, had smouldered for weeks in the very dry summer of 1947. This would have burned most of the soil's organic content, along with bluebell bulbs. Unfortunately, Gerald never got down to the wood to show us the area where the fire had burned, or any of the secret places of the childhood recollections that must have filled his amazing memory.

Fungi were a less obvious aspect of the wood's wildlife, although they, too, came to be a visitor attraction. In those early years, autumn would find Anne scuffling through the fallen leaves with trug on arm and nose to the ground, assembling a collection of fungal mysteries to puzzle over on the kitchen table with the help of the limited field guides of the time. Identifying mushrooms and toadstools is not easy, and even more of a challenge when self-taught, and it took several seasons for her to recognise even the common species such as penny bun and honey fungus with enough confidence to add them to the family supper.

Compared with trees, and the carpets of spring flowers and summer foxgloves, toadstools were more elusive and therefore more entrancing, which slowed Anne to a dawdle on our autumn walks. We in time came to realise that they were not just a colourful addition to the autumn scene, and sometimes a free meal, but an indispensible part of the jigsaw of woodland life. Like the plankton in the sea or the bacteria in a compost heap, fungi play a fundamental role in a woodland ecosystem. As nature's recyclers, it is fungi that decay all those dead leaves, twigs, branches, and wood. We humans go to a lot of effort and expense to prevent fungi from getting a hold, by keeping timber dry, and using preservatives and paint; unless it is naturally rot-resistant, such as the heartwood of oak and sweet chestnut. Some fungi invade living trees as well as dead ones, including that well-known garden scourge, honey fungus. Every wood has it, including ours, but it seldom kills more than a tree or two, and there's nothing to be done apart from enjoying its fruits for supper. As a practising forester and arboriculturalist, I had to have more than a passing knowledge of the symptoms of fungal attack, for it would have done my reputation some harm if I had missed a tree likely to fall on smart cars in Belgravia, where I advised on tree matters. Similarly, one had to know appropriate hygiene measures to prevent outbreaks of trunk-decaying fungi in our valuable trees, and for this reason we never lit fires in conifer plantations for fear of encouraging *Rhizina*, a fungus which grows on old fire sites and causes groups of trees to die via their roots.

Some of the largest and most colourful groups of woodland fungi, including the boletes, brittlegills, amanitas and webcaps, get their living from trees in a manner which is beneficial. They have evolved with trees in a symbiotic relationship, called mycorrhiza, or fungus roots. The hidden, underground "body" of the fungus consists of minute threads of mycelium, which draw carbohydrates from the rootlets of the trees, and in return the tree sucks mineral nutrients and water from the fungus. We realised that this explained how our trees in Wilderness Wood were managing to thrive in a soil with so few nutrients, and many forest transplant trees are now sold ready-inoculated with the right mycorrhiza to speed their growth when planted out.

Over the years Anne identified some hundreds of different species in our wood, and they formed the basis of very popular guided walks each autumn. What comes up, and when, and in what quantity, is extremely variable. Anne gradually built up a mental map of what to expect, and has an improbable ability to remember the Latin name of a toadstool that she hasn't come across for years, although, like me, she is often stumped for the name of a human friend.

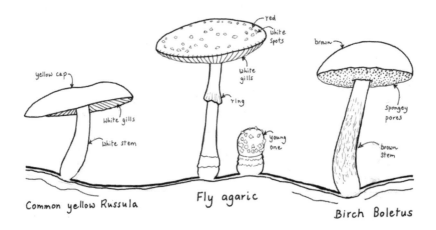

Common yellow Russula

Fly agaric

Birch Boletus

Mushrooms and toadstools have an unjustified reputation in Britain for being poisonous, and Anne at first reassured visitors that she knew of nothing deadly at the wood, until one year she happened on a couple of death caps growing by a path near the pond. This is apparently one of the most poisonous living things, and one mouthful can kill a child, and half a cap finish off an adult. It was a preferred assassination method among the Caesars, although these days you may survive if you are hooked to a kidney dialysis machine quickly enough. Anne was glad to show her fungus hunters an actual specimen, and she put up explanatory warning signs next to the innocuous-looking toadstools, so that people could learn to avoid what is quite a widespread danger. A few years later she spotted a couple of specimens embarrassingly near the play area, and we had to cordon off the site, and each morning carefully remove any that had "mushroomed" overnight. Unlike ragwort, you can't simply pull it up to eradicate it.

We were sharing the wood with a variety of wildlife, from beetles to deer, that brought pleasure and interest to ourselves and our visitors. This gave us the opportunity to interpret its many aspects to the general public, and to the thousands of schoolchildren who came each year. Some elements, such as the bluebells, were splendid enough to be attractions in their own right, whilst other less obvious ones, such as the myriad fungi, enabled Anne to attract a following of enthusiastic students. Diversity and abundance were sufficient to provide us with venison and mushrooms for the table, but there was nothing so rare as to need special protection, and thus impinge on our freedom to manage the wood for the variety of outcomes we had planned. It was fortunate that both of us had enough knowledge and interest in the subject to be able to manage and keep in balance those elements that might so easily become pests, and undermine our efforts to nurture healthy and productive trees.

WOOD AND WOODY
THINGS

One frosty morning, as I split yet another log with my fibreglass-handled maul, I pondered: when was the last time we had bought a ladder, sledge, wheelbarrow or rake made of wood? If wood is now used at all, it is for a small element such as the handle, machine-made by the thousand. Everything else is made of plastic or metal in some distant factory. The coppices of old relied on craftsmen whose skills died out with the demise in demand for products that could not compete with machine-made items. It would have been pure romanticism to think we could somehow swim against the tide and make a living bodging at a pole-lathe, besmocked and chewing on an oaten straw. Not only would we have to compete with factory-made items, but those made by cheap labour in the third world.

We had always realised that income from sales of standing wood and unprocessed timber would yield small returns. To survive, we had to harvest the wood ourselves, and add value by converting it efficiently into things people would buy direct from us, avoiding the middleman who would take half the profit. But what should we make?

Our early attempts had confirmed a demand for simple

Wilderness Wood

HADLOW DOWN NEAR UCKFIELD SUSSEX TN22 4HJ TELEPHONE HADLOW DOWN (082 585) 509

PRICE LIST Jan. 1987

All Hardwood (chestnut) unless otherwise stated.　No VAT charged.　Delivery extra

GARDEN FURNITURE

Seats

| 2 seater | £42 |

Other sizes to order

Tables

44 x 20　ins.

£30

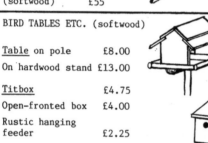

Picnic tables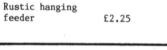
(softwood)　£55

BIRD TABLES ETC. (softwood)

Table on pole　£8.00
On hardwood stand £13.00

Titbox　£4.75
Open-fronted box　£4.00
Rustic hanging
feeder　£2.25

OTHER ITEMS

Special Orders　Articles made to measure
e.g. climbing frames, dovecots, foot bridges.

Pot-grown conifers　£1.50 – £2.50

Christmas Trees　Freshly dug or pot-grown
trees.　Also holly.

FIREWOOD

	COLLECTED	DELIVERED Hadlow Down
Hardwood sack: loose 80p bagged 90p		95p
2 cu.m. (tonne)	£31.00	£37.50
Pine sack: loose 60p bagged 70p		75p
2 cu.m. (tonne)	£24.00	£30.50
Mixed Pine/Hardwood	£27.50	£34.00

All logs are sold by volume, not weight.
We try to sell air-dried logs, but further
storage under cover may be desirable.

ROSE ARCHES　AND CHESTNUT GOODS

Rose Arch　3' wide　£25.00

Other widths to order

| Sawing Horse | £13.50 |
| Small Gate 3' wide | £11.00 |

(other sizes to order)

Gate hurdles

| 4½' x 2½' | £11 |
| 6½' x 3½' | £15 |

Trelliswork to order
Approx. 60p/sq.ft.

POSTS AND POLES

Chestnut Poles:　Price depends on size –
see post pricelist.　Examples:

	1½"	2½"	4"
5'	25p	40p	80p
7'	40p	75p	120p
10'	85p	125p	215p

Pointing, peeling extra

Fence Posts

5–5½', 3" top, pointed, peeled	55p
Straining Posts 6½', 5" top	£1.75
Bean Poles 10 x 7' or 8'	£1.80
10 x 6'	£1.45
Peasticks (Birch) Approx 20 x 6'	£1.25
Plant Stakes 10 x 4'	£1.00

CRISS-CROSS FENCING

Price per 10' run,
peeled

Height	5ft	4½ft	4ft	3ft
	£16.75	14.75	13.75	11.00

An early price list

gardening requisites such as bean-poles, pea-sticks, and plant stakes, but our predominantly chestnut coppice was less suited to these than hazel would be. On the other hand, our chestnut poles were ideal for rustic garden items. As word got around, we rapidly became known as a source of poles for gardeners wanting to build their own fences, fruit cages and other constructions. We displayed them on a rack by the yard, with dozens of different lengths and diameters, right up to twenty feet (six metres).

We had soon designed a range of simple trellis panels, rose-arches and pergolas, which I could quickly make with the most basic tools and skills on the ground in the yard. We could certainly have made traditional cleft fenceposts, but farmers had to buy at the best price, which only an experienced old-timer working with minimal overheads and reluctant to pay taxes could meet. On the other hand, we were well placed to provide limited quantities of specialist raw materials for craft workers, such as "pimps" for the trug-makers based around Herstmonceux which commanded a good price. These are straight, knot-free pieces of chestnut, up to twelve centimetres diameter and one and a half metres long, cut from the lowest section of the pole, and with bark completely undamaged. They are cleft and shaved for the frame and handles of these iconic wooden baskets, made only in East Sussex. One maker ordered a large number, complaining he could find no-one to supply him. Having located and extracted his order at short notice, we learned why. He never came to collect it, and it turned out he was notoriously unreliable.

One unusual order was for a large number of poles for a Roman battle scene in a film, and the scene-builder didn't bat the proverbial eyelid when I quoted double our normal price, ostensibly because they were wanted at short notice. At this point my chutzpah failed, and I forgot the usual trick of following up the quote with "plus VAT", so excited was I that our produce might feature in a blockbuster. By this time we had a website, so the world was our market, if not our oyster. A Californian emailed to order genuine chestnut poles for his Italian-style vineyard. Being reluctant to ship low-value material halfway round the world, we emailed back that bio-security rules would forbid it, and trusted he would not actually look them up. No wonder Britain exports so little!

Film set material was not the only strange request. One day we had a 'phone call from a foreign-sounding man, requiring dozens of six-metre-long chestnut poles, not unlike traditional hop poles. The customer, a typically entrepreneurial Dutchman, was offering an attractive price, but for collection the following Wednesday. Somehow we had them ready when Willem's massive lorry came down the drive, but the time spent locating the order at such short notice probably obliterated most of the profit. They were destined for dyke reconstruction, replacing outlawed pressure-treated wood, as chestnut's natural durability makes it a suitable alternative. This astute man had sought out return loads for his lorry, and we could only applaud his economic use of transport.

With the passing of the coal pit-prop market, early thinnings from pine plantations are very difficult to shift, so I was delighted to get an order for a variety of pole lengths from a local fencing contractor, and too many hours were spent cutting these to size with minimum wastage. The produce waited in the yard for some weeks in early summer, so that most of the poles were too dry by the time the buyer came to collect our efforts. There were several lessons to be learned, including getting a firm collection date and deposit up front.

We had three and a half hectares of plantations, and I had always envisaged converting our trees into timber by means of our own sawmill. I devised a rack bench which would fit round the McConnel circular saw on the back of the tractor. Blacksmith Ben, who had made so many of my designs before, did a good job constructing it out of sheet steel, angle iron and other parts, and with it we managed to convert logs up to two metres long and 30 centimetres diameter into short weatherboards and "four by two's". But it would not mill accurately, and within a couple of years we disposed of it as expensive scrap. Even before the 1987 storm felled much of our timber, our business advisor gently dissuaded us from creating a sawmill to process the few tonnes of pine we would be harvesting, pointing out it might be better to buy in planks of the quality and quantity we needed. In other words, it would be a long time before our plantations yielded the quality of timber we needed, and such a small-scale sawmill would be a poor investment. We could either sell softwood in the round, or, if we wanted to use it ourselves, have it accurately converted at a local small sawmill.

Gardening is a leisure activity and, as such, a luxury. Few question the cost of the roses growing on their arbour, and we found people were delighted to find a source of the garden materials and products they wanted, especially if they were made to measure. We developed a range of products that could be made with relatively unseasoned chestnut and local bought-in oak, constructed without recourse to complicated jointing techniques. We shamelessly "borrowed" ideas for products and designs, just as others would in due course copy ours. A chance visit to Herstmonceux Castle suggested an early design - a simple two-person bench made of poles nailed together, which we sold for all of fifteen pounds. As the seat was of round poles, it looked less comfortable than it was, but suited customers wanting an appropriately rustic addition to some remote spot in their garden. However, it did not appeal to those requiring a fashion statement for the patio. An early lesson was that, in this market, few items sell on price alone. Appearance and quality of service are as important, and so that simple bench over the years evolved into a range of sawn oak and chestnut furniture, costing up to £350.

One of our seat range

Supermarkets have prior warning of the programmes of TV chefs, and can stock up with special ingredients needed for the recipes. We were often surprised by a sudden flood in demand for items that had been featured on TV. Not avid watchers ourselves, we had to rely on our staff for information. Mike came in one day saying he had seen a gardening programme featuring uprooted tree stumps, and for years thereafter we sold as many dead chestnut stools as we could unearth. People came with their own designs, and many of the products on our later catalogues were first made as bespoke items, including tree seats, dining tables, welly racks and mini hurdles. One such product was our log sawing horse, which became a steady seller. A woman customer was delighted to be able to buy one as a Christmas present for her husband, but a few days later he returned asking if he could exchange it for a garden seat. Perhaps ideas on leisure differed in that family!

Our range was limited by my own skills and those of our staff, and by our green, unseasoned wood. Although I had only one year of woodwork at school, making things comes naturally, and if I didn't know something, I could always look it up. It was therefore a shock to find that many who passed through our workshop were uninterested in learning about basic matters such as wood seasoning, and the implications of using the wrong material.

Perhaps culturally the English eschew technical knowledge, in the same way as classically-educated people are often happy to parade their innumeracy. It is not necessary to take a degree in timber technology to appreciate that dry wood soaks up preservative more easily than wet, or that summer-felled poles, peeled and in the sun, will split as they dry. Even our two experienced part-time carpenters did not know that wood shrinks five times as much across the grain as along it, or that even seasoned timber can decay in moist conditions. Had they never wondered what wood preservatives did?

Every "lifestyle" magazine is stuffed with adverts for sophisticated oak and teak garden furniture, and it was something of a struggle to meet the expectations of a clientele that did not understand the shortcomings of a rustic product. If you have never known anything other than plastic garden furniture, or products made from tropical hardwoods, the cracks and stains in our benches and tables must have seemed alarming. In due course we produced a leaflet that warned customers that the rain would wash tannin out of new oak and chestnut furniture, so initially it should be kept away from light paving, and that the drying cracks on round chestnut poles would not affect their strength. We needed to sell items as quickly as possible. Irrespective of how much care we took in manufacture, our small storage and display area was damp or dusty, so that things soon lost their newly minted look.

At first we stripped poles of bark with a drawknife or garden spade, a process unchanged since Roman times, but a tractor-powered peeler-pointer machine made light work of this task, and suddenly we could produce fenceposts economically. Initially, simple carpentry was done in the Barn. As visitor-related functions took over, we needed a separate workshop, and in the winter of 1986 built a simple timber one on the opposite side of the yard. It had a smooth concrete floor for safe working, and double doors big enough to allow the passage of our largest trellis panel. We had three-phase electricity, and so were able to install a commercial dimensioning sawbench. This speeded up and greatly improved the quality of repetitive jobs such as milling bird box parts. In addition to the normal range of hand tools, over the years we acquired the usual powered workshop equipment such as a planer-thicknesser, which smartened up the sawn timber, and improved the quality of our finished products. Unfortunately its din often drowned out the voice of whoever was trying to keep the attention of schoolkids on the other side of the yard, and periodically production had to be put on hold.

Despite our mechanisation, we couldn't compete with mass production. Our manufacture tended to be small batches, using a single tool, such as the sawbench, to carry out a number of different tasks. Working flat out, I could make a picnic table in one and a half hours. This compared with a competitor who sold them by the hundred and had a separate bench and machine for each task, reducing his production time to 35 minutes per table. What's more, because of his large throughput, he could buy his timber more cheaply. At the other end of the scale was the retired handyman, equipped with saw and hammer, working in his shed and selling for little more than the cost of materials. Once we had to add VAT to prices, our products became even less competitive.

In many respects our production business fell between the stools of the arty-crafty and commerce. The basic materials, skills and methods at our disposal, coupled with the utilitarian nature of our products, would never produce an object that would end up in a collection or be handed on as an heirloom. Years earlier, I had hand-carved pairs of yew-wood salad servers as Christmas presents; but, although finely shaped and finished to a glossy sheen, to the untrained eye they were not very different from the £5 ones at the kitchen shop in Lewes High Street. On the other hand, that same year I saw a polished yew stick in a gallery window labelled "Water Snake" and priced at £60, although it had probably taken no longer to make than my servers. One was useful, the other was "art."

We never really got on top of pricing, even though we used a formula which added percentages to materials and labour costs, and a profit margin and retail mark-up. A small percentage change at any one stage could result in a big difference in the final price, because each stage was multiplied by the next. The acid test was whether items then sold, and people or their friends came back for more. When, at the Weald Woodfair, a staff member reported that someone was selling an item for twice our price, our retort was "No, it's on sale at that price. They may sell none". They were not there the following year.

Our different styles of seats and trellis were demonstrated around our tea garden, and we soon had regular requests to install rose-arches, trellises and fencing in people's gardens. Pricing a contracting job unseen was the trickiest problem, for digging holes through buried rubble or concrete would quickly demolish any profit. Sometimes we priced unnecessarily keenly, and the team turned up to discover the establishment indicated an ostentatiously wealthy client not needing any charity on our part.

Because we offered a bespoke service, the list of products we quoted for now seems endless, ranging from swinging seats to cat hutches. Our woodland adventure playground spawned many requests for climbing frames and even tree houses, and the money people were willing to spend on their children was an eye-opener. My mother's phrase "nine-day wonder" often came to mind as we erected yet another item of play equipment for some over-indulged child. Eventually, we were able to turn down requests when regulations required engineer's reports and periodic inspections for such items, so that play might become totally risk-free.

On our small scale, it was possible to indulge our ethos of trying never to waste anything, whether raw material or by-product. All our wood had an inherent value as stored sunshine, especially as energy costs were mounting inexorably year by year, but some pieces had greater value than others. Generally speaking, the longer and straighter poles were harder to find, for coppice is usually less straight than conifer trunks, and therefore they were priced at more per foot than shorter ones. It soon became clear that cross-cutting poles to minimise waste was one of the most important jobs in the place, as cutting a long straight pole into several shorter lengths lowered the overall return. Inevitably, there were offcuts that could most simply go for firewood. However, if possible we preferred to incorporate them into products, so developed a range of items to do just that, such as log-roll edging of different heights.

Whereas others might leave significant amounts of wood at a coppice site, we extracted the short or bendy pieces to dry as firewood. It may be fashionable to leave deadwood as wildlife habitat, but we forget that in ages past peasants must have gleaned every last stick for fires and ovens, and yet somehow wildlife survived. We used offcuts from logging, from pointing fenceposts and the workshop to heat the house and Barn, and for barbecues, and we supplied sawdust to the riding stables across the road. Our sawdust output was never large enough to justify accumulating it for collection by a wood pellet manufacturer, geared up to weekly bulk collections from sawmills and joinery works, and we resorted to dumping surplus in the nearby plantation to rot and return its nutrients to the soil. Our peeling machine produced a small mountain of bark from rustic poles and fencing, and this we sold as low-cost mulch for beds, paths and play areas; it was so popular that we supplemented it with bought-in woodland mulch and hardwood chips, so we could offer a range of coverings at different prices.

The rising cost of gas, oil, and electricity for domestic heating was boosting the demand for firewood, and we were able to sell as much as we could produce. One of our abiding principles was to be as flexible as possible in our sales. Firewood was sold loose or bagged, collected or delivered, and the price reflected our labour input. The customer had a choice, depending on his pocket and degree of energy. If the customer chose to fill bags or his trailer, he had the added advantage of selecting the logs that suited him best. As in the case of a Christmas tree, no size fits all. Some customers bought the occasional bag to provide a token log for the Sunday fire as they sipped a G and T before lunch. They would specify a certain size of log, and preferred ones that burned slowly, which did not suit our predominantly coppice chestnut output. This was usually of small dimension, in the round, and with a reputation for spitting.

Even full-time firewood merchants can be surprisingly amateur, incompetent or downright deceitful. One day just before Christmas, I was delivering to a regular customer some logs which had been seasoned for two years, while, next door, a log merchant was unloading freshly-cut birch logs. When I questioned their suitability, the fellow retorted that, despite having been felled only that week, they were perfectly good, and anyway, the customer wouldn't know the difference. Most of the energy given out by such logs would be used boiling off the sap. To add to my feeling that the world could be a better place if only we worked harder at it, a neighbour came out and complained that my trailer was blocking his drive. I replied I'd move if he was in a hurry, to which he rejoined that it was "a matter of principle". Anne later suggested that he must be pretty short of principles if he had to invent that one. And anyway, what about some Christmas spirit?

For market research purposes, Diana, one of our long-term "all-rounders", one November bought a sack of firewood from a merchant who assured her the logs were "fully seasoned". Over the next three weeks, I left a selection of these obviously wet logs in the kitchen, weighing them regularly on the kitchen scales. They lost over a third in weight, and must have been cut that summer - almost worthless as fuel. Other suppliers advertising in the local free newspaper quoted "£50 a load", but were unable to work out the volume. One even referred to "two square metres" of logs!

Because they are enclosed, stoves make wood an efficient and competitive heat source. They also provide foresters with an ideal outlet for coppice wood, as smaller dimensions burn more efficiently in such stoves than larger ones. Initially we cut logs to length with a chainsaw, but soon bought a second-hand McConnel sawbench with a moving table. This harnessed the power of the tractor, and one could cut cordwood at waist height for hours on end in comparative ease and safety, provided you kept thumbs away from the circular saw. Larger logs were then split with a threaded cone which, powered by the tractor PTO, bored into each with a satisfying cracking noise. Because the cone splitter tied up a tractor, we bought an electric log splitter, which did the same job with a hydraulic ram, silently and without fumes. Over the years, firewood processors in all sizes came onto the market, and at the Weald Woodfair of 2006 I was seduced into ordering a Finnish machine. This cradled the log on a swinging table, cut it behind a guard, split the log into two or four pieces, and elevated the stream of logs into the awaiting delivery vehicle, all in comparative safety and comfort and with minimal effort. At about this time, we also bought a replacement Land Rover truck with a tipping bed, which greatly speeded our unloading time. Unfortunately, a few of our older customers hailed from the era when the coalman carried the sacks right to the cellar, and expected us to wheelbarrow and stack our logs at their back door. We soon evolved a price for this service, which must have seemed expensive to those who used it. In fact, one such delivery possibly contributed to a widowing; the elderly gentleman who signed the cheque died before we presented it the next day.

Within a few years, demand for firewood outgrew our ability to produce it, and we had to buy in increasing quantities, both from local woodsmen and larger producers. David, our ex-trainee, had set up his own harvesting business, and for several springs we took delivery of 30 tonne loads of three-metre ash cordwood, which was stacked in our top car park to dry, ready for processing. But it was often difficult to get through this pile before we needed the space for our Christmas crowds, so we had to resort to more expensive

The processor makes short work of log production

deliveries of wholesale logs straight into our covered sales bay at more frequent intervals. The same woodsmen who supplied us with logs were often able to sell us chestnut poles cut to length, to meet our increasing retail trade. The arrangement was mutual beneficial, as we provided them with an outlet they would find difficult to replicate.

Many visitors and fellow woodland owners asked why we didn't make charcoal. After all, it had been a Wilderness Wood product from the Roman period to the 1950's, and with the fashion for barbeques there was an estimated UK market of 60,000 tonnes each year. I did go on an introductory charcoal burning course, but concluded that it would only be economic on a semi-industrial scale, using far more wood than we could produce, and belching out clouds of smelly steam that would hardly be welcomed by our visitors (or neighbours). In any case, we could sell all our fuelwood as logs, without the effort of converting it. Most cheap charcoal on petrol station forecourts is from the tropics, made by third-world labour at a wage we did not wish to compete with, or is in briquette form with a high clay content. Selling English charcoal at a premium price only works by appealing to people's better nature in a small niche market, and we bought in relatively small amounts from a local producer for re-sale. It was interesting to read the labels on the charcoal bags that our barbecue hirers brought with them. The price they had paid for the charcoal often reflected the low cost and quality of their sausages, whose flavour could hardly have been improved by the use of the oil-based firelighters we could often smell as far away as our house.

Over time we bought in other products we could not, or were unwilling, to make. There was always the temptation to become a woodland-sited garden centre. Anne's brother, Jim Keeling, makes high quality terracotta pots which we could have sold to a very similar client base to his, but the question was: where would it stop? We decided that anything we sold from elsewhere should be made of wood; as local as possible; and robust enough to withstand exposure in our display area. Any items of value would have to be small enough to have on sale in the Barn, such as the faces carved from roots that we sold on behalf of Tach, a local wood-carver. Our bought-in products were therefore limited to bean-poles, pea-sticks, hazel hurdles, wood chip, mulch, and the like, and these we sold with a normal retail mark-up.

Cheap transport has accustomed us all to expect goods to be delivered from afar, but at great environmental and social cost, as anyone who lives close to a major road or airport will confirm. When, after eight car-free years, we reluctantly purchased the battered Saab 95 to get us to and from the wood, it enabled us to deliver our first products. Its large tailgate and flat loading bed facilitated carriage of all sorts of goods, and over-sized items were lashed to a groaning roof-rack. This poor little beast of burden was further laden with an ancient Post Office trailer; I managed to drill a hole into the petrol tank when fixing the tow-bar – a silly, costly and potentially fatal mistake.

By 1985 the scrapheap was beckoning the Saab, and for years a seven-seater Volvo estate doubled as shared school transport and delivery vehicle. Filled to the gunwales inside, with the roof rack resembling an Indian bus, and pulling an equally overloaded trailer, we would make our way gingerly to and from Agricultural shows where we had a stand. Eventually we gave in to our staff's entreaties, and a long-wheelbase Land Rover with its four-wheel drive made sure we got off those muddy showgrounds.

Many customers selected their own poles, saving us time and the possibility of choosing material too straight or too rustic for their needs. Some turned up with suitable vehicles, but many pristine seats were scuffed by fenceposts or poles. One driver refused to be helped with loading his Jaguar, which was just as well, for when he slammed down the boot, a pole resting on the dashboard went through the windscreen. Another young man had ordered six seven-metre tepee poles, from the first thinning of the Douglas firs. He turned up in a Morris Minor with a minimal roof rack. On this occasion I refused to have any part in loading, as I could imagine what might happen with his over-long load on the way home. We were more comfortable selling long "pioneering poles" to the Scouts, whose leaders turned up with trucks borrowed from indulgent employers.

"Free delivery" has to be paid for, and we saw no reason to penalise locals by charging a flat rate. We encouraged customers to collect their purchases, as part of a visit. Even a ten-mile delivery might cost us £20, and more if one took account of loading time. Small items therefore appeared outrageously expensive to deliver, and bulky products, such as logs, were only economic to deliver locally. Most road hauliers refused to carry our bulky goods such as poles and trellises. Only when a customer ordered a full load, such as ten six-foot woven hurdles, was worth our while to drive to a distant place such as Margate, sixty miles away, and the unit delivery price made sense. Our experiences of the actual cost of making deliveries have led us to question how national firms can make pay "next-day" deliveries, with their ensuing rush of white vans. The environmental cost must also be immense.

Under our management, the plantations and coppices were supplying increasing quantities of versatile raw materials. We were proving that we could run a small business making useful items, and that this resource could be harvested sustainably and in harmony with other benefits, such as wildlife and visitors. As the enterprise grew, our self-sufficient efforts had to be augmented with outside assistance, and we found ourselves providing useful employment; or so we hoped!

WOODWORKERS AND OTHERS

As soon as we bought the wood we had invited a stream of friends at weekends to share our excitement of ownership; hoping that they would also enjoy helping with the myriad of tasks to be done, from clearing the rides of invading brambles and birch seedlings, to fencing the first small Christmas tree plantation by the stream. Many did indeed slog away for nothing more than food and a warm glow of satisfaction, but after a few forays to our winter-time wood they somehow found that family commitments and their gardens were greater priorities.

Our idea was to run Wilderness Wood part-time, alongside consultancy work and other commitments. By nature I would like to have worked unassisted, and never be an employer other than of professional help dealing with tedious matters such as tax. But it soon became clear that there weren't enough hours in our week, especially if Jo and Kate were to get any undivided parental attention, and we were therefore going to need regular outside help. Even before we moved to the wood we took advantage of the Youth Opportunity Programme, one of a succession of government schemes to give training to less academic youths. The employer only had to pay his expenses. Our first "YOP" was a carefree lad whose grandparents ran a tiny pub in Lewes; he and I would drive up from Lewes each Thursday and Friday, and set about those early tasks of ride-clearing and fencing. The next YOP broke the mobile sawbench in two by driving the tractor too close to a tree stump. So much for "free" labour!

By the time we moved to the wood, the Youth Opportunity Programme had evolved into the college-based Youth Training Scheme. A forestry course was up to three years long, consisting of both theory and practical modules such as chainsaw use, tractor maintenance and general estate work, and each student would be with us full time for several weeks each term. We paid an agreed weekly sum, and in most cases got value for money, while acting *in loco parentis* to youngsters away from home. One lad had been going through a bad patch following his parents' breakup, and one day he and the carpenter were caught throwing sharp tools at each other. Not long after, we received a 'phone-call from his landlady, asking us to come and collect his things, as she would not be spoken to in the way he had at breakfast. I hot-footed it along the road to mollify her, later reinforced by the apology and bunch of flowers we insisted that he give her. That mixed-up kid went on to great things in the tree department of a London borough.

A woodlander's life may seem idyllic, and many youngsters must dream of its being the local embodiment of the Python "Lumberjack's Song". But despite the delights of morning mist in the valley and birdsong at dusk, the life is hard, dangerous, and poorly paid, and their mates working at a factory at Crawley are in the dry and better rewarded. It may be different in more remote parts of Britain, where rural work is more the norm and living costs lower, but in the South-east it is increasingly difficult to attract and retain young people in our tiny forest industry. Time and again, we would hear one-man operators say that they couldn't afford the insurance costs, or found the associated paperwork of employing people too burdensome; and, once trained, "they go off, work for theirselves and pinch moy customers."

Despite college instructors' best endeavours, a holder of a chainsaw certificate will know little more than how to avoid cutting his foot off, and it takes years to reach commercial standards of output, so training up a recruit can be a major commitment. However, we employed youngsters from the start not just because such labour was inexpensive, but because it was our philosophy to provide both training and employment. Some of the youths who passed through our hands went on to successful land-based careers, while others discovered that work on the land was not what they wanted to do for the rest of their lives or even the next few days; like Boris, who left us to train as a mason and, the last time we heard from him, had a job for life repairing one of our great cathedrals.

There was so much to get done – cutting and extracting coppice, thinning the plantations, making our increasing range of wood products, building up our facilities for visitors, dealing with customers. I could not be on site all the time to supervise, as I had to give priority to consulting work, and we soon decided that we could not survive on trainees who required constant supervision. We needed permanent staff that would become competent all-rounders, and so kept on some of our trainees as full-time employees. David and Paul, who did such sterling work clearing up the damage from the Great Storm, carried on with us until the former moved on to set up his own firm and the other was attracted to an employer with much bigger machinery. Andrew, who first came as a teenage "Saturday lad", returned after a degree course, and was still with us as woodland foreman when we handed the wood on. Diana was so keen to stay on after her agricultural college placement that she commuted daily from north Kent, and became an accomplished all-rounder until motherhood dictated she get a job nearer home as a teacher at a local wildlife centre.

As demand increased for furniture and other made items, we advertised for a part-time carpenter, and had a succession of cheerful semi-retired men who were happy to come in a couple of days a week. This supplemented their pensions, and they were able to show less experienced staff both wood-working skills and a mature approach to work.

In 1988 we bit the bullet and advertised for a graduate forestry assistant – someone who could help with the relatively lucrative consulting work whenever needed, and turn his hand to woodland work the rest of the time. Now we could take holidays confident that both businesses were in safe hands! Ross was soon succeeded by fellow forester Tim, who became our longest-serving employee; he was our dependable manager from 1990 until he took over the consultancy 15 years later. His broad theoretical knowledge was a sound basis for developing his practical skills, and he successfully led the team with the tact I sometimes lacked.

A school "demonstration". Andrew helps a nine-year-old to cleave a chestnut pole.

The day-to-day work of the woodland business was amazingly complicated, as we were running such a varied range of activities. Because each member of staff had to lend a hand wherever needed, they had to have not just a passing knowledge of what was going on, but to be able to do it. This made for interesting work, as no two days were the same. A day might include a kids' party, making pea-sticks, composing an advert, answering the 'phone, and dealing with a complaint. Because of the seasonality of the enterprise, it would take at least a year to gain a full understanding of the job. Thus, an employee who had joined us in January would have no concept of how the Christmas period worked. Each person became increasingly valuable, with his growing store of knowledge, not just of how things were done, but why and when. Only after someone had left did we realise that even the humblest had accumulated a wealth of knowledge.

Over the years we had some splendid staff, who were both fun to be with and hard-working, and contributed all sorts of ideas to the business. We were not always good at heaping them with praise at appropriate times, and our shortcomings as employers must often have been disheartening. Several stayed over a decade, while others went on to opportunities which allowed them to use their talents more appropriately. Some, including the father of one YTS student, graciously wrote and thanked us for the skills and personal development they had acquired during their time at the wood. Letters like that made it all worthwhile.

Although we strove for self-sufficiency, often our own workforce was not big enough for seasonal or one-off tasks, such as Christmas tree sales, spraying, or coppicing. Hadlow Down is in an area of marginal farming which has been becoming less viable with each passing year; those small farmers still holding on were often part-time, and glad to cut hedges, top grass or erect fences in return for cash in hand. We tapped into a network of one-man bands, who could be relied on to do a tidy job at a fair price. A quiet word in the New Inn would usually bring results. One such person was Slavik, a young Pole with a thick accent made worse by a paucity of teeth. Alone, he felled, cross-cut, transported and stacked over sixty tonnes of early pine thinnings from Owl Wood, to be used as firewood. But this was before Poland joined the EU, and suddenly he disappeared, and his 'phone number went unanswered. In those early days our only transport was our decrepit Saab 95, so we used a father and son from nearby Buxted for delivery of larger loads. Les was as wiry as his son was large, and they had voices to match. Nothing was too much trouble for them, and they also helped out in the wood. A regular visiting woodsman was Johnny, who pressed us for standing coppice to work. A drink problem and years outdoors had aged him prematurely, and it was often his missus who delivered him because of a driving ban. One Saturday afternoon he turned up reeking and barely able to stand, asking if he could have money due to him the following week. We would normally have complied, aware of the cash-flow problems of small operators, but knew he would spend it until he was paralytic; so we lied that we were right out of cash, but could let him have a cheque. We later learned that Gerald at the pub had driven him home, both to do a favour and to get him off the premises.

Periodically we had to advertise seasonal or part-time posts, revealing a wide range from hopefuls to downright incompetents. One chap, who came with a good reference, would only work on an agreed day-rate, but had a disappointing output when coppicing. A foreman in a well-known firm of tree surgeons had told me the trick of waiting at a distance until you knew the men were taking a well-earned pause, and then springing on them with a "Is this the way you spend all your time?" Unfair perhaps, and the equivalent of the lumberjack foreman's practice of firing a man daily, *pour encourager les autres*. I went down to see how the hired help was getting on, and found him staring vacantly into the bonfire. He explained he was working out how best to proceed, and after a pep-talk I withdrew, glad to hear again the buzz of an active chainsaw. Once I was out of sight, the buzz ceased, not for the minute it would take to pile up poles, but some time. After ten minutes I could no longer contain curiosity and suspicion, and returned to find him sitting in his pickup, reading the local free newspaper.

Here was a man who loved his work so much he would lie down and sleep with it. Caught red-handed, there was every reason to discontinue his contract on the spot, but we failed to get back a loan I had made him. Several lessons hard-learned – take up more than one reference, don't lend money to a stranger, and pay by results.

We learned not to judge by appearances. "Swampy" gained the nickname on account of his shoulder-length dreadlocks, and because he lived in a large old van of the sort that used to travel round pop festivals, perhaps sporting a rear bumper sticker: "Don't laugh. Your daughter might be in here". At interview he made it clear he would be prepared to go along with any dress-code we might inflict, but the dreadlocks were non-negotiable. A couple of rubber bands held them out of the chainsaw's way, and honour was preserved. He parked up his van for two or three nights a week in the car park, and it wasn't long before the charming barmaid at the New Inn fell for him, and soon his semi-nomadic days were over. Now he has his own local forestry contracting business.

Wilderness Wood offered an abundance of training in life skills and the work ethic. Many were the local teenagers whose working lives started as Saturday morning jobs, filling bags with logs, sweeping the yard or staining picnic tables. Youngsters who were unwilling to help at home would submit to boring work, under often uncomfortable conditions of heat or cold. Because most parents work away from home, children have little appreciation of the working environment; to counter this, schools were charged with finding placements for a week's work experience for every teenager, and we agreed to participate with two local schools. Some of our student visitors asked for jobs the next summer holiday, others were put off the great outdoors for life, and a small minority played hooky after day one, usually no surprise to the teacher with their pastoral care.

At the other extreme were the graduates who had yet to find their metier, and I have always felt that "attitude rather than aptitude" is the commercial equivalent of the army maxim of one volunteer being worth a dozen conscripts. One such early worker was Andreas, son of two writers, and later to become a university philosophy lecturer. Living in a Brighton squat, he would cycle eight miles solo on an ancient tandem to arrive in Lewes by eight am, having paused only to buy a hunk of bread pudding at a lay-bye. At that time he held the opinion that Man had evolved to run, and would think nothing of jogging the twenty miles between Brighton and his parents' home in the middle of the night. The rucksack full of weights to add to his exertions was of particular interest to the police who once stopped him mid-journey. Here was a man whose challenging brain would be working out a more efficient way of doing some thankless task, rather than letting it get him down.

Some of our best workers were farmers' sons, for they had been inoculated with the work ethic and practical common sense at birth. Not only did they do a full day's hard work, they already knew how to drive a tractor or construct a fence. On the other hand, the lad who had drifted into casual work with a dodgy forestry contractor after leaving school had to be re-educated as to how taut and straight a fence should be, and to take a pride in his work. Youngsters who had been brought up in the era of cheap, disposable goods did not see the point of caring for tools and other equipment, and many times we found hand tools rusting where they had been left at the end of the day. On one occasion, I resorted to hiding the chainsaw that two of them had left in full view during their lunch break. Unable to locate it, annoyance turned to panic when they believed it to be stolen, and to incredulity when we suggested they fund its £400 replacement. That was a relatively easy lesson to teach. Another time, a chainsaw was wrecked by someone filling it with ordinary petrol rather than two-stroke mixture, so that it lacked internal lubrication; but the saw was used by several people, and no-one would take responsibility. In former times a craftsman had to provide and maintain his tools at his own expense, to ensure their care. Now it is the employer who takes the risk.

One of our first tasks in which volunteers played a part was clearing the pond with the BTCV, mentioned in an earlier chapter. When we set up our Friends of Wilderness Wood, one of the membership benefits on offer was the chance to help at the wood. One such volunteer session helped replant the front plantation in March 1988, after the Great Storm. We tried several other tasks with members, including path-making, but initial enthusiasm soon wore off, and we failed to pursue the opportunity as vigorously as we might have done.

A local social services department asked us to provide a placement for adults with learning difficulties, and each Wednesday half a dozen would turn up in a mini-van with Brian, their supervisor. A highlight of their day was the free hot chocolate or ice-cream. They were a likeable bunch, and, although slow-witted, we never doubted their wisdom as they stood watching Brian slog away at building a trail, while they voiced encouragement. We were not known for political correctness, and one steep part of the main trail has a section that we fondly referred to as the Loons' Steps. Sadly, declining local authority budgets saw an end to their outings. Less rewarding for us were visits by groups of town-based, long-term unemployed who were being exposed to countryside skills. For many, the woods must have been a totally alien environment with unfamiliar elements such as mud, trees, and unpaved tracks. With the passing years, safety issues became dominant, and risk assessments so protracted that the biggest danger was that some actual work might get done.

Forestry has a high accident record and we were fortunate that we had no serious incidents at the wood. Much of what we did was relatively low risk. We had, for example, few large trees to fell, and no huge machines to crush people. There were nonetheless some near-misses, as when David overturned the tractor by using the winch to pull a log from the side, rather than in line with the tractor. People need training and supervision if they are to work safely and productively, and this places a huge burden on woods too small to afford proper apprenticeships.

Youngsters presenting themselves for woodland work often had a deficiency of both common sense and self-preservation. One such lad was Ben, whose fag dropped out of his mouth while he was refilling his chainsaw. He appeared up in the yard sans eyebrows and arms to his jumper, and told us he had put out the flames on his hands by putting them in his pockets, while he kicked the chainsaw around until its flames died out. Another misuse of fuel involved re-lighting a reluctant fire by throwing petrol onto a pile of sticks with concealed embers. The resultant explosion threw the wood pile several metres in all directions. In both cases we were lucky no serious injury resulted, but at least the cause and effect taught a lesson. A more puzzling incident was when F appeared up in the yard, limping and dazed, with off-road tyre marks imprinted up his back. This slightly simple lad, whom we had taken on at his mother's pleading, had been sent to pick up some logs with the dumper. He had driven it many times supervised with no problems, and had been judged competent to do this task alone. Our subsequent site investigation revealed the empty dumper, engine running and still in gear, trying to climb a tree, wheels digging pits in the soft ground. All we could surmise was that he had somehow fallen off, and the rear wheel had run over him and, incredibly, done him little damage.

Working in a wood can be hazardous both to oneself and anyone who comes within range. As time went by we realised the wisdom of health and safety legislation, but it was always debatable what "reasonable" precautions meant. Our problem lay in balancing ideal safety measures with the need to make a living in a marginally profitable business. We marked off with red and white tape areas where we were felling trees, but the feller needed eyes in the back of his chainsaw helmet to ensure no-one had wilfully ignored the "keep out" signs. Working with machinery in the yard was problematic, as there was a constant flow of visitors to and from the Barn and car-parks. Fortunately, most people were sensible, and enjoyed the opportunity to observe our work at reasonably close quarters, and we never had any significant problems.

My academic training was no foundation for managing staff, and I am by nature a loner. I have a theory that people who are drawn to forestry prefer the company of trees, which have the added attractions that they don't answer back, and those that do not measure up are for the chop. There has been a loss of deference and devaluation of knowledge, and it must have been so much easier for our forebears to say "Do as you're bloody well told!" A sound organisation incorporates good ideas from all sources, but there are limits to the democratic process, especially in the middle of a job, when "works meetings" can be a costly time-waster.

The combination of an unsubtle manager and a worker with a personality problem could lead to serious trouble. We had one chap in his thirties who was developing an ever-shorter fuse, which would ignite at the slightest provocation. He almost left the Barn roof we were shingling, as he "flew off the handle" in response to an innocuous suggestion that he try to match the shingles better. Soon afterwards he was diagnosed with diabetes, and his sugar levels and moods became better controlled. More serious was the time that a carpenter neglected to follow correct procedures while using a sawbench. By using his hand to clear scraps, instead of the stick provided, he removed the ends of two fingers. Although our insurers found us not at fault, they settled out of court rather than fight a costly case; yet another reason for banning solicitors' "no fee" advertisements in A and E waiting rooms.

One of the challenges to any small employer is that few employees have his enthusiasm for productivity. Working for ourselves in 1981, Anne and I could each earn a tolerable £5 per hour making bean-poles and pea-sticks, then well in excess of the minimum wage. We found that few could match our rates of production, even though we were hardly more experienced. I explained until blue in the face that, although a task might be repetitive, one's mind was free, not only to dream of more exciting things, but how to save time by performing the task more efficiently. You know you are getting old when you do up your laces and look around to see what else there is to do while you are down there. It is a joy to watch one of the old-time workers making hurdles. One such craftsman was Bill Thompson, from whom we bought woven hazel hurdles for resale. Never appearing to rush, he had a steady daily output of five large hurdles, and still had time to discuss all manner of things over a cup of tea. He was amazingly well read, and before his untimely death was well into writing a book on hurdles, from their use as roadways across prehistoric bogs to the modern age.

Setting the right level of remuneration is always a problem, especially with the wide range of skills and experience that we had. After the '87 storm, a young couple from the Liverpool area turned up looking for work, and we employed them to saw fallen trees. Within a week David, our YTS lad, came up crestfallen that they would not let him work with them unless he was paid their hourly rate. I explained to the Scousers that he was a trainee, and receiving free board, lodging and education, but they preferred to walk off the site, never to return, than work with "scab" labour.

Among the less reliable and conscientious staff, we found obtaining a full day's labour for a full day's pay a constant challenge. Loic, a French forestry student who worked for us one summer, suggested the French went to work in order to work, whereas the English went to socialise. Despite their 35-hour week and six weeks' holiday, the French are reportedly more productive than we are. The early morning chat whilst ostensibly getting out the equipment might go on for up to half an hour, and the ten minute tea break ("breakfast") mid morning might take another half hour. Six people chatting in the workshop could run away with two man-hours of the firm's time, but this was never seen as virtual theft. Staff who are conscientious on this matter are often viewed as "boss's men", as are the ones who stay past the official end of day to finish off some task. A foreman can make himself unpopular enforcing good working practices until they become ingrained, but over the years his impact will be immense, and he can be the most important member of any business.

Our training and background had not prepared us for managing staff, let alone the number and variety who passed through our hands. Like them, we were learning on the job, and we could only hope that their remuneration, job satisfaction and training matched the contribution they made to the wood's success over the years.

Wilderness Wood

TRAIL

30p

This trail takes you past some of the wood's interesting features. It is just under a mile (1¼ km.) long. There are some steps, moderate hills, and muddy patches after rain. The route is marked by wooden posts with white arrows and letters.

Also available: *Children's discovery trail leaflet*
Trail quiz sheet
Easy access path leaflet

Wilderness Wood is 61 acres (24 ha.) in area, at the head of a small valley. It is a working woodland, managed to produce a crop of timber and wood. You may walk where you like, but only cross fences or hedges if there is a stile or gate.

To protect the wood, please :

- *Guard against risk of fire*
- *Leave no litter*
- *Keep dogs under control*
- *Do not pick or damage plants or toadstools (you may pick tree leaves)*

The Main Trail leaflet was regularly updated

THE GREAT BRITISH PUBLIC

With our encouragement, Hadlow Down residents carried on their traditional free access to what was, in effect, the village park. These visits ranged from the twice-daily dog walk to the ex-banker who brought his labrador for a pre-Sunday lunch outing, and the network of well-maintained rides and paths proved very popular alternatives to the often nearly impassable local public rights of way. Unlike many landowners, especially those new to their role, who try hard to keep people at bay, our vision for Wilderness Wood involved actually welcoming the public. We set out to show that woodland should be productive in every sense of the word, including public enjoyment and education, and visitor income would be central to the financial success of the project.

Our intended target market was the general public looking for a day out, and indeed the largest element over the years was what we referred to as "casual visitors": that is, those who simply turned up unbooked. We wanted to provide a woodland experience and an affordable day out, where it was not necessary to spend constantly, and where you could eat your own picnic, perhaps supplemented with an ice cream or tea. Coming from frugal backgrounds, we felt that, if we were to be part of the commercialisation of leisure, we should at least be seen as good value. Unlike most large visitor destinations, we were not going to insist people made their exit through the gift shop. This approach proved popular with grandparents charged with entertaining during the school holidays, and it encouraged repeat visits, not just for walks but for our other products. In terms of return on effort, visitors can be the most profitable element of a rural enterprise. A family paying a £10 entrance fee added almost £10 to the day's profits, as the only additional costs were the issuing of a ticket and information leaflet. To make the same profit on catering or made goods would require significant extra input of time and materials.

We decided our main market would be the family. However, to satisfy it, each member would have to find at least one element of the visit to their taste. The young would be happy to play on the zip wire for hours, and den-building kept both children and parents entertained. Granny would enjoy tea and cakes, and Dad could find ideas for garden constructions – although he would miss his pint, unless he brought his own. Like most countryside sites, we would find it difficult to engage with teenagers - Wilderness Wood was just not "cool" enough, even with a fresh northerly blowing.

Wilderness Wood is just an ordinary Sussex woodland, lacking superlatives of rarity, landscape or history. So how would we be able to charge people to visit, when there are so many public footpaths running through lovely wooded scenery in the surrounding High Weald? Just five miles away are the two and a half thousand hectares of Ashdown Forest, with free access for all, and several freely-accessible Forestry Commission woods are within an hour's drive. But Wilderness Wood would have the unusual distinction of being a working woodland, where people could see, and learn about, wood and timber being grown and used. It would not be a visitor attraction that just happened to be in a wooded setting, but visitors and their activities would be an integral part of modern forestry in its broadest sense. In addition, the wood should appeal to those needing to feel they had "gone somewhere", in other words, be seen as a destination: a day out in the country, and a place where people would feel both comfortable and secure, with a range of facilities and recreational opportunities.

A major disadvantage of our location was that it was not accessible by public transport, with Buxted railway station two miles along a busy road, suicidal to walkers, and just one weekday bus. Against our own ethos, we were inevitably in the business of attracting almost exclusively a car-borne public. This could have resulted in serried ranks of cars parked on tarmac, but instead we installed discreet wooden signs to rubble-surfaced parking areas, edged with log barriers to prevent tyres from venturing onto grass or tree rooting areas, or onto the object of attraction, whether picnic site, play area or tea garden. Capacity at peak times such as bank holidays would never be adequate, and I could be seen burning off my breakfast by charging round urging people to park neatly, so that precious spaces were not lost. On a walking holiday in France we came across parking spaces demarcated by thin larch poles pegged to the rubble surface at 2.5 metre intervals; these ensured sensible parking in situations where painted lines would soon be obscured by mud or leaves, and we used this approach in a later car park. Why hadn't we thought up this simple idea ourselves?

To justify our admission charges we would have to develop facilities such as toilets, trails and picnic sites. Probably our greatest attraction, at least for children, was the play area not far from the Barn. It started life as a simple climbing frame constructed from chestnut poles bolted or nailed together, and a zip wire, affectionately known as the "death-slide", crafted from some abandoned cable I found in a hedgerow, left behind when a telegraph pole had been removed. Items involving movement are always the most popular, and sometimes the queue for the death-slide was almost as long as the slide itself. We tried as far as possible to build with our own timber and labour, to keep down costs and ensure an appropriately rustic appearance, although we did have to buy in some elements such as climbing net, and slide for the toddlers' fort. Over the years, the climbing frame expanded into a considerable structure with monkey bars, ladders, and fireman's pole.

The play area combined fun with an acceptable degree of risk. Occasionally we received complaints from parents whose children had hurt themselves, but fortunately the vast majority saw such injuries as part of the process of growing up. One irate father returned with six-year-old son with an arm in plaster, complaining that he had fallen one and a half metres from an unguarded platform. When we inspected the apparatus, the boy explained he had deliberately jumped, from half that height, and landed badly. To save the father from loss of face, I agreed to add a rail to prevent such jumping in future.

Our first play area

In deciding how to design our developments, we were fortunate in having sufficient skills not to need to employ outsiders to interpret our wishes. I had studied forest recreation design in the western USA, and was itching to implement my take on those concepts. Clearly, a US Forest Service density of 2.5 picnic tables per acre would not be applicable to a small Sussex wood, but gravelled tracks, simple tables, and wood-chip ground cover were all appropriate. The play area of chestnut poles, the rustic wooden fences and simple routed wooden signs, all lent a deliberately unsophisticated, rustic feel to the place, where design was determined by function, and function by what we hoped our clients would want. For me, the most telling vindication of our approach came one day shortly before we handed over the reins, when I overheard one old gent say to another "This place is really *genuine*".

One of the ideas that I imported from Montana was the barbecue stand. No US Forest Service picnic site or campground is complete without its opportunity to burn steaks, and, given the chance, the British are just as keen. I devised a couple of "portable" stands that could be wheeled between the picnic areas, or placed near the Barn for evening functions. They always seemed to be in the wrong place, and we soon replaced them with permanent brick structures. Customers could buy a bag of locally-made charcoal, or a sack of wood off-cuts with an instruction sheet on how to make their fire with wood.

Family barbecue

A small business cannot offer its staff much career progression, so a trickle of new ideas and projects was needed to keep them (and ourselves) stimulated and motivated. Sarah dreamed of creating a "little house in the woods", and persuaded us to open out a clearing near the bottom of the wood and build a hut there, as a focus for picnics half-way round the trail. The resulting small cruck-framed structure, with shingled roof and wooden floor, barbecue pit and log seats, was immediately popular. I muttered about the staff time taken in the construction, but it indirectly led to one of our most successful enterprises. That summer was a hot one, and soon we had requests for overnight stays. All we were offering was a tiny open-sided hut, a clearing to pitch a small tent or two, and a place to make a fire, in your own little bit of Sussex countryside. Access was a half-mile walk (uphill, in the morning), with wheelbarrows provided; water supply was a plastic container; sanitation, a spade. But "wild camp" was an instant success, and soon we added a second site nearby, with canvas shelter, and then two more. Undoubtedly, the opportunity to light a fire was an attraction many other campsites lacked, and scavenging your own firewood enhanced the feel of wild camping.

We saw ourselves as educators on matters of forestry and natural history, and by 1982 had devised a trail that would encourage people to explore the wood, guiding them along routes they might otherwise miss, and explaining what they were seeing. We didn't want the wood cluttered and tamed with signboards, which would anyway be expensive and prone to vandalism, so the route was marked at points of interest by white letters on wooden posts. The accompanying leaflet could easily be updated as time passed. At point X, for example, the leaflet originally said "From here you can see the Barn, over the pines planted in 1970". Within three years that view had become obscured by the growing trees, and we had to amend the text to refer to the pines instead. We charged a nominal sum for the leaflet, to avoid its being discarded as litter. With her years of experience writing visitor guides for other sites, Anne ensured the right words were used in sentences of the appropriate complexity; aim for a twelve-year-old, and your text will be comprehensible to most people. To complement this trail leaflet, and the others that followed it, we provided simple quiz sheets so that children could be involved in exploring and learning.

Not all children required such encouragement, for they loved to tear ahead and find the next marker-post, and the chance to be off the leash and away from traffic must have seemed magical to many.

Despite lacking formal art training, Anne rose to the task of drawing the illustrations for these quiz sheets and trail guides, later helped by Sarah. Some of these simple line drawings leaven the prose of this book.

As time went on, we developed seasonal trails to complement the permanent one and encourage repeat visits. Our first was the Bluebell Walk through the best spring flowers, explaining their natural history, uses and folklore. Although our bluebell displays were nothing special, people flocked to see them in the unusual setting of a wood that was still actively coppiced. On an autumn break in south-east France, we came across a Chestnut Festival that took the form of a whole village devoted to the culinary delights of the sweet chestnut. Realising that we were missing a trick, we next autumn instituted a Chestnut Celebration of our own, with chestnut soup, cake and ice cream, demonstrations of cleaving chestnut wood, and a Chestnut Trail, giving the opportunity for visitors to pick up nuts. To fill the summer gap, Sarah developed a Forest Folklore Trail. This encouraged lots of visitor participation, and by the end of the summer season one part of the wood was adorned with fairy gardens, and another with clay faces leering from pine trunks, while the Barn was festooned with charcoal drawings and woodland poems. These seasonal trails did involve signs around the wood – simple laminated sheets, easily and cheaply replaceable. Less firmly fixed than the permanent trail, the temporary arrows were prone to "re-direction" by enterprising nine-year-olds.

Encouraging the public into the furthest parts of the wood was not without drawbacks. Once mobile 'phones had become commonplace, we began to get calls from lost souls, and learned to use directional terms such as "uphill" rather than "northwards" to route them back to the Barn. One Saturday lunchtime, we noticed a police helicopter hovering a few hundred metres below the house. Apparently, a four-year-old had thrown a tantrum and run off round the corner of the path. Instead of waiting for sense to prevail, or asking our staff to form a search party, the mother had immediately 'phoned the police, who straight away instigated a missing child search. We were not sure if our ire was more deserved by mother or police. What, we wondered, might have been the consequences if the silly woman had glimpsed me on one of my squirrel-shooting forays, with shot-gun under my arm?

In order to broaden the wood's appeal and comply with the spirit of access for all, we built a quarter-mile "easy access" path, taking in plantation, coppice, and a view over the Christmas trees. The wood has little level ground, and, although we kept gradients as shallow as possible, wheelchairs needed a hearty push to get up the final slope to the yard. It was popular with the more cautious baby-buggy pusher, although most took a commendably four-wheel-drive attitude, and were undaunted by the steps and mud elsewhere in the wood. One intrepid wheelchair-bound visitor even managed to get her electric vehicle to the very bottom of the wood, and enjoyed it so much that she came back with her family to camp there.

In keeping with our environmental evangelism we never provided a single rubbish bin for visitors, and almost everybody complied with our plea to "Take your own rubbish home." Even after a busy Bank Holiday, a litter-pick would seldom fill a single carrier bag, possibly because we took care always to remove the smallest sweet wrapper on sight, so litter never begat litter. What did surprise us, however, was the food we discovered when barbecue hirers left behind large bin-liners of "waste". I would often sort the bag contents, to do their recycling for them. Along with drinks containers might be half-eaten steaks, whole containers of salads, and even unopened packs of sausages. This seemed scandalous to us brought up in the "austerity" years, but we decreased our frustration by feeding any waste food to the hens.

Good behaviour is infectious, but sometimes lack of consideration for others drew deeply on our reserves of tolerance. On one hot Sunday I had to persuade a father and young sons that the gents toilet was not the most suitable place for a water-pistol fight, despite the ready availability of ammunition and towels. Another time, a group of young Russian picnickers found the English custom of keeping down the volume of music in the countryside after seven pm was not what they had expected in the Free West.

In our rare contacts with local police, they were amazed, and probably horrified, at our trusting nature. We had neither locked gates at night, nor staff in the yard to oversee self-service, but relied on customers to come and tell us how many stakes or sacks of firewood they had loaded into their cars. Many visitors remarked how they appreciated being trusted. We judged that it would not be worth employing extra staff to prevent the inevitable pilfering or unpaid admissions that must have slipped through. We did occasionally notice a customer teetering under an overfilled bag of logs, or five children playing for nothing in the playground while a designated mum made a single cup of tea last an hour. For several weeks a man and a woman used to arrive in separate cars at lunchtime and make their way down into the wood, carrying a blanket and little else. They reappeared some time later, hand in hand and with smiles on their faces, and went their separate ways. We were too bemused to ask for entrance fees, so avoided any possible charge of profiting from immorality. They would have appreciated the sign "Smile, you're <u>not</u> on CCTV" which I considered erecting in my fight against ubiquitous surveillance.

Professional hosts such as hoteliers and publicans develop the art of remembering their clients from one year to the next. Neither of us was adept in this field, and often had to feign recognition when an apparent stranger approached in Uckfield High Street like an old friend, and proceeded to tell us how well their child had enjoyed the hot chocolate or party game. I was not well suited to face-to-face dealings with many members of the public, and would score low marks in any test of empathy. For me, the idea that "the customer is always right" was often patently incorrect, but over the years I did manage to temper the desire to correct all shortcomings. Sometimes our advice was ignored, as when a man ventured down the snow-covered drive in his shiny BMW in spite of the "4-wheel-drive only" notice at the entrance, and filled his boot with logs. Anne innocently enquired whether he had four-wheel-drive, and he informed her it was a new car with a powerful engine. So he used the powerful engine to spin two wheels very fast, and no way would he listen to a mere woman explain how to drive. Reluctantly he allowed me, with two Montana winters' driving experience, to take the wheel and gently steer the vehicle up to the Main Road, but could not manage so much as a nod of thanks as he drove off.

It was therefore Anne who had the unenviable reputation for being better with "difficult" people, even before her Tourist Board training on customer care. Actually we had very few unhappy customers. Even if they arrived in a bad mood after a long hot journey, with squabbling kids and grumpy aunty, Wilderness Wood usually worked its magic before long. If someone complains, remove him from his audience, sit him down, smile, and give him your whole attention and a free cup of tea, and that's usually the end of it; a well-handled complaint can create a happy and loyal customer. But it doesn't always work. Anne had to deal with a letter complaining, amongst other things, about paying to use the barbecue stand. She wrote a detailed reply explaining the economics of the wood, and offering a refund if they still wanted their money back. She thought it would take some cheek to claim anything after her careful exposition, but claim he did, and also on behalf of an accompanying family. Much to my disgust, she remitted £23.50 to what was clearly a professional complainer.

The recreational elements of our enterprise could have developed in so many ways, and the ultimate decision between the possibilities lay with us alone. Activities had to be compatible with one other; for instance, horse-riding permits might have been profitable, but horses churning up our paths would not have fitted with family walkers. This compatibility also applied to the character of the place, and the tone we were trying to establish. No place can cater for all tastes, and we had to choose our market. Like many other small entrepreneurs, we were guilty of defining our market as PLU – People Like Us. In other words, what we provided, and its style, largely reflected our own tastes, and we sought to attract those who shared them.

We did from time to time make an effort to nail some hard facts about our visitors, rather than rely on assumption and observation. From Kate's teenage maths assignment onwards, the occasional student would bother visitors with a questionnaire of dubious rigour and statistical significance. Of more use was our own questionnaire which we for some years invited visitors to complete, with the incentive of a monthly prize draw if they added their name and address. This revealed that about fifty percent of visits were repeats, and that recommendation was the biggest source of new customers. The replies confirmed that the great majority travelled less than 30 miles, and that the proportion of elderly visitors rose at bluebell time. Overall, over 90% were family groups, and, in spite of our efforts to make our paths easy for walkers, we continued to be seen as a place primarily for children. Club organisers would say "I don't think our members would manage a woodland", although in our experience older people were often fascinated by the place. For many, an actively-managed woodland was a breath of the past. The survey forms had spaces for recording what people liked most, and suggestions for improvement. Anne scanned the latter every week, as they often identified easily-fixed problems such as dogs' mess or badly-checked loos. The "likes" ranged widely, but the play area figured prominently, and many could be summarised under the heading of "peaceful woodland environment".

In the early days, our main problem was how to make people aware of our existence. When politicians can go to jail and yet still sell their books by the million, it would appear that there can be no such thing as bad publicity, but Anne drew the line at actions that might lead to "Bearded forester has affair with vicar's wife" headlines in the local newspaper, and we had to resort to conventional means to spread the news of our rural delights. Thousands of cars pass our entrance each day, for the Main Road is a major commuting route to places such as Haywards Heath and Gatwick. For good reasons, we had deliberately hidden ourselves behind trees, but this discouraged the less curious from turning off the road. Some years earlier we had advised a hotel group about a site near Salzburg, and the local tourism officer had stressed the need to have its car park visible from the road; but we ignored this sound advice until, years later, we built an overflow car park behind the front hedge. Repeated remarks that our customers had driven by hundreds of times before venturing down the drive, and the comment in the visitors' book that we were "a hidden gem", should have persuaded us to bring our light from under the bushel rather earlier. Our first entrance sign was a stout pole in the front hedge, with routed wooden signs protruding drunkenly from the side, giving an accurate preview of our unsophisticated enterprise. As we became a little smarter and more businesslike, it was replaced by a larger wooden sign, and then a professionally sign-written one – but still in a rustic wooden surround.

Some sort of publicity leaflet was essential, and although it evolved from photocopied sheet to commercially printed leaflet, we again made sure it gave an accurate flavour of what was on

offer.   We didn't want expectations of a mud- and dust-free
environment, or fancy entertainment for the kids.   Our leaflets
were obviously home-designed, and printed in just two colours,
with the cover drawing by our artist friend Colin, supplemented by
Anne's sketches inside. Later, the design of our website followed
the same principle. In spite of our best efforts, we did inevitably
have the occasional disgruntled visitor, like the man in his car who
was blocking the drive as he waited for his wife to make a final trip
to the loos. He suggested the place was "a rip-off, not worth the
money". I delved in my pocket, fished out the five pound entrance
for two, and rounded it up by a fiver per hour for the time they had
wasted. Such coals of fire, I felt, were cheap at the price.

Having printed thousands of leaflets, the next challenge was
to spread them around without breaking the bank. They could
be freely distributed to Tourist Information Centres and other
attractions at annual "leaflet swaps", which were an enjoyable
way of catching up with owners of similar ventures. Bundles of
leaflets cluttering the car were dropped off whenever we passed
suitable businesses, and we were eventually lured into paying a
leaflet distribution service. Although many must have ended up
in the bin unread, we did occasionally get a 'phone call checking
how prices had changed since the date of their five-year-old leaflet.
Local associations for promoting rural tourism came and went,
often depending on the enthusiasm of a single member to keep
them running. The most effective and long-lasting was Sussex Top
Attractions, which still annually prints and distributes a million
maps with members' details, and many cars came down the drive
with the navigator clutching their leaflet.

Satisfied visitors would recommend us to friends who might
also like the place, which is always the cheapest and best form of
advertising. Eventually, when asked how they had heard about us,
visitors would say they had "always known about you". Gratifying,
as if we were the Tower of London, but not much help when
deciding how to spend our limited advertising budget. With the

passage of years, visitors with children sometimes introduced themselves as having first come as a child themselves, and it can only be a matter of time before their grandchildren are playing on the zip wire.

To encourage those all-important repeat visits and build up a regular clientele, Anne came up with the idea of a membership scheme which we called "Friends of Wilderness Wood": essentially a season ticket, with five percent discount off all purchases, a periodic newsletter, and opportunity to attend a members' barbecue and volunteer days. In its early days the Friends was a small and close-knit bunch, and some became personal friends. As membership grew to over a hundred families, the social aspects declined in popularity, and we concentrated on offering early bookings and special offers. The internet became a boon in this respect, and we did get as far as electronic circulation lists and e-newsletters. Anne attended an early Tourist Board day on "social media", but it was left to our successors to take the business into this area of the modern world.

Advertising is horribly expensive, so we were almost always pleased to be featured in the press. As early as April 1983 we had a double page spread in the Brighton *Argus* entitled "They've hearts of oak at Wilderness Wood", complete with photos of the girls on a primitive swing, the half-built Barn, and me with an axe over my shoulder. Often such articles were picked up by the regional TV station, who would ask if they could come and film us - that same day, for we were NEWS. We might spend half the day being repeatedly interviewed, only to have the clip displaced by a bank robbery in Chatham.

As members of the regional Tourist Board, we took advantage of courses on marketing, website design and other tricks of the trade, including the art of writing catchy press releases, which were sent out to local newspapers, radio and TV stations on all suitable occasions. One such opportunity for shameless self-promotion was hung on the strap-line "Wilderness Wood Loves Cats". Before catalytic converters were standard, we offered a large discount to visitors whose car had a "cat"; but soon discovered the average driver was unaware of the existence of such devices, let alone knew if his car had one. Our green proselytising would face many challenges, but at least we got publicity from the press release we had put out.

Generally, we declined the many offers of a stand at a local show or fair. Although the expense might be modest, the costs in time and effort could rarely be justified by sales or publicity. We did for many years support the nearby Heathfield Agricultural Show on the last Saturday in May, which afforded us a day out and the chance to display our wares on a stand constructed with examples of our furniture and trellis panels. We achieved the heights of a runner-up rosette for the best small trade stand, judged by two rosy-cheeked gents in dark suits and bowler hats, which they politely doffed to the ladies. In later years, our loyalties switched to the Weald Woodfair each September, which more closely mirrored our fields of interest.

We were increasingly asked to talk to groups about the wood, and did the rounds of local village halls, complete with slide collection, projector and screen. Fees were small, but we looked on these talks as a way of promoting the wood. As time went by, searching for a chilly village hall on a dark winter's night began to lose its appeal, and we never brought ourselves into the twenty-first century with Powerpoint presentations.

The proprietor of a tourist attraction such as ours has to assess the safety of all the associated developments, as well as the trees themselves. It is a popular anthropocentric misconception that woods and forests *need* to be managed; they actually thrived for millions of years before the human species had even evolved. We choose to manage them for our own, human, ends, which in our case included visitor recreation. Even if you decide to leave your woodland entirely to its own devices, you still have a legal obligation to prevent your trees doing harm to anyone who may venture onto you land, or adjacent to your boundaries. This duty of care and avoidance of negligence can be irksome. Clearly, in a fun-fair nobody wants his roller-coaster car to come off the rails 30 metres up in the air, but, as natural places, woods have inherent hazards such as stumps and fallen branches to trip over, and muddy places on which to slip. The law requires "reasonable care" to be taken to avoid hazards, so we inspected regularly everything we had provided that could develop faults, such as nails protruding from seats, or broken slats on bridges, and the play area had to be inspected daily. We of course had public and product liability insurance, and our dealings with our insurers and the Health and Safety inspectors, who might turn up unannounced, were always cordial and positive, and these professionals usually took a balanced and proportionate view.

Safety checks are just one of the inevitable overheads of transforming an ordinary piece of woodland into a woodland park, and we developed a roving eye for litter, breakages and maintenance jobs. In May and June, the brambles in sunlit areas would have encroached thirty centimetres or more since your last weekly round. Visiting schoolchildren often remark that "everything is made of wood", but even our rot-resistant chestnut decays in due course, and there was a never-ending round of repairing and replacing steps and bridges, signs, seats and play equipment.

Recreation planners have devised the concept of "carrying capacity", and one of its several aspects is the physical ability of land to cope with human use. Of the thirty thousand annual visitors to the wood, many concentrated in a few places, such as the picnic site and play area. The impact of so many feet will rapidly lead to root-killing soil compaction, with decline in the health of trees and other plants. Compaction possibly contributed to the spread of the root disease *Phytophthora* among the chestnut trees. Like many a park-keeper, I had to water, fertilise and re-seed the picnic site, an impossible task if there was a hosepipe ban.

Of the many visitor activities taking place at Wilderness Wood, visits by the general public formed the dominant theme with which all others were harmonised. It was essential that all these elements should be compatible with one another, and with the woodland management. We were able to demonstrate that, if properly planned and managed, public access could complement traditional forestry, and did not conflict with normal operations or even timber output.

SCHOOLS, PARTIES
AND EVENTS

Putting a sign up on the Main Road saying "Open today" or an advert in a local newspaper might entice a few curious souls down the drive. To build up a worthwhile number of visitors it would be necessary to invite groups of people, and to lay on special events over which we could exercise control and timing of visitor numbers.

Our very first paying visitors at Wilderness Wood were schoolchildren. As soon as our entrance road was complete, together with a basic network of reasonably passable paths and tracks, we had been eager to initiate the "education and recreation" part of our vision. Someone had remarked to us that if you provided education you were on the side of the angels, meaning, in our case, that few would object to kids learning about the countryside. With our recent Balneath experience in mind, schools seemed a safe place to start. Even before we lived on site, we could book school visits, and drive up from Lewes to meet them.

Apart from our own education, we knew little about schools and school visits, and it was fortunate that a former colleague of Anne, the County Environmental Studies Advisor, was at hand with help and encouragement. His advice was "Just do it": offer the wood as a place to visit, and teachers could make of what they would. He circulated East Sussex schools with our particulars, but it quickly became apparent from enquiries that most teachers did not have the knowledge or confidence to make the most of the natural history potential of the wood, never mind explain subjects such as coppicing. They wanted help and guidance, and we realised that we needed to offer guided walks and worksheets (later re-branded as ranger-led activities and activity sheets). We found the prospect of a class of thirty six- or eight-year-olds as daunting as the next person, and so Anne went off on a week's course in the Peak District on outdoor education for primary schools, which included teaching a group of Manchester schoolchildren for an hour. She was relieved to discover the power to engage and delight of a simple activity such as a bug hunt, and returned with basic crowd-control tips such as "Always keep ahead of the walk". A couple of free guided walks for local schools, in exchange for advice and frank criticism from their teachers, and we were ready.

Our initially very amateur teaching efforts to maintain the interest of a six-year-old were competing with some of the best nature programmes in the world. I became adept at making a fool of myself, for example by using two chestnut leaves as donkey ears to demonstrate tree leaf shapes, or pretending to be a bunny frustrated by a rabbit fence. Another party-piece was a demonstration of "birching", as an example of the uses of the birch tree. The adults in the back row would smirk knowingly while the liveliest boy in the class volunteered to find out what the word meant. At a time when corporal punishment was being outlawed, we were promptly put on notice by a seven-year-old with a strong American accent: "If you hit me with that, my dad will sue you!" This wasn't the only time we realised we might be out of touch with current thinking, and had to mend our ways on what we might accidently say or do. Reluctantly, I ceased calling our home-made mallet a "cave-man's wife-basher" when a teacher gently told me domestic violence was not uncommon in his school's catchment.

It wasn't long before demand for school activities outstripped the capacity of the two of us, especially as I had to give priority to the more profitable consulting work. As we gradually accumulated staff, most had to double up as teachers when required: Tim might take a bunch of six-year-olds before writing a tree report, or Andrew emerge from the workshop to give a wood-working demonstration. It was Anne's assistants, first Liz and then Sarah, who really helped develop the schools programme, and when we eventually got round to formal job titles and descriptions, Sarah became Education Manager.

In the early days, many school visits were simply fun events towards the end of the summer term, accompanied by almost as many mums as children, and teachers often asked us to lead a walk on "whatever you like". The currently unfashionable "nature walk", which includes collecting things along the way, has much to commend it, as it encourages observation, exploration, and "ownership" by the children of their finds and observations. For some city children, a visit to Wilderness Wood may have been almost the first time their feet had left a paved surface, and they needed to experience the novelty of kicking leaves or splashing their mates with muddy water before they could concentrate on the science curriculum. We always tried to include our message that woods are useful places where we cut down trees for all sorts of uses, but that doesn't matter as long as we grow new ones. Our demonstrations of turning chestnut poles into fence posts or shingles using hand tools such as axe and wedges, with full audience participation, were always a great success, and injury-free apart from the occasion a small boy accidentally bloodied my knuckles with a mallet. When told that evening, eleven-year-old Jo's reaction was "Poor boy!" Clearly, she empathised with the child's embarrassment more than Dad's pain.

We attempted to be as flexible as possible, with walks geared to whatever topic the teacher requested. When the national curriculum extended its heavy hand, we tried to make subjects such as growing plants and habitats as much fun as possible, finding inspiration from books such as Joseph Cornell's *Sharing Nature with Children*. As the curriculum gradually eased up again, topics again became more varied, and we might be thrown the challenge of gearing a woodland walk and activities to Vikings, dinosaurs, or Little Red Riding Hood. In later years, our "castaway" activities of shelter-building and campfire cooking were seen as a great way for schoolchildren to develop teamwork and resourcefulness.

A woodland offers endless opportunities for "learning through doing", but the current fashion in that direction is undermined by increasing, and usually irrational, risk-aversion. Some teachers were horrified when we encouraged their charges to taste young beech leaves or the bitterness of wood sage, or to help wield a sledgehammer. How can this over-protected generation ever produce adventurers or explorers? We worried that our schools business could be at risk as teachers became ever more bogged down with carrying out risk assessments, eroding their energy and enthusiasm for field trips.

We made reasonable efforts to reduce hazards, but could not foresee them all. In one memorable incident, a convent class had been told to follow me in a crocodile round the pond by the West Ride, and I turned to see tail-end Patrick running down the bank to take a short-cut across the "grass" – actually duckweed. Patrick found not even he could walk on water, and Anne led a shaken little boy back to the house for a clean-up. With great reluctance he allowed this strange lady to shower the duckweed out of his hair, and the shame was further heightened when he had to don Kate's pink tracksuit as the only available dry outfit. When Anne suggested to the nun in charge that it must have been rather a shock, her retort was "Sarved the little bogger roight!"

Before long we developed a "Teacher's Pack": essential information about a visit, including a booking form, the trail leaflet and quiz sheet, and activity sheets aimed at different age groups, on subjects as varied as "signs of spring", and "get to know a tree." Photocopying and collating the packs was a tedious and time-consuming chore, so we allowed schools to photocopy their own. It was a relief when comprehensive packs for a variety of ages and topics could be made available on-line from the website. We always encouraged pre-visits, and many conscientious teachers came after school or at weekends to discuss and plan their activities, often with their own families in tow.

With parking space for two coaches, we were able to take two schools at a time, but our capacity was limited by wet-weather shelter. We could just squeeze two classes into the Barn, even before we had expanded it, but to avoid chaos they did need to be from the same school. The situation eased over the years as we added canvas shelters over the tea garden picnic tables, and eventually a pole-framed marquee which accommodated two school groups with room to spare, but sometimes we were turning away business for lack of capacity. An obvious difficulty with running an outdoor attraction in England is that most people want to come in the summer months, and schools are no exception. Before the Barn was enclosed and heated, there was nowhere for children to eat and warm up on winter visits, and on one particularly bitter day we had a whole class encamped in our kitchen, Rayburn blazing full bore. Children's clothing has become a lot more sensible over the years, but we have often found ourselves assisting little ones into gloves, or cajoling older ones to put on hats or do up zips. For children ferried between centrally-heated home and over-heated school, exposure to typical winter weather for more than an hour is usually a novel experience, and they have yet to develop a sense of self-preservation. We could never comprehend why it is cool to go under-clothed: more like frozen.

A few schools came several times a year, many came every year; and others every second year. One Brighton primary came every year since we started. We kept records of each visit, and would note that one class was well prepared and enthusiastic, or another lacked concentration. Not that our predictions were fault-free. A head teacher might leave, and the school suddenly change for better or worse. As a governor of two schools, Anne knew only too well how crucial was the Chief Executive.

Our prices for visits were modest, for we were in competition with places subsidised by industry or charities, and schools could no longer charge parents for visits that were part of the curriculum. With the help of our leaflet distributed each spring by East Sussex education department, and with varying co-operation of neighbouring local authorities, the number of schools soon reached fifty a year. We built a solid base of repeat business, and satisfied teachers would recommend us to their colleagues, so that in 2008 the number of schools broke the hundred barrier, with over 4,000 children visiting. Each child would go home with one of our publicity leaflets and a free entry ticket. With two kids of our own, we did not under-estimate "pester power", and reasoned that one happy child could bring back a whole family. The play area was perhaps the best investment of time and materials that we made.

We were open almost every day of the year. Our original intention had been to attract a steady flow of visitors through the seasons and through the week, and not to rely on large numbers on a few occasions. In this way we could minimise development for car-parks and the like, together with the large crowds which we and neighbours might find annoying. But we soon realised that some were unable to amuse themselves with a simple trip to the countryside, and needed the additional excuse of an "event" to attract them. People would 'phone up at a weekend to ask what was on, and were probably not satisfied to be told by me that the birds were singing and the leaves rustling in the sunshine. Before long we found ourselves devising an events programme, to entice those who have "always been meaning to visit you", and provide an excuse for a press release to remind the world of our existence. Our biggest problem was one which dogged us in everything we did: the matter of capacity. We could not put on a big show because of lack of adequate parking, which never exceeded about 80 car spaces, plus about 25 percent overflow. It is a truism that you can never economically provide permanent facilities for peak demand, whether toilets or parking spaces, for they will be unused for most of the year.

The annual working horses day was always popular

Events are expensive and time-consuming to set up and run, and therefore we tried to get others to do it for us. The Working Horse Trust was glad to bring three giants to pull out coppice poles on a Sunday each March, attracting up to a hundred families who might not otherwise have thought of coming. It gave the Trust publicity and something useful to do, and we were pleased that most of the organisation fell to them. For several years some appropriately clad enthusiasts enacted a weekend of Medieval

Mischief, with mock sword fights, and popular but alarming archery displays. A charcoal burner with a mobile kiln was a fittingly "woody" event, but the additional visitor income over the three days did not cover even the charcoal burner's charges. On the other hand, a retired couple for several seasons demonstrated their pole-lathe without charge, in return for a summer location for their caravan. This proved a valuable additional attraction, as did any of our tasks, such as peeling poles, which we could do in the yard. When the Barn needed re-roofing, I made sure I cleaved the 5,000 shingles outside the workshop if visitors were about and the weather clement. Manufacturing is so often done by machines in far-away factories that hand-work is a fascinating spectacle, even when not masquerading as a "country craft".

We seized on appropriate seasonal dates. Christmas was already busy with selling trees, but we increased our Easter trade with a "Bunny Hunt", with plywood bunnies hidden in the "warren", and eggs as prizes for spotting them. Hallowe'en may be American-inspired, but it was an excuse for a Hallowe'en Happening. Our staff took to the idea with enthusiasm, preparing a route along which Anne or Sarah, disguised as witches, led guests in pitch blackness and holding onto a long rope. Mike, Andrew and crew delighted in hanging up wool to simulate spiders webs, devising a "corpse" hanging from a tree to be glimpsed in the torchlight, and firing a shotgun blank on cue for the tale of the highwayman. We somehow avoided twisted ankles and eyes poked out by twigs, but the killer was the wage bill for all the hours so enthusiastically put in by the staff. We judged that we could not charge enough to make a profit on what was essentially a very unsophisticated piece of entertainment, and after a few years we reluctantly dropped it; but not before a neighbour, out for an early walk the following morning, almost had a heart attack on seeing the "corpse" still swinging in the breeze.

One Hallowe'en, I made a spur-of-the-moment decision that on reflection I regretted. I turned away a man who had arrived with plastic fluorescent wands to sell, hardly the type of product or image we wished to promote. He had read of our event, travelled down by train from London, and walked the two miles from Buxted in the hope of being allowed a better sales pitch than the public highway at the entrance to the wood. Here was a man, probably down on his luck, who had taken the initiative to try and make some seasonal money, not unlike so many street vendors in Dickensian England. I was later reminded of the Leiermann, or hurdy-gurdy man, in Schubert's *Winterreise*, surely one of music's bleakest portrayals of the world's outcasts, and whose pathos can melt the hardest heart:

Barfuss auf dem Eise	*Barefoot on the ice*
Wankt er hin und her,	*He staggers to and fro,*
Und sein kleiner Teller	*And his tiny platter,*
Bleibt ihm immer leer.	*Has ne'er a coin to show.*

As a forester with a mission, I never missed an opportunity to stress that woodlands were useful places that needed management We originally envisaged that clubs and societies would want guided walks, in the way our friend Tony Phillips had great success with groups such as Rotary and Townswomen's Guilds. He related interesting snippets about wildlife and aspects of management, while his wife prepared cold chicken, salads and French bread back at base. Probably our marketing and presentation were not good enough, but guided walks never really caught on for us, with or without catering. Maybe the subject matter seemed too worthy, and we found that, on open days where a choice of guided walks was presented, wildlife won hands down over woodland management. Was this yet another example of the British distaste for industry and a preference for a vanished Eden?

We did have occasional bookings for our walks, and one summer's evening notably failed to cover ourselves with glory. Both of us had been out at a village meeting and, returning down the drive at around nine o'clock, were surprised to see the Barn shining with light. Our hearts turned over as we simultaneously recalled the booked evening walk. In the Barn we found a jolly bunch of Women's Institute ladies sipping tea. It transpired that Kate, aged twelve, had answered the door, and told them that Mum and Dad were out, but that she could show them all that she knew about the wood. Being a good-natured bunch they took the changed arrangements in good part, and were evidently charmed by a girl's view on the wood and living in it. And no, there was no way they would accept a refund.

Woodland management might not be much of a draw, but fungi turned out to be quite a different matter. Anne had been fascinated by natural history since childhood (although the addiction had to be carefully hidden from her peers during teenage years); with her poor eyesight, plants were easier to observe than birds, and, having got to grips with flowers and trees, fungi were next in line. Identifying fungi is far from an easy art, and each autumn at the wood brought fresh fungal challenges to puzzle over, in seemingly never-ending variety. In 1985 she acquired an early copy of Roger Philips' *Mushrooms*, which was to become the amateur mushroom-hunter's bible, and, with this at her side, the picture gradually began to fall into place.

A few years later the County Council was developing a guided walks programme, and a former colleague of Anne gave her a ring: he had heard she knew something about fungi, so would she lead a walk at the wood on the topic? A date in October was advertised, and we waited to see if anyone would be interested. Fifty-six people turned up. There was obviously a big market out there, and in future it would be essential to limit group size by pre-booking. The following autumn, we filled several walks with the title "Woodland fungi – death or dinner?", and over the next decade expanded the programme to include day courses, family fungus hunts, and fungal fry-ups, as well as walks for clubs and societies, and schools. Public interest was stimulated by TV programmes and new identification books for the amateur, but there were few people locally to teach people the basics, and Anne had the field almost to herself. With our Barn kitchen facilities, we could offer people the opportunity to taste what they had collected, and learning to forage safely was a great attraction. In later years the subject became rather less fashionable, but fungus programme, Chestnut Celebration, and Christmas tree reservations still combined to make autumn one of the busiest seasons at the wood.

Our early approach to entertaining children's groups such as Cubs or Brownies was a "quiz walk" game, based on old uses of woodland plants, such as bog moss for wiping bottoms and mopping up blood, bluebell bulbs for glue, wood sage for flavouring beer, and so on. Each team would collect these in a bag, and at the end there would be a race for the teams to bring the right item when a clue was given. This required careful manipulation by the game-master so that the least able group had a chance, by redistributing adult help or asking for something already in a child's hand. The game did not appeal to groups such as the Woodcraft Folk, who disapproved of competition. More appropriate was the Tramp's Rubbish game, where a dozen items such as false teeth, welly-boot and beer bottle were placed along a stretch of ride-side, and each child would write down what he could see. The concept of a tramp often had to be explained, so perhaps it was no surprise when an excited bunch of seven-year-olds, on passing the vegetable garden after the game, spotted a bearded Chris in his old gardening clothes and shouted out "There's the tramp!", probably with no sense of irony. Like Mary mistaking Christ for the gardener, visitors sometimes took me for a woodsman as I filled log bags in the yard, and once one asked what an educated, well-spoken man was doing, performing such a menial task.

It was often up to our younger staff to keep us up to date with the outside world. Liz, Anne's first assistant, had previously been running a holiday programme for a County Naturalist Trust, and suggested that we too should be offering activities to keep children amused for half a day in the school holidays. Anne had been lucky enough to be brought up with a patch of neglected woodland at the bottom of the garden, where she and her younger siblings were encouraged to make camps and campfires, and "cook" items pinched from the vegetable garden, well away from adult supervision. I, too, had trespassed on others' land with my gang of ruffians. Presumably modern children too would relish such an opportunity, and she and Liz devised an activity later christened "castaway": building shelters from branches and bracken, making a fire, and cooking sausages and marshmallows on sticks, led by one of our staff and with the assistance of parents. This was an instant success. Very often the adults enjoyed the activities as much as the kids, and fathers could get very competitive over who could build the best shelter, before Anne or one of the rangers made everyone get inside and tested it with a couple of litres of "rainwater".

Castaways were perhaps the single most popular thing that happened at the wood. Parents were soon begging us to run castaway birthday parties. Each had up to sixteen guests, so we then received dozens of bookings for repeat performances. Next, we had requests for activities suitable for little children, and an ever-expanding programme ranged from fairy gardens and Gruffalo-hunting to Robin Hood and "survive in the wild", and seasonal activities such as Christmas wreath-making. Most were both part of the events programme and also available as a bookable activity for parties and groups, which blossomed to the extent that two rangers were each leading four sessions almost every weekend. Parents seemed to appreciate our relatively unsophisticated outdoor activities, without elaborate or expensive equipment.

A castaway party

We quickly found that groups that include both adults and children require special skills on the part of the leader. An overbearing or uncooperative parent could easily undermine the confidence of the inexperienced, so it was necessary to formulate reasonably strict "rules" for activities, as well as give appropriate training. It takes a certain amount of courage to take on sixteen over-excited eight-year-olds, and child management requires great skill, especially when the birthday child is overwrought, or guests or parents unhelpful. Safety is a modern obsession, and one member of staff wryly renamed the castaway activity "Desert Island Risks". One could philosophise at length about the modern child's upbringing, but the lack of freedom to live like Richmal Crompton's William has led to our being unable to distinguish between danger and risk, and too few have experienced the scrapes that are crucial to growing up. Our minds were certainly concentrated by the occasion when a child tried to put out a burning marshmallow by swinging the stick, with the result that the flaming sweet landed on another guest's face, narrowly missing a blinding. Our rangers' introductory talk included the avoidance of stupid behaviour, as well as the fun in store. Another modern obsession is hygiene. The occasional parent was concerned at eating something dropped in the fire, and we hated clearing up those foul-smelling wet-wipes without which no outdoor picnic can now take place. Anne's stomach turned over when, walking back one day after a castaway, a parent announced that she worked for the Health and Safety Executive. "That was just the sort of thing children should be doing. You've worked out everything really well." Phew!

With delightful surroundings, toilets and parking, it was inevitable that we should be approached by people wanting to hold celebrations at the wood. The Barn, barbecues and kitchen suited families who wanted to run their own parties, especially on summer evenings when younger members could play outside while grown-ups did boring things like talking. Over the years, weddings had become an increasing market we hadn't really noticed, and the wood appealed to those wishing for a natural setting to celebrate their nuptials. Having completed the legalities at the Registry Office, the happy couple would descend on us to have their marriage blessed deep in the wood, sometimes by a friend clad in Druid-like robes. On one occasion we hosted a wedding with a Highland theme, with groom clad in a kilt, a dirk in his sock, and more or less bare to the waist. Periodically we went over from the house to check everything was going well, tearing ourselves away from the TV where, by bizarre coincidence, *Braveheart* was showing. Even more bizarre was the fact that this reception had been organised by the groom's ex-wife. As our daughter Kate responded when we expressed surprise, we "needed to get out more".

We had to emphasise that the festivities would have to be adapted to the limitations of the setting, and it was sometimes tricky to enforce the reasonable quiet by midnight rule, in order not to upset neighbours. While the bride might come in silver wellies, less well-prepared guests would not appreciate their finery being spoilt in the muddy conditions that dominated much of the wood, even close to the Barn. There would always be a fine line between the "natural" setting the happy couple wished for, and the level of comfort many expect, and we did not have the facilities of country house hotels, such as ballrooms or converted stables, which can be enlisted in our less-than-reliable climate.

Inevitably, at times there were conflicts between different activities, and it was our job to ensure they were minimised. Over the years we learned not to book courses requiring relative peace at the same time as children's parties, and so on. In the daytime, there was little we could do, short of shutting the wood to the public, in order to ensure the peace and privacy of a private party, and we had constantly to judge what the best interests of our customers and business would be. The many letters of thanks and appreciation suggested we might be getting some of it right!

THE BARN AND ITS STAFF

We had sited the Barn so that it would be the first building our visitors saw on coming down the drive, and always intended it should be the focus and reception point. Its traditional rustic design, as a modest structure of on-site or local materials, would set the tone of our business and be an icon of our endeavours. Building it without planning permission as a woodland workshop may have been a gamble, but it enabled us to forge ahead and construct it as we thought fit. The use of oak beams, split chestnut, and wattle and daub would probably have sent officialdom crazy, so putting it up without the benefit of the local Building Inspector's inputs undoubtedly reduced costs and delays. We avoided modern refinements, and an architect noticed the purism of our omitting a damp-proof membrane under the sill beams, and the lack of felt under the shingles. Understandably, many non-specialists assume the building is ancient. We wanted a structure that was honest, rather than a pub chain pastiche.

Even before it had a roof, it was performing its intended function. A very early photo shows perhaps our first party of schoolchildren, munching their packed lunches inside the roofless oak framework - the nearest approach to comfort and civilisation we could offer! Initially open at the front, with an uneven mud floor, the Barn at first served as our workshop, and shelter from the rain for schoolchildren as they ate their lunch or bought souvenirs. When we built the Barn we did not foresee the variety of uses it would accumulate, or the sheer volume of visitors it would need to hold. As its functions evolved, and visitor numbers increased, we had to refurbish and extend it. In 1986 we moved its workshop functions to a new building across the yard, and in 1990 the open front was enclosed, and an extension added with a small kitchen and toilets, its roof clad with shingles and the walls with weatherboards. We installed a second-hand wood-burning stove, obtained complete with insulated stovepipe for a modest sum. Fuelled, like the house, with scrap wood, waste paper and cardboard, this gave us virtually free heating and was a popular place for visitors to sit, as well as a subtle advert for carbon-neutral energy. Three wall-mounted electric heaters supplemented the stove, but we turned them off as soon as the Barn was warm, always aware of their running cost and carbon impact. The primitive construction and thin wattle and daub walls meant that the building would always be on the cool side, and many visitors kept their coats on whilst sipping their hot chocolate. We considered mounting solar panels on the roof to heat the water for kitchen and toilets, but the trees shading our tea garden would also have obscured the panels to sub-economic levels, so we dropped the idea.

As well as shelter from the worst of the English weather and some warmth in winter, the other fundamental requirement for school groups and family picnickers is a toilet. Initially, a sentry box structure housed an Elsan toilet of a type familiar to early caravanners and campers. This evinced a mixture of delight and disgust among the children who used it, but, even with access to the downstairs loo in the house as well, the queues would be extensive after the arrival of a large party from a distant school. By this time "access for all" was obligatory, so the new Barn toilets incorporated a disabled cubicle and ramp outside. We coated the concrete floors with liquid lino in a fetching shade of red, but tile-work was limited to the immediate vicinity of the floor, washbasins and urinals. At the time the toilets were of an acceptable standard, but with rising expectations we realised they would eventually need to be revamped.

Inevitably the Barn became too small, and a wet weather school lunch-break could see sixty children and a dozen adults crammed together. Unlike many farms, we had no range of unused outbuildings to convert and expand into, and for every square metre of building we had to clear the trees and build, from footings to roof ridge, with our own limited capital and labour. As a result, development was slow and piecemeal. The Barn was functioning as visitor reception, check-out for product sales, souvenir shop, café, and exhibition. Running a tea-room had not been part of our original dream, and at first our catering was limited to booked groups; I would take them on a walk round the wood, while Anne organised tea and cake from the house kitchen, or carried across the salads to accompany a barbecue. It soon became obvious that the general public expects a cup of tea and an ice cream on their outings, and that a tea-room would help create the "buzz" that the place needed as a visitor attraction. Adding our tiny Barn kitchen allowed us to offer tea, coffee and cakes, and before long a second-hand deepfreeze and microwave meant that ices, filled rolls and soup could be added to the menu.

Our minute kitchen could turn out over £1,000-worth of food and drink on a peak day, and a nasty burn accident drove home that it was plain dangerous to have up to five staff working in such a small space. In 2007 we bit the bullet, almost doubled the size of the Barn, and trebled the kitchen area. Using a friend's oak for framing, and weatherboards milled from our own pine, we added a light and spacious extension behind the original Barn, divided from it by the now slightly wormy frame of the back wall stripped of its cladding. We had just finished staining the outside when we received a letter from the District Planning Department, enquiring if we had carried out development without consent. "Guilty as charged," I pleaded over the 'phone. We submitted plans, a letter of justification and the required cheque, and received post-dated consent a few weeks later. With many years advising others on buildings in proximity to trees, I had reasoned that a *fait accompli* was a smaller risk than having to argue the possible damage to, and value of, a couple of pine trees with the over-zealous tree-lover who held the post of District Council trees officer.

We developed the adjacent area as a tea-garden, with canvas awnings as protection from rain and the all-too-rare sun. This was where school groups and birthday parties ate their sandwiches and cakes, with the mice and robins clearing up after them; unless the weather was so bad that we took pity on them and allowed access inside. The tea-garden was also popular with families bringing their own picnics, who for the most part augmented their meals with drinks or ices bought from the café. We reasoned that if it was acceptable for us to eat a packed lunch with a beer at a pub in our youth, why should we discriminate against those with limited means now? Publicans don't insist the fags smoked in their gardens must be bought at their pub, but why do so many nowadays object to a hiker with his sandwiches?

Selling food and drink enabled us to extend our green living philosophy, as well as be evangelical about it. Not for us the easy option of a free freezer full of mass-produced ices, cans of sugary drinks, and packs of cheap food, swigged down to an incessant background of pop music. We had decided that our catering would avoid packaged food and drink, and that we would have no disposable tableware. Any waste food would go to the hens or compost heap, and paper and cardboard were used to heat the Barn. As a result, we made do with just one domestic rubbish bin for house, Barn, office, and workshop.

Sourcing supplies was a dilemma. Was it better to buy from one of the more responsible supermarkets, or spend time and petrol scouring the countryside for small, local suppliers? Should we buy bread and rolls from a local baker who made disappointingly "commercial" products, or source ciabatta or sourdough from further afield? And how far should we impose our ideas of healthy eating? Fortunately for our visitors, we were not vegans or even vegetarians, but when we overheard a father say to his son "It's not that sort of place" in response to a request for a coke, we realised we were establishing our chosen image. As ever in life, we had to make an endless series of compromises which by necessity changed over time. To reduce packaging, for many years we scooped portions of local farm ices, and a cheaper supermarket alternative, into cones; very popular with children and parents alike, but getting a scoop quickly and efficiently into a cone is a lot trickier than it looks on an Italian ice cream stall, and eventually we gave up the challenge of training our teenage staff, and succumbed to tubs. Requests for bottles of water were met with the offer of a free glass of tap water, or, for those unable to walk for three-quarters of an hour unrefreshed round the wood, a recycled bottle filled from the tap. We offered no canned drinks, not only to save on packaging and avoid a potential litter problem, but to make a stand against big business purveying empty calories, although we did sell fizzy lemonade by the glass. Local unfiltered apple juice was available by the glass, and was so delicious that we sold many bottles to take home. A German guest liked it so much that he asked to sip it after dinner in preference to the malt whisky on offer!

As demand increased, our capacity to make enough cakes was soon overwhelmed, and so we would pick up cakes twice a week from a Crowborough mum, after the school run. When she moved away, a West Sussex farm business supplied us with wonderful cakes made to ethical standards similar to our own. While we never set out to be primarily a tea-room, we did have a number of regular customers, including a couple of well-built spinster sisters,

Xenia and Zara, well into heart attack territory, who came regularly to top up their cholesterol levels with large slices of cake while they pondered which of our chestnut constructions they could shoe-horn into their little garden. Derek was another regular, coming several times a week with his small terrier for a walk and a specially discounted lunch of coffee, cheese toastie and slice of cake, which he enjoyed over a charity shop paperback. He became an honorary member of staff, always willing to lend a hand with washing up if we were overwhelmed.

How far to go down the catering route was always a vexed question. Wilderness Wood was a location where a whole variety of enterprises could take place, and we had to decide what we *wanted* to do and what would fit in, as well as what might be profitable. Serving all-day breakfasts would, we reasoned, imbue our pure air with the smell of frying, and our limited parking might not suit the inevitable white vans and lorries we would attract. Cooked meals, apart from the occasional catered barbecue, would put us in competition with the numerous pubs in the area and require sophisticated kitchen equipment and specialised staff. We always regarded refreshments as a necessary service to visitors, rather than an end in itself. We wanted to be a woodland with a café, rather than a café that happened to be in a wood.

All in the "hospitality industry", that ugly term that presumably embraces both brothels and convention centres, and in which we were now included for business classification purposes, inevitably suffer from peaks and troughs in demand. We could not afford to have staff standing around idle, and in early years visitors who wanted to pay for a bag of logs, or order tea and cake, had to ring a bell unreliably connected by an old telephone wire to the house door-bell. As the frequency of these calls increased, we found ourselves in the Barn more and more, until it became obvious that, at least for certain times in the week, it would have to be manned.

Helen was our first such person. She had run a tea-room at her cottage in a nearby lane, but it was too off the beaten track to have much trade, so she leaped at the chance to help us out. Her forte was cream teas, complete with her own scones and home-made jam, and she operated as a concession, paying us a percentage of takings. She moved on to run the Ludlow food festival for a number of years, and maybe her experience at the wood helped her secure this much more prestigious role.

Peak periods, such as summer weekends and school holidays, would see Anne in the Barn for much of the time. Sarah, who quickly became an indispensable full-time member of staff, initially answered an advert for a weekend Barn supervisor, assisted by casual weekend staff. For some years Anne and Sarah managed to run the Barn, supplemented by temporary extras in the school holidays. Casual staff ranged from acne'd teenagers through to ladies of a certain age looking to get out of the house for a few hours. Numerically, we must have been the village's largest employer apart from the school. Weekend or holiday work at Wilderness Wood became almost a rite of passage for local teenagers and students, including Jo and Kate and their friends. If there were a medal for domesticating youngsters, we should have been awarded it, with bar. The average fifteen-year-old has perhaps been into the kitchen at home only to help him or herself to something from the 'fridge. For many, the concept of working for some hours without getting on the 'phone to their mates was quite novel. More than one turned up late on a Sunday morning bleary-eyed or with a hangover, and we had to make clear the requirements of the real world. At home, any washing up had been limited to loading the dishwasher, so working in our kitchen must have been an eye-opener. We had no disposable cutlery or plates, and, even after we had invested in a glass-washer, everything had to be pre-washed by hand. To minimise use of expensively-heated water, I evolved an efficient washing up system, which meant learning how to work logically and quickly.

Our better staff quickly made it to "front of house," where they had to deal face to face with the people who ultimately paid their wages. Brought up in the 1950's, we had both absorbed the Queen's English from the BBC and other sources, and had been encouraged to believe clear diction, eye contact, and an aura of self-confidence were helpful in a world where incoherence equated with poor education or simple-mindedness. On starting their training, our beginners were asked if they knew the main reason for customers not returning to a business, and the smarter needed little prompting to elicit the answer of poor service, rather than price or poor product. Most had flown, even if only on a budget carrier, and they were reminded that the air hostesses smiled all the time, and our customers would like the same courtesy. We certainly didn't succeed with all of them, but it was very satisfying to help a gauche and self-conscious 16-year-old blossom into an 18-year-old who could confidently welcome visitors, deal with 'phone enquiries, and serve food and drink - unfortunately just in time to spread their wings and leave us for university life.

Britain, once the "workshop of the world," has turned from manufacturing to being reliant on service industries. Although we have become a nation of consumers, rather than that much more dangerous concept of citizen, most of us are pretty bad at offering service. Perhaps the servility once required of domestics gave service a bad name, and many still look on those who serve us as inferior. In the 'States this is usually not the case, and a cleaner is just somebody doing a job that you haven't time to do yourself. No wonder the staff at their eateries are so enthusiastic, but "Have a nice day" and "Enjoy!" can sometimes grate in the ennui-blocked English ear.

As well as having the right personal skills, we needed staff who were willing to turn their hand to a variety of jobs, and explained that performing the same task hour after hour was boring; the more varied the work, the faster the day would go, and the more transferable skills they would learn. We were always happier employing those who were conscientious, convivial, hard-working, and willing to learn, even if they had little previous experience. Youngsters new to work were surprised that we considered that wasting time whilst being paid was akin to theft. There was always something to do, such as checking outside tables, sweeping the floor, or restocking the shop. We expected both sexes to use spare moments for whatever needed doing, be it filling log bags or cleaning the WC's, although it was clear from their reactions that some had preconceived expectations of their roles. Some rangers doubled up as Barn staff, and during the lunchtime rush would quickly scrub the castaway mud and charcoal from their hands, and set to at the sink or behind the counter.

We tried to predict likely visitor numbers by referring to previous years' records, and looking at the weather forecast. What we could not plan for was an unannounced influx, as when some 25 three-wheeler cars congregated one Sunday morning as a meeting point for their rally, and all wanted coffee. A sudden rush such as this would entail all hands on deck, with even office staff dashing over to toast tea-cakes, make sandwiches, or serve on the counter. Although we welcomed the extra business, a surge of unexpected arrivals prompted by a national newspaper recommendation, and of which we were blissfully unaware, could prove challenging. All-too-frequently the 'phone would ring at eight am on a busy weekend, with a member of staff announcing she was sick, and Anne would have to find a stand-in or, more commonly, resign herself to losing yet another promised day off.

Eventually we accepted that employing a reliable Barn manager was high priority, so we could take time off at weekends or get on with other things. The job was part-time including at least one weekend day, which suited only a few, greatly diminishing the size of the pond we could fish. One otherwise excellent applicant withdrew at interview when we pointed out that checking and cleaning the loos would sometimes be required. Perhaps she had a cleaner at home. At the interview Anne resisted relating how I once had to empty the overflowing septic tank on a bank holiday weekend with bucket and wheely-bin, illustrating that we expected staff to be flexible, and to lead from the front rather than delegating unpleasant tasks.

We had to part company with one manager who was happy in the kitchen but avoided front-of-house customer contact, which was half of her job. Another might be all sweetness and light one day and the next have the staff in tears, and customers complaining. While it may have widened our experience of life, this was no *Fawlty Towers* episode, and our livelihood could be at risk. There is a business theory that there is no such thing as bad workers, but only bad managers, and perhaps we had only ourselves to blame.

As well as a place to eat or buy an entrance ticket, the Barn was also part of our efforts to open people's eyes to how Wilderness Wood produced wood and timber. We knew that most of our patrons had little knowledge of forestry matters, so the walls were lined with displays explaining plantations and coppicing, the wildlife associated with the coppice cycle, the uses of sweet chestnut, the internal structure of a pine tree, and how the building was constructed. We included a pine tree sawn in half from tip to base, and a badger skin, which somehow survived being stroked by countless children. These modest displays really didn't merit the title "exhibition". Had we started an educational trust, we could have devoted more money and time to developing and maintaining better interpretive facilities. The home-made laminated sheets of Anne's drawings, our amateur photos, and typescript blown up from our original Amstrad computer, soon looked hopelessly dated. We had intended to renew the displays every few years, but there was always some more pressing task. Those visitors keen enough to read the panels had difficulty squeezing behind the café tables, although we did occasionally overhear tea-drinkers commenting on what they were reading on the walls behind. We later added cards on the tables themselves, explaining our "green" ethos and suggesting how visitors could help, both at the wood and at home.

Taking tea in the Barn, with our display on the walls

We encouraged visitors to get more out of their walks by taking a trail leaflet. For children there were "discovery" versions and seasonal "I-spy"-style spotter sheets, illustrated with Anne's simple line drawings, to focus their enthusiasm and curiosity. We cannot overestimate the importance to a young mind of a basic understanding of the natural world, and how this may shape an appreciation in later life of our dependence on the biosphere. How gratified we were, on a school guided tour, to find that the child with its hand up had come that summer holiday to the wood with Granny.

As parents of school-age children, we were only too aware that spending your 50p or £1 was a highlight of a school trip, and we realised that souvenirs would be expected, could make us some money, and help raise awareness of Wilderness Wood. At first, we carried a pedlar's tray of pencils, notepads, and I-Spy books, and a small cash box, back and forth from the house. The notepads and pencils featured the distinctive Wilderness Wood lettering that our graphic designer friend Colin had already created for our notepaper. With the help of a library book or two, Anne drew a wood-mouse eating an iconic sweet chestnut for the notepad's cover, and lettering and mouse became our logos.

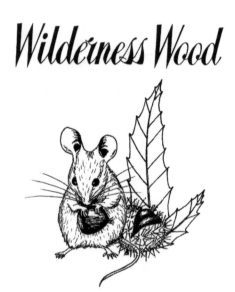

Lettering and mouse became our logos

In time, the "shop" became an important part of the business. As with catering, we had to decide what to stock. Our ideal would have been locally-made items of wood or with a woodland theme, but in practice we found ourselves stocking a wide range of cheap plastic goods made in the Far East, in order to find attractive items suitable for our market's limited purchasing power. Nonetheless, it came as a shock to find that children who were barely able to count their coins sometimes had more to spend than we had charged for admission and tuition. A few children bought wisely, but the most popular items were "maggots in slime" and other items with a high "yuck" factor. A bright object, even if made of easily-broken plastic, usually had more appeal to an eight-year-old than a wooden spinning top, no matter how well the latter was crafted.

I put up some shelving to divide the café from the shop area, and this soon filled with an ever-growing range of products, from Sussex-made trugs to a range of wooden toys from a firm in Yorkshire, and local apple juice, honey and chutney. For bodies such as the National Trust and many tourist attractions, it is mandatory to exit through the shop. We lacked both commercial drive and space to emulate this mercenary trick, and our shop display was little more than something to gaze at as one queued for refreshments or admission tickets. At least we managed to avoid that all-pervading aroma of pot-pourri and scented soaps that distinguishes many such places! Books were a natural thing to stock, but over the years their sales declined, and we noticed customers making notes so that they could order more cheaply off the internet. In our cool and dusty Barn, both books and other items soon lost their brand-new look, which discouraged us from carrying large stocks.

Hadlow Down had lost its shops, and had few places to congregate; given drive and capital, there is no reason why we could not have expanded the shop element so that it became a village store. Such a venture would integrate its commerce more closely with the community, but our declining energies meant any such departure would be left to our successors. From a simple shelter, the Barn expanded over the years to become the focal point for visitors to the wood, and it would have made sense for us to incorporate our office into its structure. In retrospect, we should have grasped the nettle and accepted that catering merited being run as a separate business, and staffed it accordingly, or let it out as a concession. Nevertheless, we were proud of how successfully this primitive building adapted to fulfil its multitude of roles.

CHRISTMAS AND ITS TREES

Neither of our families had ever bought a Christmas tree. In Lewes my family made do with an evergreen branch stood in the corner of the room and decorated yearly with the same baubles, which, although mostly cheap plastic and in dubious taste, had almost heirloom status. The idea of buying a tree was then quite alien to us, but, as with so many aspects of leisure, the proper Christmas accessory has become a necessity in our increasingly commercialised society.

So how did we feel about Wilderness Wood's role in what a cynic friend calls the "Festival of Great Takings"? We had always intended that our wood should yield a range of products within the context of financial viability. We were aware that people bought Christmas trees, so there was money to be made. Moreover we had land, and if a forester couldn't grow a Norway spruce tree to six feet, who could? Unlike proper forestry, where a tree becomes useful after several decades, an average Christmas tree needs only five to seven years, which in forestry terms is instant riches. So where would we start?

When we bought the wood, the top pine plantation was ready for a light thinning. That first December, we had felled some trees and managed to sell a few tops at our girls' primary school in Lewes. But although many parents had radical-chic leanings, evidently unpruned Scots pine tops were not attractive enough, even at a modest £1.50 each. We would have to try harder, and decided we should grow our own proper Christmas trees. Early the next year, we rabbit-fenced an area of poorly-stocked one-year-old coppice down by the stream, and planted 1,250 Norway spruce, together with Douglas fir, ash and wild cherry to form a long-term crop. The broadleaves failed miserably because of the poor soil, but the spruce and Douglas thrived, especially after liming and fertilising. In December 1984 we dug fifty trees, the first that we had both planted and sold! Sales from this small plantation continued for the next four years. The remaining spruces were too big, or spoilt as Christmas trees by their proximity to other trees, and were left to grow on and form part of the mixed plantation we had planned.

Having established that we could market trees successfully, we began buying in trees for re-sale, to supplement our own production. Like beginners in any field, we were sometimes fobbed off with stock others had rejected, and soon discovered there were growers and dealers out there who were unaware or uncaring that trees they supplied were poorly shaped, or had been harvested far too early, so that needles were dropping even before our customers got them to their centrally-heated living rooms, let alone had been indoors for a week or two. It seemed sensible to grow more of our own, so that we could have a reliable supply of trees of guaranteed quality. In spring 1983 we coppiced an area by the West Ride, surrounded it with rabbit-proof fencing, and planted 1,200 young trees, mainly the traditional Norway spruce, as well as Douglas and noble firs and a few Scots pine. We chose the location because it was close to the Barn and yard. Furthermore, its outstanding view across to the Cross-in-Hand ridge would not be obscured because, unlike other forms of forestry, Christmas trees are cut before they reach much more than two metres.

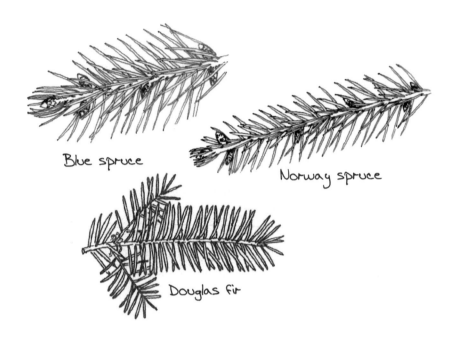

Blue spruce

Norway spruce

Douglas fir

The noble firs soon died. This turned out to be just as well, as larger growers were finding that this tree loved to die a year before it was ready to be sold. They are renowned for retaining their needles, and we had to resist selling a dead one to a customer admiring the interesting tree with the copper-red needles. Our pines were likewise a failure. They dropped needles after two years of growth, leaving bare, woody branches with too few needles at their tips. The Douglas grew so well it needed pruning three times each year, and we built up a loyal market for this sweet-smelling species with its long, soft needles. Unfortunately, as time passed they began to die back, probably due to the soil compaction caused by the boots of customers exploring the plantation for their perfect tree.

Some of the space was taken up with the coppice stools up to two metres across, and these had to be killed chemically if their re-growth wasn't to stifle the Christmas trees. Gradually, the stumps decayed and were uprooted to be sold as garden ornaments. Even after 30 years the larger stumps remained as trip hazards, particularly when one was laden with a knapsack sprayer, killing off weeds or pests.

After a further expansion in 1993, the plantation extended to half a hectare, space for 4,700 trees. In order to provide ourselves with an additional supply of trees, we also rented a hectare of land a mile away and planted ten thousand transplants; so by 1995 we were self-sufficient, apart from the very largest trees, and even had a small surplus to sell wholesale.

Centuries of coppicing had depleted the soil of nutrients to an almost inert state. Our ancestors would have removed everything: even twigs for faggots, dead leaves for soil improvement and animal bedding, and lower branches for summer livestock fodder. The wood would have been a virtual mine. Saleable Christmas trees must have copious foliage, and to produce this they need fertile ground, but our soil was extremely acid (pH 3.9), and almost completely lacking the main plant nutrients. We would therefore have to improve the soil by adding lime and fertiliser. Lime reduces the soil acidity, and this allows nutrients such as phosphorus to be absorbed by the tree roots. No supplier was interested in delivering just one ton of lime, so I drove to a lime pit near Glyndebourne to fill up our trailer, and broadcast the powder by hand from a bucket, up and down each row. By the end I was white from head to foot, with an aching back, and elbow cemented at right-angles from holding the bucket. After that, a pinch of fertiliser was carefully spread around the base of each tiny tree. Subsequent soil tests indicated that we needed to top up nutrients almost yearly, both to build up overall levels and to replenish the nutrients our hungry trees were removing, the amount increasing to a handful for a two-metre-high tree. We made sure any available bonfire ash was spread around the trees, as this had exactly the minerals the soil lacked. So do human ashes, and I toyed with the idea of offering an ash-scattering opportunity, with special rates for deceased airline pilots if done from my microlight.

A common complaint about commercial forestry is that its trees are in straight lines. Like all plantations, our Christmas trees were in lines, about one metre apart, and as straight as stumps would permit. The logic is simple. Trees in lines are evenly spaced, to benefit from equal light and rooting area. Additionally, the young trees are easy to find when hidden by weeds, and can be fertilised or sprayed without fear of omission or accidental damage. This is particularly necessary for newly-planted trees in an older crop, for we practiced the CCF approach: whenever a tree was harvested, we planted a new one. More commercial growers remove all the trees, clear the ground, and replant the whole area in one season - a form of very short rotation clear-cut forestry.

Little weeding was needed that first year, because the soil was more or less sterile and no weeds were growing. Until a tree is established, it has to rely on a tiny root system for its water and nutrients, and competition from surrounding vegetation, especially grass, will slow its growth or even kill it. The most effective weeding is by chemical herbicide applied at the beginning of the growing season. Often we missed this because of competing work, poor weather, or to allow the bluebells growing between the trees to die down; and we had to reduce the weed height of mid-June with a sickle or brush-cutter, or a combination of the two, before spray could be applied.

Christmas trees are a high value crop and can be worth tens of thousands of pounds a hectare, so good care at the right time is essential and worthwhile. Lose a tree to drought or accidental cutting in its first season, and a six-year rotation is lengthened by a year; a drop in productivity of seventeen percent, plus the replanting cost. May 14th 1985 saw us watering hundreds of newly-planted trees with a hose-pipe, such was the severity of the drought, exacerbated by a cold east wind. What had happened to those April showers?

During the 1990's we became aware of a major change in the Christmas tree market. With the general increase in living standards, people were becoming more demanding and particular in their choice of tree. Whereas it had been possible to sell tops of first thinning plantation trees, now the market demanded denser crowns, to hold ever-increasing numbers of lights and baubles. Even young trees can grow in height by up to a metre a year, and the resulting gap between branches would make them unsaleable to the modern market; so trees require pruning to increase their bushiness, often twice a year. Both leading shoot and side branches are trimmed to encourage a dense cone, and, like the supermarket apple, this is now the desired style. Performed with secateurs and shears or shearing knife, tending a small plot such as ours can be a satisfying task, but I would hate to prune tens of thousands, as is necessary on the larger estates. One can shape wayward trees with a variety of techniques, including the use of cane splints, and I always felt gratified to see a skimpy or distorted tree shape up after careful treatment and another year or two's growth.

In summer 1988, a visiting specialist noticed that many of the spruces had browning needles. We had put this down to the aftermath of the 1987 storm, when many trees were burned by salt blown in from the Channel. However, he immediately diagnosed spruce aphid, a sort of greenfly that multiplies prodigiously in the right circumstances. My heart sank. We do not belong to that hopeful tribe that believes Mother Nature will always sort things out. Ladybirds may love to consume aphids, but we would need millions *that week* if our trees were to be saved from defoliation, so we reluctantly resorted to chemical warfare. I say reluctantly, not only because it is undesirable to spray toxic and expensive chemicals about, but because spraying manually is a most unpleasant task. The operative has to wear a protective suit, rubber gloves, boots, and mask, and carry a 15 litre backpack sprayer, while walking up and down each row and dowsing every needle with a chemical that only works at temperatures above 15 degrees Celsius. One could easily die of heat exhaustion. This reinforced our intention to interfere only when necessary, and not to join more commercial growers, who, like orchard owners, spray to prevent outbreaks of any disease at great financial and environmental cost.

With all the intensive maintenance, Christmas tree production is expensive, but the rewards can be high. While a thirty-year old conifer sold for pulp or woodchip might fetch just £3 before felling, as a six-year-old Christmas tree it is a luxury rather than a commodity, and could fetch five times that sum. Christmas was a season we could not afford to ignore.

When we decided to sell trees retail, we at first concentrated on dug ones, as this was what the market demanded at that time. In my earliest memories of Christmas trees for sale outside the High Street greengrocer, they always had a knob of roots at the base, roots it was rumoured the grower had boiled to prevent survival when planted. It seems people thought that the tree would last longer indoors if it had roots; even though they probably never had success planting it in the garden, as water uptake would be through the fine roots which had been left behind in the plantation by the rough and ready digging of the time. Until our own were ready, we bought in a variety of rooted trees, including some we carefully dug from a friend's field and immediately wrapped in bin-liners to stop roots from drying out; advising customers that they would grow on in the garden, if properly cared for.

Needle drop was common, especially in households where the tree had to tolerate weeks of central heating. Few customers were converted by our telling them that in Germany, home of the Christmas tree, they were not brought into the house until 24th December. In a culture where shops have "seasonal" Christmas goods for sale by mid-autumn, who were we to suggest that any sense of the special would be destroyed by prolonged exposure? Imported trees may be cut in October, so would be at least two months old by the Big Day, and even locally-grown trees could lose their needles because a mild autumn had failed to harden them off.

So needle-drop was on everybody's mind, and by the millennium "non-drop" varieties such as Nordmann fir were becoming increasingly popular. These suited the larger outlets in the way that Golden Delicious apples suited the supermarkets – they had a long shelf-life. To our minds, "Nords", as the trade calls them, resemble plastic trees, and are stiff and heavy to handle. Nonetheless, we bought in and planted increasing numbers of this species; although we grew it with some difficulty, as it prefers better soil than ours, it came to constitute about a quarter of our tree sales.

At about the time Nords became popular, details of water-holding tree stands were falling on our doormat. These support the tree and supply it with water, in the same way as a cut flower in a vase. We had by then realised that the most popular sizes were 1.7 to 2.1 metres, which would require a root-ball a metre in diameter in order to survive when planted out. So gradually we weaned our customers onto water-holding stands and cut trees, and sold the more expensive Nords to those who were determined to have "those trees that don't drop their needles". Pot-grown trees had a small but steady market, and at the end these were the only trees with roots we sold. We bought them in, as they needed far greater care than we were able to offer, especially on hot summer days when we had better things to do, such as being on holiday. One day's missed watering, and years of effort could be wasted, and we decided we should leave pot-grown tree production to the experts.

All trees were sold by height, priced to be competitive with other local outlets, of which there were up to ten within a three mile range. In line with our "waste-not-want-not" philosophy, our price labels were initially hand-written on strips cut from old fertiliser bags. These were stapled round the tree; each label was removed as the record of sale, and counted on the kitchen table that evening. We retained labels for next year's use, and some eventually had five or more rusting staples from previous years. We did in the end succumb to the colour-coded strips recommended by the growers' association, and our favourite suppliers delivered trees with height-band labels already attached.

Word spread that we sold good trees, and soon we were selling over two thousand a year. Our own production could not keep pace with demand, and each year we had to buy in more and more. We tried to use local suppliers as far as possible, but tree production is cyclical. A glut year depresses planting, so that five or so years later there will be a shortage, and we sometimes had to top up from the big wholesalers who sourced their trees from wherever they could, of a quality that left a lot to be desired.

Eventually we settled on three growers, establishing a cordial relationship by prompt payment, and in return were reliably supplied with good trees. We would order in early autumn for weekly delivery in two or three batches from about 21st November. Often a lorry-load of five hundred trees would arrive mid-afternoon, and it would be all hands to unload as quickly as possible, for no driver wishes to set off home just as rush hour is starting in the South-east. Next morning we had to sort the trees by price and stack them around the yard, and even up the drive. We offered a size range from 60 centimetres to over 6 metres, and ordering the right numbers of each size was an art we seldom fully mastered.

Living in the wood, we took our lovely surroundings for granted. In due course it dawned on us that Wilderness Wood had a very special atmosphere at Christmas, and buying a real tree from a real forest was what the marketeer calls a Unique Selling Proposition. Not only did the hundreds of freshly-harvested trees smell of the forest, so did our pines around the yard. We realised we could offer the special treat of choosing and cutting your own living tree in a woodland setting, and also save ourselves the harvesting cost! "Dig-your-own" became a family event, and people would come from miles away to tag a tree in November, and return the next month to cut it or dig it up. In this way we enjoyed two visits per sale, and had the opportunity to sell refreshments or logs at an otherwise quiet time of year.

The DYO plantation had the capacity to produce only 500 to 600 trees a year and most of these were reserved well before the first harvesting day, usually the first Saturday in December. Human nature being what it is, a small number of labels were torn off each year, to be substituted by the name of a less scrupulous family. Usually the victims took it stoically, but we often felt sorry for a child who had chosen a "special" tree. Latterly, many families hid their reserved tree under a coat of decorations, personal messages and even photos, to make label substitution too onerous.

Although the customer did the work of harvesting, we gave no discount, reasoning we should be charging for the entertainment. Dig-your-own was hugely popular, but a headache for us. Despite exhortations to fill in the holes, we often found Somme-like pits after a busy weekend, and lost a significant amount of our precious soil on the roots. We therefore strongly recommended cutting, and using a tree stand, and ended up charging a hefty premium for dug trees, both to discourage diggers and as a contribution to soil replacement and hole-refilling.

To help a tree to survive its Christmas ordeal with most of its needles still attached, all customers received a leaflet advising on tree care. Some people were successful in planting out their rooted tree, and one family told us how their garden had fifteen from Wilderness Wood. There was one such Douglas fir just across the road from the wood in a friend's garden, seventeen metres high and 36 centimetres diameter after sixteen years; we wonder what the record for one of our trees would be.

One of the main advantages of the Christmas season was that it brought people to the wood who would otherwise come only in summer. If they bought a tree, they might also buy firewood, holly, wreaths and mistletoe. Get them into the Barn and they would discover the delights of hot chocolate and mince-pies in front of the roaring log fire, and the opportunity to buy the Christmas decorations and small presents which Anne and her assistants had tastefully arranged around the jolly scene. We deliberately insisted tree purchases were settled in the Barn in order to expose customers to our other earthly delights. Before long we were victims of our own success. On a cold day that Barn was just too comfortable and people stayed too long. Not only was there not enough room in the building, but their cars were clogging up the car-park.

Despite offering weekday discounts, most trees were sold on just three December weekends. It would not have paid to create sufficient parking for those six peak days, when we might sell over four hundred trees in eight hours - an average of almost a tree a minute. It was not always easy to get the first arrivals to park neatly; two cars would take the places of three, and we could be stuck with that parking pattern all day. Unable to park, many a would-be purchaser drove off in frustration. It was my job to ensure everything went smoothly outside. Trailers, vast Chelsea tractors, large white vans, and people who couldn't reverse all added to the challenge. We enlisted Boy Scouts to assist with the parking, and those who were big enough to direct traffic rather than just rattle collecting tins helped maintain my sanity.

Trees were displayed round the yard according to size. The most popular sizes stood up to five trees deep, and it was here that most of the purchaser indecision was manifest. I swore I could detect latent divorces from the body language of the person, usually the husband, holding the tree. Poor devil! He had to rotate one in his right hand, while trying not to fall over under the weight of another in his left. Then, let's compare that other one against that, no, the other.... and so on. I was tempted put up a sign reminding people that a tree is not for life, just for Christmas, but the dog people might have claimed copyright.

Once chosen, the tree was netted, paid for, and carried by the customer to his car. At peak times it was difficult to give customers help, but it was amazing how the lads found time when an attractive blonde in an open-top car smiled in their direction.

Fortunately everyone seems to have a different idea of the perfect tree, and we were amazed how miserable specimens would be happily selected from our own plantation. On the other hand someone might bring back a tree that had just one small twig broken. We had little sympathy with the attitude that everything must be perfect and, if it isn't, someone must be to blame. We were also expected to provide infinite choice, that holy grail of the free market. A lady turned up fifteen minutes after opening on the first day of tree reservations and complained that all the best trees had been taken. We pointed out that only ten had been tagged and there were at least 500 more to be chosen, but she would not be mollified.

Every business should have a good idea of its customer base, and at quieter moments we asked people how they had heard of us. Most were repeat customers, and the next largest group had been recommended by friends. Advertising agents, eat your hearts out! One year we crossed swords with the highways authority, who removed our temporary Christmas tree signs from the verge at the entrance. Despite the fact that each had "Wilderness Wood" in fifteen-centimetre letters, they said they didn't know their origin, and so had taken them to their yard. The signs were quickly returned when we told them we had informed the police they had been stolen!

Our road frontage was always low key, with a tasteful sign indicating our existence behind the roadside wall of Scots pines. Despite ourselves, we nailed a small Christmas tree with a string of coloured lights atop the sign. Every year the lights would disappear, presumably a seasonal challenge to the local lads, undeterred by the barbed wire wound round the tree like the

Amnesty symbol. I stopped short of connecting that to the mains only because it would trip the fuse box every time it rained.

Loss of lights was not our only annoyance. After the 1987 storm we had interspersed a cash crop of spruce Christmas trees between the broadleaved trees we planted along the road frontage. One night four years later, a hundred of their stems were deliberately snapped. This must have been done by a pretty brawny soul, and we suspected it was the young bloke I had admonished for blocking the pavement between the pub and the village school with his car. Fortunately we were able to splint the stems, and most healed. The incident was the unique example of vandalism against us.

One tree that did grow well on our poor soils was holly. Chatting over a pint at the pub shortly after we moved to the wood, we learned that in a recent year there had been a general shortage of holly with berries, except for one large tree in the wood; and legend had it that the resultant sales exceeded £1,000, in the days when that was worth several thousand pints. We never had such luck, but did find holly could be a useful seasonal crop, along with foliage we could obtain by pruning branches from our Douglas fir and Thuja.

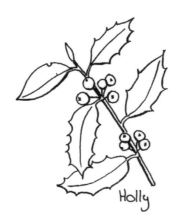

Holly

Unfortunately, if there was a cold snap in late November, the berries would be stripped by birds in a day. So we outsmarted them by harvesting earlier, storing the holly boughs under a tarpaulin; this time it was wood mice that had a surprise harvest, with berries at their level and out of sight of raptors.

There was, however, Mr. Smith from south London, who each year turned up in a battered pick-up for two loads of berry-free "blind" holly for wreath-making. While his wife sat impassively in the cab, we would load up, and a useful quantity of used notes changed hands. Holly berries have a tendency to fall off, and he preferred to add tastefully-designed plastic ones, along with cones and ribbons. Wreath-making is a welcome source of cash before Christmas for many families, and we bought wreaths from several sources in order to offer a variety of styles and qualities. Mr. Smith insisted on a descriptive receipt each time, "in case Oi get stopped by the Bill". One year we had no 'phone call in November, and our attempts to contact him went unanswered. Next year we supplied him as usual; there was no mention of the pause in demand, and we imagined that he had not been free to travel and trade as normal.

The first three weeks of December were a time of unremitting slog, for in this short period we might take twenty percent of annual turnover. At the end of each day I would work out tree sales, and over the years built up the sales pattern we might expect, allowing for the weather. If a weekend was wet, those 200 trees bought at the less muddy car park behind the supermarket in town were sales lost to us, and only our New Year bonfire benefitted. On the other hand, while December snow transformed the wood into a picture-postcard scene, it discouraged all but owners of a large four-wheel-drive car. Sales would plummet, and, against our best romantic instincts, we prayed the snow would go before the next weekend.

Then came the counting of the takings. Until we had a till, all sales were recorded on paper, and we fondly imagined it gave our venture a quaintly uncommercial flavour. Once we had bought a till, we wondered how we had ever managed without. Till or no, those five, ten, twenty and occasional fifty pound notes needed bundling into hundreds, and secreting somewhere in the house until we could get to the bank. Credit cards reduced this burden, but at a cost of almost three percent commission. We sometimes discussed what we would do if the proverbial robber came down the drive on a Sunday evening to relieve us of the weekend's loot. A near neighbour had this happen for a modest sum and his shotgun, while he and his wife were tied up and badly beaten. Tree theft was easier to foil, by parking the Land Rover across the entrance each evening, so that any wholesale thief would have to carry trees 80 metres uphill to his truck parked in full view of any passing police patrol. To our knowledge few trees were stolen at night, but at busy times we did occasionally find someone taking a tree straight to their car without any intention of paying. Our informal sales methods possibly encouraged dishonesty, but we did not wish to impose more secure systems which would have been disproportionate to the problem. Britain is one of the most surveillance-dominated countries in the world, and we saw no reason for installing CCTV on the remote chance that blurred pictures of a hooded figure might record theft of some low-value item. Besides, we wanted our customers to feel trusted.

Each year, on the staff's last working day, we would hold the Christmas lunch. Knowing that the typical "Christmas fayre" on offer at nearby pubs would be overpriced and underwhelming, the spirit of DIY again rose to meet the challenge. Anne is a splendid cook, and sixteen of us could squeeze into the hall of the house. The pattern was always the same. Anne would spend the morning preparing the meal, and I would get the hall organised. At 12.30, woodsmen, carpenters and other outside staff, appropriately scrubbed, would troop over to join the girls who were giving Anne a hand, and bubbly was served by the living room fire. It soon became obvious that cans of lager had already been opened in the workshop, and more than one less experienced drinker would have to be collected later that afternoon.

Our food can be classed as robust and traditional. We are not too fond of turkey, so a joint of pork, beef, pheasant or Wilderness Wood venison would be served, once crackers had been pulled and wine glasses filled. In the spirit of self-sufficiency and enlightenment, home-grown creamed parsnips might join the more conventional vegetables, but goodwill and tolerance permitted one young member to garnish whatever was on the plate with copious quantities of tomato ketchup. This was usually followed by mincemeat tart in some form, and the port went round the table, followed by strong coffee, or tea. If a customer needed serving they would be attended by the youngest first, and I, as the oldest, would hope for once that sales weren't too brisk that afternoon. It became a tradition for each to receive a plain envelope with something more than a Christmas card in it, reflecting the efforts each had made that year, and no doubt these were compared in the pub where several repaired later. The dinner party was the start of family Christmas for us, and from that evening we could relax and enjoy the rest that the turn of the year demanded.

We were very fortunate that Christmas and its trees provided a lot of activity and income at an otherwise dead time of year. We all enjoyed the hard work, and rejoiced in the success we so clearly achieved as a team. Each Christmas was a celebration not just of that season's efforts, but the culmination of the care that each tree had received over several preceding years, and a reminder that our lives were inextricably entwined in the ongoing cycle of seasons.

A WHOLESALE MISTAKE

On any rational assessment, I must have been crazy. By 1994 we had lived at the wood for a decade and its business was on an even keel, with the graph of yearly turnover climbing steadily upwards, even if the profit line stayed nearly horizontal. We had survived the Great Storm, and the replacement trees were rocketing skywards. Joanna was in her last year at Oxford and likely to get a first in rowing if not in her degree, while Kate had plans to study medicine. Job of raising offspring: pass, with distinction in certain aspects. The economy was coming out of recession, and the flourishing consultancy business meant our assistant Tim was at last paying his way doing tree surveys, and did not have to spend most of his time in the wood. All things considered, life was going swimmingly. But my restlessness resurfaced, and once again it seemed time for a bit more creative crisis management; except that this time there was to be too much crisis and not enough management.

We knew that there was a steady demand for Christmas trees, and no-one was going to delete Christmas from the calendar. The trees we bought in for re-sale were often difficult to obtain, and in many cases of poor quality. It seemed obvious that, if we had the land, we could grow all the trees we needed, and have plenty to sell to other outlets. Some years earlier we had rented a hectare near the wood as a Christmas tree plantation, but the lease would soon run out, and we figured a new plantation could take over if we planted now. Further, Tim wasn't yet married and had time on his hands. He would do most of the manual work, and I would provide the finance; and so we went into partnership, with a formula that rewarded each with shares until the venture showed a profit. We looked forward to selling 75,000 trees at a profit of £5 each, a useful pension pot for each of us.

Tim found nine hectares of pasture ideally located between his house and the wood, nicely hidden from prying eyes down a narrow lane. A soil survey revealed that, although heavy, the soil had good rooting depth compared with the thin stuff at the wood. On balance we considered trees would grow well, and after a little negotiation we bought the land in late 1994. As well as providing a retirement nest-egg from the sale of trees, our intention was to intermix the Christmas trees with oaks and ash, thereby creating a broadleaved wood which would be eligible for a Forestry Commission woodland creation grant.

As we had found at Wilderness Wood, it was always a good policy to keep neighbours on side, so we approached the two closest. The lady to the north could not have been nicer, only regretting she had been unable to afford the land herself. To the south was a man who had imposed a restrictive covenant preventing change of use from agriculture on our small front field. Despite our offer to plant trees of his choice on his boundary, he was adamant that the term "agriculture" ruled out forestry, although identical in planning law. Furthermore, he would pursue the matter to the High Court if need be, as he had already done on a similar issue elsewhere. As we would have our hands full planting the remaining nine-tenths, we decided to withdraw from this skirmish, and rented the hectare to a nearby farmer for hay. It turned out that our neighbour had done us a great favour, as the field was impossibly wet and planting would have been a total failure; though we never gave him the satisfaction of this knowledge.

The area for planting consisted of two fields of similar size, separated by a hedge. The lower was steeper, and as a result better drained. It was only when Peter, whom we had hired to build our access road, ventured into the lower field and had to use the digger bucket to pull his machine up the modest slope, that we realised how difficult our site would be to work. Even with its caterpillar tracks he could make no progress uphill, for the underlying Wadhurst Clay becomes impossibly slippery when wet. Buying land on this clay was our first mistake. We would need to extract our trees uphill in late November, usually the wettest time of year, and a task normally done by tractor and trailer. The only consolation was that we were able to dig out a pond for wildlife, fire control and spraying, that stayed full of water even in the driest year.

We had to fence both fields against rabbits, a total boundary of 1,600 metres. Because of the large scale it was worth getting a farming friend to plough a single furrow as close to the boundary hedge as possible, so that we could easily bury the bottom part of the rabbit netting, a great saving in time and digging. He also lent us a tractor-mounted post-basher, and the fence-posts at three-metre intervals went in like pins into soft butter. I suspect no forest rabbit fence has ever been put up more efficiently.

The biggest constraint to the growth of young trees in pasture is the grass, which competes for moisture and nutrients in their early years; so it is standard practice to kill it off before planting. Early in March, in came an agricultural contractor with a 24-metre sprayer boom, and in only four passes and less than half an hour he had covered the whole field with glyphosate, considered to be one of the least toxic sprays. Knowing we were entering a competitive business, we had to ensure that all subsequent tending could be as mechanised as possible, and this meant machine access in both directions between accurately spaced trees. I hit on the idea of scoring the ground with parallel lines 1.1 metres apart by dragging behind the tractor a six-metre-long pole with spikes, which scored five parallel lines in the sod. This was then repeated at right angles, and planting positions were at the lines' intersections. To allow subsequent mechanised spraying, a three-metre-wide lane was left every 24 metres. Our rows followed the gentle curve of the lower field boundary, so nobody could accuse us of regimented straight lines of trees. The trees had arrived from a Scottish nursery, and we were ready to plant.

March 1995 was unusually warm, and by 10 am each planter was stripped to the waist as he worked along the lines, inserting a young tree at every intersection. For ease of planting, we had chosen cell-grown trees with roots confined to plugs of peat about three centimetres wide and ten centimetres deep. Unlike large, bare-rooted stock, they were small enough to insert into the little hole made by a narrow spear-like spade. We could carry up to 450 trees in a special planting harness which fitted comfortably on our backs. With the easy conditions, team members each planted over a thousand a day, and were rewarded by a generous piece-rate and a celebratory pub supper when we had finished.

Most of the trees were the traditional Norway spruce, plus a few thousand of the more valuable blue spruce, as these were both species suited to the heavy clay soil. In order to create a broadleaved wood we planted oak and ash at double spacing in each direction, i.e. 2.2 metres. The spruce occupied the alternate rows and spaces, and so formed seventy-five percent of the planting. To complicate matters further, we planted the route of a future circular access ride with just Christmas trees, and lined it with shrubs, to avoid unnecessary tree clearing when it came to harvesting the broadleaves in future years.

The planting had progressed like a dream, and it even rained soon after we had finished. Our luck could not continue, and that year was to be one of the driest and hottest on record. As the rainless weeks continued, the clay demonstrated its propensity to shrink as it dries. Like imperfections on a Champagne glass forming the foci for bubbles, the planting holes seeded cracks by the tens of thousand, and the roots of the tiny trees were exposed to the merciless sun and dry air in canyons three centimetres wide. Death by dehydration seemed certain. The ground was rock hard, so heeling in the cracks to close them was out of the question. We investigated filling around the roots with sand, and quickly ruled it out on practical grounds. Had we used the more traditional "bare-rooted" transplants, the planting would have been a disaster. Against all odds, the plugs lived up to their reputation for good survival rates, and, when autumn rains came at last, we counted a failure rate of only two and a half percent, which is well within the range of a normal year, let alone drought conditions.

Spurred on by our initial success, the following year we planted the upper field. Although cooler, the summer of 1996 was almost as dry, but we were not too worried as we again used cell-grown trees. Our main concern was that the numerous rabbits living in the adjacent Crab Wood might tunnel under our new rabbit fence to get to their accustomed grass. Just like a woman new to motherhood, I frequently checked on my baby trees. To my horror, there were the tell-tale signs of rabbit damage, with tops nibbled off; but nowhere could I find holes under the fence. Puzzled, I visited the plantation one evening, and spotted a rabbit nonchalantly chewing our trees. As soon as he saw me he dashed for the fence, and, to my total amazement, clambered up the metre-high netting, tumbled down the other side, and no doubt told his family about his lucky escape once he had caught his breath.

Rabbits are not supposed to climb, and our fence, built to the approved specification, should have been rabbit-proof. Like the blue-tits who in the 1950s discovered how to pierce milk-bottle tops to get at the cream and spread the knowledge year by year further afield, we were petrified our mutant rabbits might teach others how to climb fences, and the forester's main defence would become useless. With the adjacent owner's consent, we engaged ferreters to kill off every last rabbit in the warren, and perhaps England has us to thank for eliminating a plague with a similar potential for damage as the grey squirrel.

If the field our neighbour had prevented us from planting was little more than a clay bog, most of the adjacent upper Christmas tree field was scarcely better. Before planting, the farmer who lent had us his post-basher went over the whole area with his "Shakeaerator", a device that drew tines through the soil and vibrated them to break up the clods. But, despite the improved conditions, the tree roots that penetrated more than a few centimetres in summer were under water most of the winter, and drowned. The next summer, the increased size of crown could not be supported by the remaining roots, and many trees died of drought. As a result, we had less than half the predicted number of Christmas trees to sell from this field. Because the Forestry Commission expected a plantation to be fully stocked with trees, we had to replant hundreds of broadleaves to have sufficient at the end of the five-year period to qualify for our woodland grant. Despite our desire to establish a productive wood with valuable timber trees such as oak and ash, we accepted that "weeds" such as alder and willow would thrive in these trying conditions, and it was these that we planted in the gaps. We have to admit that public money contributed in part to establishing yet more scrub trees in the High Weald.

Our overall application of weedkiller had done an excellent job of killing off all the green vegetation before we planted, but this left a fertile seedbed for any seeds that cared to fly around the countryside and see how our land suited them. We now know that we should have put up a "Full" sign by sowing an uncompetitive cover crop such as clover, but, as it was, the thistle family moved in *en masse*. Within a short time our trees were thigh-deep in scratchy plants which threatened to smother them. Unwilling to use chemicals on a wholesale basis, we attempted to cut the thistles with a hired flail mower, which chugged along between the rows, mashing everything to a fine pulp. This had limited success, so, until the trees reached about two metres high, future outbreaks were controlled by the return of the 24-metre boom sprayer, which rapidly applied the fearfully expensive product that knocked back thistles alone. Because we had broadleaves mixed with our conifers, we could not find a chemical to apply overhead that would kill weeds without harming the broadleaved trees, and we had to resort to pushing a special mono-cycle sprayer which applied neat Glyphosate below the level of the lowest branches, in minute but precise quantities. To cover the nine hectares of plantation both along and across the rows would be a walk of ninety miles, so we compromised by spraying in one direction only. Forty-five miles is still quite a trek in midsummer pushing a barrow, no matter how ergonomically designed, and especially when the weeds are high enough to touch the spray guard. A similar level of legwork was required periodically to distribute fertiliser near the base of each young tree, by means of a specially adapted wheelbarrow.

In order to supply supermarkets with blemish-free apples, a grower may have to spray his crop up to seven times a year. For our market, "blemish-free" meant trees with most of the needles still on, and not discoloured. Green spruce aphid and red spider mite were constant threats, as a light infestation would brown the needles, and a heavy one cause total loss of all but the newest foliage. Again, the boom sprayer had to be called in at short notice whenever an outbreak occurred, to apply the appropriate insecticide. The interplanted ash quickly outgrew the spruce and, once above two metres, were too tall to allow the boom to pass overhead, so we had to resort to hand dousing. Despite these endeavours the blue spruce lost most of the previous years' needles, and were unsaleable. It was a matter of judgement whether to throw good money after bad, and we put many out of their misery when it became clear they could never make the grade.

Christmas tree pruning in the patch back at Wilderness Wood could be done almost at leisure, over a few half-days. Here, we had fifteen times that number, and needed extra labour. Tim and I had an increasing consultancy workload as a result of the 1995/96 drought, which caused hundreds of subsidence insurance claims for which expert tree advice was required. Fortunately a stalwart man called Matt answered our small-ad, and he pruned, sprayed and weeded over several seasons. He was trying to renovate a vineyard some miles away, and fighting both planners and difficult neighbours. He needed all the money he could earn, but one season his mobile 'phone number was not recognised, and the caravan down his muddy track seemed unoccupied. Had he fled abroad to stay with his step-son, or had his troubles and the tedium of our tasks turned his mind? We never learned.

In the first year we had employed Peter, our ever-helpful digger driver, to construct the line of a forest road for harvesting the trees. He had excavated the "formation" by scraping off the soil to create a gentle camber, so that water would drain into side ditches. When dry, the road made a fine route for driving the 450 metres to the lower field by Land Rover, but in winter it was impassably slippery and soft by any vehicle. So, the summer before our first tree sales, we bought, spread and rolled several lorry-loads of hardcore; but we spread it thicker than calculated, and didn't have enough to finish the job. Hardcore was always expensive when bought through a dealer, but small builders often had loads they wished to dispose of at short notice, and a "free dump for clean hardcore" notice in the local newspaper soon attracted enough to make up our shortfall. One risked the occasional piece of wood or plasterboard, but these could be dealt with easily enough. What we hadn't reckoned on was the use that would be made of our access track by some dubious friend of the hardcore dumpers.

About one month after the track was completed, the police 'phoned one morning to tell us it had been used by thieves to gain access to a scaffolding firm in the neighbouring village. They had driven several times across our little trees in a stolen four-wheel-drive pickup, through a hedge, and across two further fields; liberated a large number of valuable scaffolding clips; and made their getaway courtesy of our fine new road in what must have been a sizeable truck. We reflected that better use might have been made of the ingenuity behind the operation. Not only had they carefully recce'd the land, cut our padlock earlier that day, and stolen a suitable vehicle, but they had waited for a full moon so that the raid could be done without lights. Fortunately the driven-over trees were bent rather than broken, and most recovered.

This incident highlighted the vulnerability of our precious crop. Christmas trees in unguarded locations with good access are an obvious target in the weeks before the festival, and growers are bombarded with adverts for security measures including near-ballistic thief-scarers. Never one to spend money when low technology might suffice, I laid several planks in the ruts along the track, with 75-millimetre nails poking through, which would puncture any tyres driving over them. In the interest of safety, the nails were protected by a thin board, so that an innocent walker would not be maimed. We reasoned few vehicles carried more than one spare tyre, and that no truck with two or more flat tyres would be leaving at three am. I was almost sad my invention was never tested in action.

Unless we can persuade the authorities to move Christmas to midsummer, as in Australia, trees must be cut and extracted from the plantation at the wettest time of year. Tractor and trailer were useless on our clay, and the first year we carried and dragged out the few hundred smallish trees for our own sales, sliding and cursing in the mud. In future years we would have thousands to extract, and it was clear that a solution had to be found. Acting on a brainwave, I devised an overhead cableway, similar to the simple drag-lifts used at ski resorts. With the help of my engineer friend Phil, I spent several frosty early November evenings in the yard and workshop building a tower to fit on the tractor power-take-off, with a large pulley wheel set horizontally at the top. The whole was welded together from scaffold poles and car transmission parts, and drove a 400 metre cable looped round another tower at the bottom of the field, by way of three intermediate towers with wheelbarrow wheels to support the cable. A cord loop was knotted every five metres on the cable, to which a tree could be hooked.

Extracting our Christmas trees across the mud

With the tractor engine ticking over, the cable was drawn up the slope at walking speed. All we had to do was to drag each tree to the cable, attach a cord loop with a modified meat-hook to the stem of the tree, and hand it up to the bloke on a platform, who hooked it onto a passing cable loop. The system transported up to 500 trees per hour up the slope, and it was a surreal experience to see a line of inverted trees appearing out of the mist across a sea of treetops. Ever-keen to promote ourselves, we managed to get the regional TV to feature it on their news, and we are told that our fame spread as far as a West Midlands newspaper.

By the turn of the millennium, the lower field had hundreds of marketable trees. We were able to supply ourselves with well-shaped, absolutely fresh trees, and no longer needed outside purchases apart from the largest sizes. But next year there would be thousands to sell, and we began to approach possible wholesale outlets. Obvious candidates were local garden centres, all of whom would be selling hundreds each year. Many smaller, family-run firms told us they preferred to buy from their regular supplier, and we admired their loyalty. The larger chains would only purchase centrally, and it was here that the misery really started. We at least in theory knew how to grow trees, but in the field of marketing we were hopeless beginners.

There are people who could sell snow to Eskimos, but neither we nor any of our staff had any feel for the high-pressure selling needed to shift thousands of trees. Frustration quickly turned to desperation. When we approached buyers in May, we were told that we were too late, as they ordered in February. Others told us to contact them again in September - by which time they had already ordered. The smaller outlets, who loved our samples for both quality and price, would not commit to an order, despite our weekly calls. A large marketing group promised in August to take several thousand at a good price, but repeatedly delayed a firm order, until announcing in late October they no longer needed them. A savant in the trade later told me this was a ploy to keep us out of the market. Another buyer actually marked a sample of trees he liked, and said he would have 1,600 at £8 each, netted and delivered to Bedfordshire on a certain date in late November. A couple of weeks later I had a 'phone call. He was standing in a field in Luxembourg, surrounded by beautiful trees he could get for seven euros. If we weren't prepared to meet that price, the deal was off; and this was at a time when the pound traded at 1.50 euros. I later pondered whether he even went beyond Dover.

We were able to negotiate the price up slightly, and on two consecutive wintry days found ourselves loading up a huge curtain-sided articulated lorry of the maximum size permitted on British roads. As all the trees came out of the lower field, we had stacked eight hundred trees per lorry-load at the bottom end of the access track. Everything was at last going to plan. All the help had turned up on time, ready to load the lorry in chain-gang fashion. The articulated lorry had successfully turned in the reversing area without backing into the side ditches, and the loading was completed in one hour without any heart attacks. We might have guessed things were going too smoothly. As the laden lorry made to drive off, the single pair of driving wheels lost traction, and, with the smell of hot rubber on greasy bricks, started to excavate two holes in the road. Somehow we had to pull the lorry to a less steep section of track. Our small hand-winch merely pulled out of the ground the stakes to which it was attached. A local farmer's four-wheel-drive tractor showed it could spin all four wheels at once, and dug four further holes. Fortunately, he had a friend who was working nearby with a heavy-duty timber winch, connected to a veritable wreck of a tractor. The winch lowered two great spades onto the track, and, as the slack was taken up, they dug right through the rubble into the ground below. The six-tonne pull heaved the lorry from its resting place, and, with the tractor escorting it up to the top field, it made its way off our premises cheered by all, and with my pocket £100 lighter.

A second lorry was arriving the next day, and no repeat of this seasonal entertainment could be permitted. The only alternative was to move the next load of trees up to the level ground of the top field, which we managed to do with Land Rover, tractor and two trailers, first thing the next morning. This time the only major mishap was the loaded lorry backing into the tractor, breaking its rear window – another £100 on the harvesting costs.

We had put ourselves in the typical position of suppliers to large retailers. Supermarkets use their buying power to dictate terms to their suppliers. In the case of Christmas trees, in the interests of easy handling the demand was for palletted trees, squashed into open-topped boxes by huge rams, like sardines in a tin. Without pallets, ram, and fork-lifts, we could not supply them. Christmas trees are a perishable crop once cut, with a shelf-life shorter than the average apple, and with the difference that apples can be sold year-round. The most popular tree size is 1.75 to 2 metres, and therefore the large middlemen will only purchase trees within this range, and with a certain shape and foliage density. All else must be discarded to waste, even though our experiences at Wilderness Wood told us there was a demand for all shapes and sizes.

The large-scale Christmas tree venture was not all gloom and doom. There is great satisfaction to be had from loading up lovely trees that you have planted and nurtured, and driving them on a frosty December morning to a happy and grateful retailer who settles his bills; and this is what Tim and I had imagined life would be like. In order to soak up some more trees, and retain the retail mark-up, for several years we sold trees out of a steel container located in the forecourt of a Lewes pub. We shifted a useful number each December, but because most trees had to be carried through the streets by their purchaser, the demand was for the smaller sizes, and year by year our trees were getting larger.

Once beyond the magic two metre limit, trees become increasingly onerous and costly to prune back to size. We had stupidly planted the whole area in just two years. Anne had questioned why we were planting our nine hectares in just two seasons, rather than spreading it out to extend the harvest. Ever impatient, I had assured her that the trees' uneven growth would spread out the sizes, but in practice we had to shift 35,000 trees in just five years. As in the run-up to an exam, it became increasingly difficult to relax, and the frustration of being unable to find markets turned to despair.

Stress creeps up insidiously, and may not be apparent to the victim or others. The lovely canon who was taking services at the church in one of the recurring "interregnums", and preaching on the theme of contentment, referred to how happy the Wilderness Wood forester must be, with such a fulfilling calling out in the woods, enjoying God's creation. "Little does he know!" Anne thought when she returned to her grumpy husband, who was complaining volubly about some minor item the staff had forgotten to do. An unwillingness to face the world, and a generally black view on life, were quickly diagnosed as symptoms of depression by our sympathetic GP. The sense of failure became overwhelming; but with medical help, assisted by giving the remaining trees to Tim to make of them what he could, composure slowly returned, and the glass again became half full rather than half empty.

Hopes of that retirement pot for Tim and myself had died for us both, but at least we broke even on the venture. What's more, we did succeed in establishing a first-class broadleaved woodland, fully stocked with trees of potentially commercial value at no net cost to ourselves. How many afforestation schemes can claim that? Disappointingly, the upper field was so boggy that many trees had died, and it yielded very few Christmas trees. The loss of revenue was compounded by the cost of replanting with willows and alders. Ironically, a few years later I sold the land and its young woodland at a good profit, but would have benefitted even more had we simply traded in land, without the bother of tree-planting. There is, however, a consolation. Few of us are given the opportunity to alter significantly the face of the earth. Our new wood is now on Ordnance Survey maps and visible from space, so we can watch its progress from satellite pictures.

MONEY MATTERS !

Most foresters know the corny joke about the man who won a prize at a circus for making Nellie the elephant cry twice. The first time he told he was a forester; and the second time, his salary. Nobody goes into forestry to get rich quick, and it is very easy to make a small fortune: by starting out with a large one and planting trees. Other chapters have related what we did, and why. This one outlines the financial side of our Wilderness Wood venture, and offers some conclusions on avoiding common pitfalls.

Christopher Bullock suggested in 1716 that *"Tis impossible to be sure of any thing but Death and Taxes"*, to which we now might add Rules and Regulations. These latter can be a major interference with the daily struggle to survive, being costly in terms of money, time and frustration. We kept our heads down as far as possible, hoping to escape under the radar of officialdom at all levels. When official circulars came through the letterbox they languished in the "pending" tray, and generally we responded only if there was a follow-up. It was probable that local officials had sympathy with our activities, and only reacted to complaints and to more blatant or substantial breaches of their regulations.

Employment law is fraught, but we tried to observe both the spirit and letter of regulations relating to youth labour. However, we were reluctant to set up tax and insurance returns for every short term, part-time worker. The first Inland Revenue lady who visited was sympathetic to our employing casuals, and took no action. Years later, the second was pleasant but firm, and we had some thousands of pounds of back-payments to make up. I find it scandalous that only recently has it become acknowledged that some of the world's richest individuals and biggest corporations have been evading taxes on a massive scale, with the connivance of our politicians and tax authorities. The lowest fruit is always the easiest to pick, if not the ripest. Neither of us was keen to spend our lives ineptly filling in forms, and, to stay sane as well as legal, soon employed suitably trained people to sort out the pay, sick- and maternity pay, and book-keeping.

Accidents can and did happen, but fortunately the inspectors from the Health and Safety Executive always gave us a clean bill of health, and it was only over-protective parents who cast doubt on the suitability of the play equipment, or hygiene at castaway parties. Inevitably, we had comprehensive and expensive insurance cover, including public, employer's and product liability. We learned the hard way that such insurance does not cover accidents where the parties agree there was no fault. A loyal member of staff refused to claim against us when her front teeth were broken in an accident with the sawbench. The insurance company agreed we were not at fault, and, without a claim against us, we had to fund the repair.

Yarrow's business rules

Below are summarised, in no order of importance, our conclusions from hard-won experience on how to keep a small woodland business afloat. Every wood is different, and every owner will have different objectives and financial situation, but I hope the information will be a guide (or warning!) to others venturing into the mysteries of small woodland management. For anyone experienced in business it may appear as little more than stating the "bleedin' obvious", but in our experience the combination of British amateurism and lack of business training has resulted in a woeful litany of failures in all sorts of ventures, no matter how well intentioned and hard-working are their owners. As I write, there is debate about introducing money management at primary school level. Why not?

- *Minimise your capital outlay.* Borrowing money is expensive, and if you are already in debt, further borrowing will be at the rate of your most expensive loan: which for many is their credit card, currently in the region of 20% interest. Every business requires working capital and, by the time we handed over the wood, equipment and stock-in-trade were worth around £80,000. This sum excluded the cost of site improvements, such as roads, picnic sites, buildings, etc. It is unlikely you will earn enough from the wood business to finance a mortgage, so you will need "foreign currency" (money earned in a better-paying activity) to buy a house, unless you do as we and Ben Law did, and build your own home on site.

- *Minimise outgoings.* Pay a fair price, but that is not always the asking price. We reduced our business rate almost 50% by contesting it, which was a huge saving over thirty years. Likewise, research suppliers, which is easily done now with the internet. Large outlays, such as insurance, are well worth putting in the hands of a good broker, who will shop around each year on your behalf.

- *Buy second-hand or hire.* Time taken sourcing good, second-hand equipment is well spent. We could never have justified a new tractor, used only intermittently; as many farmers upgrade regularly, there is a ready second-hand supply of such machinery, but you may need an expert along to assess its condition. We hired equipment for one-off jobs, such as mowing the meadow, which avoided all the costs of purchase, maintenance, storage and depreciation. Alternatively, we used a contractor.

- *Buy the best tools you can afford.* This applies to hand tools in the workshop and chainsaws in the wood. There is nothing worse than a tool that blunts quickly or breaks, or a chainsaw whose ergonomics are ill-designed or that won't start in the rain. Your "downtime" adds to the cost of an unreliable item.

- *Be practical.* Most house or car owners do the simple maintenance jobs themselves. If you can't fix a broken gate latch, or diagnose a flat battery, learn how to do so, sell your wood to someone who can, or build the business so that it can support well-trained staff. Calling out a professional will eat any profits you will make. Conversely, there are jobs you must leave to the specialists, such as rewiring the workshop to comply with new regulations. A self-taught man often has a fool for his master, and it will sometimes be worth paying experts to teach you specialist knowledge, such as how to prune or fertilise Christmas trees.

- *Pay promptly.* Contractors, part-time workers and suppliers are often small businesses, reliant on prompt payment for their cash-flow. We found we could usually get a contractor to spray Christmas trees or help at short notice, because we paid on the nail. We were fortunate always to have savings to tide us over paying for coppicing or tree planting in February, when takings were low; but, like any business, we had to operate within our means.

- *Get the money in.* Slow- or non-payers are the bane of any business, so take money with orders if you can, or at least a substantial deposit. This applies especially to booked events, where you may have turned people away, only to find the "pay on the day" ones don't turn up. Similarly, only supply on credit to businesses you know will pay. In the early years we supplied Christmas trees to more than one individual who was in the process of going bankrupt.

- *Be realistic.* Even though you are prepared to work for a pittance, you cannot expect your staff to do likewise. A full day's work deserves a full day's pay, and in the South-east we were in a high-cost economy, with wages to match, and competing with better-paid jobs in town. You will be unable to afford the wages they need unless you are well organised, and your labour is highly productive.

- *Use the right person for the job.* Trained staff with special skills are worth retaining, but it is a waste of money to use them for menial jobs. Multi-tasking is both desirable and necessary in a place such as Wilderness Wood, and it will be efficient if the foreman occasionally does a simple five-minute job, rather than finding the lad on work experience. On the other hand, it would not be economical to use a ranger paid £10 per hour to do the washing up for seven hours on the day she had no parties to lead, when a school-leaver on a lower wage might be more appropriate. Successful juggling of staff and tasks is the mark of a good manager.

- *Work out a project's viability.* Our wood could have diversified in any number of ways, but we always had to ask ourselves "Would it pay?" Charcoal-making equipment, for example, would have tied up a lot of money, and would only be an efficient use of time with several kilns burning simultaneously. Would we be able to oversee them for the three nights and days, and could we buy in enough wood to keep them busy for sufficient burns per year to justify the investment? Without a market survey, we could only guess the demand. All projects need a realistic and thorough assessment of capital, manning, supplies, turnover, profit margin, markets and competition. Even if the figures looked good, was this an activity we were enthusiastic to pursue? The same principles apply to all ventures, be they catering, Christmas trees, or buying in products to sell. No financier would invest without such an exercise, and nor should you! Having started a project, it's essential to keep sufficient records to monitor and review its success, so you can judge whether to expand or discontinue.

- *Dip your toe in the water.* We had the luxury of living on the spot, and of being self-employed. It was therefore often possible to try out flights of fancy or unusual requests, such as running a children's birthday party, without significantly risking capital. Once we had done a few parties, and worked out the ground rules for viability, including establishing a market price, we decided we could employ staff at the going rate of £10 an hour and charge several times that figure. If an idea flopped, like bush-craft weekends, little harm had been done. Initially, our catering was very basic, and it was only after a couple of seasons' experience of running a tea-room that we invested in a commercial toaster and a set of crockery, having until then used our own kitchen equipment.

- *Listen to others.* Nobody is all-knowing, and there is a danger that the sole trader will have nobody to check his foolish ideas. Larger businesses have a number of people with differing skills, such as finance, production, or marketing, and each will rein in inappropriate business proposals of the others. If you work by yourself, you ignore sound, disinterested advice at your peril.

- *Find your USP.* When it came to deciding what to do and how to market it, some of the best advice was that we should capitalise on our Unique Selling Proposition. In other words, what singled us out from our competitors? We were living so close to our project that we failed to realise that our biggest asset was the beautiful woodland itself. Our cream teas, served from a lovely barn or sunny tea-garden, would have a head start over those sold from somewhere less salubrious.

- *Price properly.* There is no point in supplying a product or service at the wrong price, for either it won't sell, or you'll go bust meeting demand. A business advisor gave a simple rule for pricing made items, which involved adding 15% to the cost of materials for wastage; multiplying labour costs by 170% to include overheads; and adding 40% to 100% for retail mark-up, and then VAT. If the final price exceeded the price others were charging, we would see if production time could be reduced, for labour was invariably the greatest cost element. A "one-off" order must take account of design time, just as one has to cost in the time of clearing up after a children's activity.

- *Chase profit, not turnover.* Don't take orders unless you can make a profit, even if there is a lot of money on offer. The time taken to locate at short notice those large chestnut poles for Dutch dyke repairs probably killed most of the profit, and we should have charged a premium.

- *Everyone needs a bargain.* For business to work, every party must benefit. You cannot use a sales agent unless his commission adequately reflects his efforts, any more than a workman will work for less than a fair wage. The 100% retail mark-up of a garden centre reflects its necessary overheads. If you cannot supply them at half the retail price, it is because you cannot compete with third world labour, or someone who is more efficient, or a retired bloke making things in his garage as a hobby. Without economies of scale, we found we could seldom drop our prices enough to supply wholesalers, so decided to retail at the wood on a much lower mark-up.

- *Find your market.* If a product is not sold locally, it may be because there is no demand, or because no-one has yet thought of supplying it. Where you could supply all manner of items, it pays to assess which are most rewarding. We had a relatively wealthy local population who were willing to pay premium prices for garden products, which were much more profitable than supplying fenceposts to farmers. In other words, we were producing luxuries, such as rose arches and Christmas trees.

- *Specialise.* Once you have established a good market with growth potential, specialise and enjoy becoming efficient in your chosen field. This will then justify investing in equipment and marketing. However, a small wood will probably not grow enough raw material to pay for your investment or keep you occupied, and you will have to buy in supplies or make use of your equipment as a contractor.

- *Mechanise!* Only craftsmen turning out products classed as "art" can afford to make products solely by hand, and even wood carvers roughly shape their work with power tools. Electrical energy is cheap compared with muscle power, and the most basic workshop should have its full complement of power tools. Some are so cheap that intermittent use is justifiable. Other items, such as firewood processors costing £5,000 or more, need quite a few tonnes throughput per annum to justify purchase, and it might be better to hire one and concentrate the work in as short a period as possible, assuming covered log storage is available. Expenditure can be avoided by joining a "machinery ring," more common in farming circles.

- *Be thrifty.* As a society we are accustomed to being very wasteful, be it through food thrown away, uninsulated houses, or unnecessary travel. To survive, a small woodland business has to imitate a Nepali village: nothing is wasted. A pound saved on diesel or electricity by turning off idling tractors or un-needed lights is a pound extra on the bottom line. Use every piece of wood harvested; time and energy have been spent on its production, and you cannot afford to leave it to rot, but must find the best use for it. That would at worst be as firewood, but better as a welly-puller, or garden log-roll. Maximum utility also applied to our daily round. The school run was combined with shopping for the café, distributing leaflets, collecting supplies, or delivering orders. The costs of car and time were worth a pound a mile each way.

- *Work smarter, not harder!* Another way of saying "Be efficient", or "It's what you put into the hours, not the hours you put in". This is particularly important on repetitive tasks, such as coppicing.

- *Be timely.* As well as saving the other eight stitches by making the one in time, actually doing something at the right time can save a catastrophe. Simply by spending five hours spraying at the early stage of an outbreak, you prevent spruce aphid wrecking your Christmas tree crop. Likewise, the five minute job of covering the winter log stack before the autumn rains, rather than belatedly when they are soaked, means you and your customers have some heat in January. The woodland life is no place for the procrastinator.

- *Process the money efficiently.* For years we had no cash till, laboriously keeping paper records of sales. A modern till with 24 different classes of sales now costs little, and records cash, card and cheque receipts, with daily, weekly and monthly totals. Notes and large value coin have to be counted, but it would be as foolish to count the copper coins each day as it would be to do a daily stock check. We transferred each week's figures to a computer accounting system, which even worked out the VAT bill each quarter. That still left the hardest part to us: writing the cheque!

- *Acknowledge your hidden takings.* Like growing your own vegetables, income from simple "unmanufactured" wood products is not taxable, so one of the fringe benefits to us was firewood, garden stakes, beanpoles, etc. There is a temptation not to acknowledge these benefits, along with the usual supply of paperclips and envelopes from the office, or help from the staff with shopping errands or house repairs. Taken to extremes, this practice makes the enterprise look depressingly unprofitable, unless you acknowledge to yourself your good fortune.

- *Charity begins at home.* There are jobs in the wood which will inevitably lose money, and some woodland charities do just that. They survive by taking donations from the public, and grants from the government and grant-giving charities. Provided you have some charitable aims, such as education, you may be able to set up a charity or not-for-profit organisation to avail itself of those funds, as well as maybe have volunteers queuing to clear paths, cut bracken, or conduct school visits for nothing. You might even take a part-time salary as an advisor or manager, provided you stay off the list of trustees. Apart from forming a short-lived Wilderness Wood Supporters Group, not starting such a charity was probably one of our big mistakes.

- *Know when to consolidate.* Unless you are spectacularly successful, or your wood sits over shale gas, it is unlikely someone is going to offer to buy you out. Once you have achieved financial stability, it is better to consolidate the business rather than ever increase turnover for its own sake. That is not to say that products and services should not evolve with changing tastes and circumstances, or that productivity should not keep ahead of inflation so that you and your staff can put money aside for a well-earned retirement; but woodlands, like any other part of the natural environment, have limits to growth. We should recognise those, and our own limits.

And how did we do?

I should emphasise that we did not set out to maximise personal income, but aimed for our efforts to be self-sustaining and not reliant on outside financial help. Profitability was always marginal, so attention to detail was continuously necessary in order to break even. Initially somewhat amateurish, we kept strictly accurate books, and over the years every item of income and expenditure was recorded month by month, as were the numbers of visitors, items sold, etc., with an annual review after the end of each forest year, 30th September.

When in 1982 we applied for permission to build the house, our statement on projected financial viability estimated that 38% of turnover would be from coppice products, 27% from visits (mostly schools), 14% from Christmas trees, 9% from timber from the plantations, and 4% from manufactured items. In our final year at the wood, the actual turnover figures were 11% from coppice products, 56% from visits (including catering and shop), 18% from Christmas sales, 0% from timber from the post-storm plantations, and 12% from manufactured items. When Diana started putting our data into the office computer, she was able to produce graphs which clearly illustrated that the level of annual sales rose steadily over the final 17 years. They also showed how visits started to outstrip other sources of income from 1999. The number of paying visitors doubled in the final ten years to 28,000, the greatest increase being the groups, especially children's parties. The income from visits increased even faster. Unfortunately, increased turnover was accompanied by a steady growth in overheads, the vast majority being labour costs. The trading profit increased to almost £50,000 in 2006, then declined when we stepped back a bit and hired more staff to do some of our work.

Although we knew which elements of the business seemed most successful, there was no business plan with "profit centre" targets, and the business grew organically under its own steam. Had we been more ambitious we could no doubt have increased turnover far more quickly; had we been more businesslike, we might have made a larger profit.

Sources of money

Although the market price of Wilderness Wood had increased more than tenfold in the twenty years of the previous ownership, the price we paid was still good value. When we bought the wood for £28,000, our savings enabled us to build the house with only a modest mortgage. Finance to buy the tractor, Land Rover and other equipment, as well as for building the Barn and constructing the car parks and so on, came from savings or out of the limited profits. By using our own labour and materials as far as possible, we were able to minimise costs. In good times, the consultancy was also a source of funds, and pre-2008, when interest rates were high, any spare money was kept in an interest-earning bank account. These back-up funds gave us the flexibility to cope with peaks in expenditure, such as buying in thousands of Christmas trees or replacing a tractor.

Grants can be useful, but one applies for them at one's peril. So often the grant-givers' requirements can outweigh the benefits, be they a higher (and more expensive) specification than intended, delay, or simply the dreary bureaucratic process. Some grants are contingent on obtaining planning permission for a proposal that might or might not require consent, and, given the lust for control lurking in some local planning authorities, we usually avoided their involvement by just getting on with things.

Forestry grants did not play a major part in decision-making at the wood. In addition to the annual management cheque there were other advantages to operating it under a Woodland Grant Scheme, and these are referred to in the chapter on woodland management. The management grant was minimal, and paid for little more than one man working for two weeks. Other grants administered by the Forestry Commission, such as the Woodland Improvement Grant (WIG), were useful if they matched what we intended to do, but we did not look to see what we could do that would attract a grant. We received a significant WIG sum for restoration of deep gullies eroded in the rides by the 2000 rains that caused so much flooding downstream in Uckfield and Lewes. Some years later, we received another to build a path diverting visitors away from a wood processing area. Our policy of allowing unrestricted access to villagers had paid off, as these WIGs were only available to woods freely open to the public.

A fifty percent grant to encourage the firewood industry enabled us to buy a firewood processor and build a log store. Unfortunately, we had bought our expensive tipping Land Rover just before the grant was announced, and they would not accept a post-dated receipt! On other occasions our timing was better, and a Millennium Lottery Fund grant enabled us to put in a path for the disabled, and paid for three resident wood-carvers to create millennium statues. Our last significant grant was in 2008, when we received a useful sum towards re-roofing the Barn. In this case, the conditions and paperwork were formidable, requiring not just a volunteer input, but signatures of attendance, a requirement not revealed until well after the often anonymous helpers had disappeared.

People own a wood for any number of reasons, and ours were peculiar to us. We were fortunate in having savings and other income sources, so that we were not solely reliant on the wood for our living. Working a small wood could rapidly bankrupt you. Only hard work and economical systems will ensure financial success. You have to love the lifestyle, and you will never get rich.

WHERE DID WE GET TO?

Thirty years is a significant proportion of anyone's life, and to spend it so wholeheartedly in a pursuit that is only marginally profitable must lay one's sanity open to doubt. The chapter "Searching for a wood" outlined our desire for pastures new. Our previous two ventures had had their highs and lows and this third one, too, could have gone so horribly wrong.

Undoubtedly we were blessed with good luck: lucky to get planning consent for our house; lucky to be financially strong enough to weather most setbacks; lucky that both of us had the resolve and persistence to make it work; and very lucky we were able to stand each other's foibles and shortcomings through good times and bad. However, the process would not have been bearable had we not both believed strongly in what we hoped to achieve: to show by example that there might be new ways of managing woodland, and that a wood could provide a wide range of benefits.

We grew up in the post-war austerity years, with mothers who made us empty our plates and who repaired clothes, and fathers who grew vegetables for the dinner table. Our generation experienced the subsequent rise in prosperity, admittedly from a low base. Guilt, or perhaps just plain perversity, led us to show we could stand on our own feet, not just on a domestic scale, but as the basis of a whole business. We reverted to the sweat, blisters and inconvenience of a lifestyle which had existed before ready-meals, a throw-away culture, and reliance on others for almost every good and service. Applying our guiding principles to the business was not without its difficulties. Our teenage staff were raised in an age of material plenty, with an economic system measured in terms of consumption. Many showed barely disguised impatience as we explained how to wash up economically, and turn off lights and taps when not needed. Maybe we should have received an award for teaching these basic skills, if not from the authorities, then from future life partners. For us not to have built the highest standards of green living into every aspect of the business would have been hypocritical, and for our efforts we did in fact receive a "Green Tourism" Gold accreditation.

There is no doubt that our interpretation of social and business responsibility sometimes cost us customers and profit. It would have been more profitable to stock sugary canned drinks instead of Sussex apple juice by the glass, or big-brand ice cream rather than that from a local farm. In every business decision we tried to assess which option would have the smallest long-term environmental impact. Hence, we refused to stock cheap firewood or hazel hurdles from east Europe, both on account of the environmental costs of transport, and our desire to support local forestry.

By its very nature, forestry must be planned over decades or even centuries. Like a runner in a relay race, you briefly hold the baton, then hand it on to the next down the track. Once we had decided on the long-term plan we avoided bending to the latest fashion, so refused to restore our "plantation on an ancient woodland site" and plant native trees. Even though we explained what we were trying to achieve, the visitors' book indicated our efforts were not always understood, as we did occasionally receive complaints that we were destroying the wood by cutting the coppice.

Our efforts to promote understanding of forestry extended beyond our woodland boundary. For some years Anne was a trustee of the Forestry Trust for Conservation and Education, and helped produce a number of regional guides of woodlands to visit, where the public could appreciate and learn more about forestry. Started by the Royal Forestry Society, it was later subsumed into the mighty Woodland Trust. The reader may well imagine our frustration when Wilderness Wood was briefly excluded from their on-line guide of woods worth visiting!

It is said that the best fertiliser is the farmer's footprint, and our frequent walks round the wood, for exercise and to keep an eye on the place, proved beneficial in many ways. There was no excuse for silviculture to be neglected, and I made sure the rapidly growing conifers were thinned at the right time, although some work was delayed by the Great Storm. When people compared photos of the wood in 1980 with what they could see thirty years later, they were often incredulous that it was the same place, and that we could have achieved so much. At times, even I found myself temporarily disorientated by the changes that had happened since I had last been in that part of the wood. The trees had literally grown beyond recognition.

Our attempts to convert monotonous, even-aged plantations to continuous cover were a marked success, both in terms of woodland structure and appearance, and we established the framework that any competent forester could take on into the future. We chose two main species to accomplish this, Douglas fir and Thuja, and the Thuja in particular thrived. There was immeasurable satisfaction in extending our retirement home with timber from trees we ourselves had planted. Fortunately, poorly-chosen trees such as ash and wild cherry showed their disdain for our dreadful soil and politely faded away like consumptive maidens before we wasted further money and effort by planting them more widely. Our policy of planting and nurturing tree species best suited to the site, regardless of country of origin, proved more successful and profitable than one guided by concepts of nativeness or perceived wildlife benefit.

We bought the wood with most of the coppice in a young and narrow age range, but over the years transformed it to a more or less even distribution of size classes, so that we were assured of a regular supply of poles. This was important if we were to build up a sustainable business. Converting parts of the coppice to larger trees by storing achieved both a source of valuable rail and planking material, and a quick change in appearance to high forest in a wood that had almost no large trees when we bought it. Combined with the growth of highly productive conifers, the "standing volume" of timber and average tree size grew enormously over the thirty years, increasing the capital value, the reserve of timber, and the beauty of the place.

We adapted the silviculture to accommodate new uses of the woodland. For example, the site of the children's play area was thinned more heavily than the growth of the trees required, in order make it sunnier and warmer. Around the picnic sites, coppice was cut on a shorter rotation than elsewhere, to achieve shelter from the wind without excessive side-shading. We continued to manage the trees so that they still produced timber, and expected every felling to make a profit. If there was a lesson to be learnt, it was that the actual productivity of the wood was hardly diminished by the large numbers who came to enjoy it. All that was necessary was the will to make it happen. Where possible, there was a synergy, where a single action would have multiple benefits, as when we high-pruned the young Douglas fir and Thuja, giving us foliage to sell at Christmas or to use for shelter-building, as well as knot-free timber at some future date. As a consulting arboriculturalist and recreation planner, I was well aware of the costs of keeping trees safe in public parks and other places open to the public, and have heard of wildlife and other woodland charities paying large amounts to have coppice managed. All our tree work was done at nil net cost, and often at a profit.

The frequency with which new diseases are arriving on our shores perturbs all who care about trees, whatever their objectives. In the decade to 2012 twelve new major threats were identified, compared with only five in the preceding thirty years. Some, such as *Chalara* (ash die-back), will have little impact on Wilderness Wood as there are almost no ash trees. Unfortunately, chestnut stools are dying from *Phytophthora*, and its ultimate impact is far from clear. If this or any of the other diseases affecting chestnut took a greater hold, the wood could quickly turn into a desolation of invading birch between the scattered conifer stands. Already foresters are looking to tree species with few known pests, but, with the complication of climate change, this may be little more than enlightened gazing into a crystal ball. Unlike woods on richer soil, Wilderness Wood will always support only a narrow palette of tree species. In the meantime, foresters and contractors are encouraged to set a good example by sterilising footwear, car tyres and so on, but wind, deer, badgers, and birds do not take such precautions, and these measures seem unlikely to succeed.

Although we never set out to maximise income, we gained great satisfaction from the money we did make from our activities. Somehow, banking £350 from supplying woodland products seemed more satisfying than receiving the same amount for a few hours' consulting work. Just as gross domestic product is a crude measure of a nation's wealth, let alone the happiness of its citizens, so the balance sheet of a small family business is an incomplete assessment of its success. Visitors often spoke with envy of our lifestyle. We never kept records of the hours worked, but were often on duty, if not actually working, for sixty hours a week. Although we usually finished each year in the black, our financial analysis did not take account of capital tied up, or make a proper allowance for depreciation. On balance the wood paid its way, bought new or replacement capital items, and gave us an income, supplemented by consultancy fees, that was sufficient for our relatively frugal life-style. It would certainly not have been adequate if we had been financing a large mortgage or employing a manager. The modest financial returns were more than compensated for by many non-monetary benefits. We lived in an enviable location in a lovely house which we had been able to design to meet our specific values and needs, with the control and enjoyment of the surrounding 24 hectares. We heated it with our own wood, and eventually installed a photo-voltaic system which produced more electricity than was consumed in the house itself, and helped power the Barn and the National Grid. We had the freedoms and satisfactions of running our own business: one which reflected our interests and abilities, and gave pleasure to so many.

Undoubtedly the financial health of the enterprise was assisted by sharing overheads with the consultancy and our domestic life. The business made use of our kitchen equipment as well as hand tools, especially in the early days, so capital outlays were minimised. Possibly more important to overall success was the time we could put in when it would have been uneconomic to employ staff. The wood could be run from the house, and our input varied according to demand, hour by hour, day by day. As the business grew, we took on staff, initially to assist in the wood and workshop, and then to take over office administration, conduct school visits, and lead birthday parties. Inevitably, when staff were ill or there was a sudden influx we would be found in the Barn or conducting parties. Willing flexibility was expected of all, and perhaps too much from ourselves. At times work pressures could seem unrelenting, and self-sufficiency combined with conscientious responsibility for too many things raised, at least for me, the spectres of anxiety or depression.

Except for a couple of small legacies, all our capital had come from our own efforts, and we were reluctant to lose it. Investment was therefore incremental and cautious, as we metaphorically tested the water. Because it was small, the business did not justify the expense of new equipment, and we had a succession of vehicles whose next home would be the scrapheap or with a restoration enthusiast. These included both tractors and the cars we so reluctantly owned. Many grant-giving bodies, especially charitable trusts, are not permitted to support commercial organisations, and we should have persisted with the idea of forming a charity or not-for-profit organisation for elements such as education and wildlife habitat work. This might also have made us a more attractive place for people to volunteer. We wondered, though, how many volunteers at large charities realise that the managers often receive substantial salaries, without the pressures of commerce bearing too heavily on their lives!

Support from bodies such as the Forestry Commission gave us credibility, even though grants were minimal. At a time when the role of green belts is being debated in light of the need for housing land, their recreational potential has been largely ignored by a planning system tilted towards NIMBYism. The Community Forests, set up in the 1990s, seem to have lost their way; starved of funds, they are low down local authorities' list of priorities. Wilderness Wood provided many of their functions at no public cost, and people travelled some distance to us because there were no comparable facilities closer to home.

The estimated billion pound annual value of forest "environmental services" offers no income to woodland owners, who meanwhile provide landscape, wildlife habitat, carbon fixing, etc, out of the goodness of their hearts. On the other hand, in the thirty years of our tenure the market values of both woodland and house increased three times in real terms, allowing for inflation. No wonder ours is called the lucky generation, with its free education and health service, and capital gains for anyone fortunate enough to own property in this period. Every generation is presented with a new set of constraints and possibilities; we had our hand of cards as dealt, but do not underestimate our good fortune at being able to pursue our dream when we did.

Our original planning application for a house was opposed by the planners, who said that we could not make a living from such small-scale forestry. From time to time advisors and landowners came by to see what we were up to, and it was for them to judge if our efforts were justified by the modest returns. We were unaware of any imitators setting up as direct copies, although it is likely a number of our ideas were implemented elsewhere. Enterprises such as ours would be impossible to patent, but we would not have welcomed the competition of imitators close by. Sadly, we received few serious requests for advice, and the recreation planning element of the consultancy withered on the vine. Perhaps we did too little to promulgate our achievements, and should have made greater efforts at the national level to influence the ways in which British forests are made available to the public.

In broad terms, we did what we said we would do in the planning application for our house, although the objector at Balneath was prescient when she predicted that, whatever our sincere intentions, we in practice would not stop at what we were proposing. Visitors like and expect at least a cup of tea and a souvenir or two, and we should have anticipated that café and shop would become a big part of the enterprise. The eventual size of the business, and numbers of visitors and of staff, were far larger than we initially imagined. Just as at Balneath, our village hall would no doubt overflow with objectors if anyone now proposed a project in the centre of the village that would attract tens of thousands of visitors a year, and over a hundred coaches. Yet that is what happened at Wilderness Wood, and, by and large, it was accepted as an asset and source of pride to the village. No small measure of our success was the affection that local people showed for the wood, and it became valued as an informal village park. Although it had no public rights of way, we always welcomed village walkers without charge, which went a long way to offsetting the inevitable disturbance that our activities must at times have caused. As a tourist destination we inevitably attracted visits from further afield than the village, but fortunately no-one could claim we were in deepest, unspoilt countryside, and the resultant increase in traffic was miniscule compared with the daily flow on our Main Road. On balance we were seen as a valued village amenity, and estate agents' particulars of local houses for sale mentioned proximity to Wilderness Wood as a selling feature. How much did we add to property values, and hence council taxes, over the years?

Despite the occasional rumour that we were going to sell the wood for building plots, we never had any intention of making money by land speculation. Prior to our planning consent for a house, it would have been entirely possible to subdivide the wood into small lots, selling the freeholds for considerably more than we paid, and then moving on. Even though the planning permission stipulated that the land could not be separated from the house, there might have been opportunities to profit from easements to adjoining properties, for garden extensions and the like. Apart from selling one neighbour a small strip to give him a safer road access, we resisted any such temptations.

It would have been interesting if, at the outset, we had written down where we thought the venture would be in five, ten or twenty years' time. For better or worse no such plan was made, and each year was taken as it came. Much to the frustration of any business adviser who strayed our way, we never put in writing a Grand Plan, and our long-suffering staff must at times have felt that mind-reading was part of their job description. None of our fine intentions would come to fruition without a financially sound business, so this had to be our first and over-riding aim. There was always the danger of pursuing sales rather than profit, and the steadily climbing graph of turnover was sadly not matched by the progress of the bottom line.

Our ability to stay in business was helped by the wide range of things we made and activities we promoted. A decline in sales for our picnic tables and dovecots was offset by the ever-increasing demand for other products such as fence panels and firewood; and the poor uptake for survival courses was more than offset by demand for birthday parties. In other words, we had many irons in the fire. We quickly dropped ideas if they didn't pay or demand was falling, and tried new ones that were appealing and seemed to have a market. Some of our original concepts came to nothing; there was insufficient water for a lake, and my idea for a touring campsite never got beyond a rough sketch. We failed to develop a market for our evening guided walks and suppers; while a later idea, "Hallowe'en happening", was hugely popular with public and staff alike, but the frugality of our own girls' treats had blinded us to the possibility that others might be willing to pay enough to make the evening viable. On the other hand, some of the ideas suggested by visitors or staff developed into major elements of our livelihood, such as the "castaway" activity and birthday parties. Brought up in an era when families generally made their own amusements, we had never dreamt that organised children's activities would become a normal part of people's lives, and that we would be hosting up to eight groups a weekend. With our mix of recreational and educational activities, together with our wood products, Christmas trees and timber production, we were clearly successful in practising the multiple-use concept we had so enthusiastically set out to demonstrate.

Any land-based tourism is in danger of becoming divorced from its surroundings, the very reason why it is there in the first place. If

UK visitors to a tropical coast never venture further than the hotel pool and bar, and fail to experience local culture, they might as well be under a heated geo-dome in Wigan, and save all that aviation fuel. Despite our preoccupation with visitor facilities, we never lost sight of the fact that we were offering a *woodland* experience. Maintenance and improvement of the woodland was what we had set out to do, despite its limited potential for short-term payback.

Having staff, from full-time, through part-time, to work experience teenagers, we were exposed to the myriad of employment and tax regulations. In our ignorance we fell foul of a few, and had to pay back-tax on some casual part-timers, and VAT on some school visits. How many businesses such as ours are too small to employ an appropriate administrative section? Our daughter Jo had to explain that the letters H R stood for Human Resources rather than a prefix to Highness or Therapy.

The wood was able to offer work experience and training to a significant number of young people, helping them towards a rural occupation. Like almost all our staff they without doubt gave of their best, often in difficult and trying circumstances, and with far less guidance and encouragement than they deserved. The hard work and loyal commitment of all staff was essential to our success. Because of the ever-varying part-time and seasonal staff, computing the number of employees for insurance purposes was always difficult, By the time we handed the wood over we had the equivalent of six full-time employees, and, after the school, were probably the largest employer in the village.

Success is hard to define, but if prizes are a measure, the various awards the wood picked up over the years indicate we were doing something right. The receipt of the Duke of Cornwall's Award for Forestry and Conservation in 1993 was perhaps our proudest moment. The Forestry Commission Centre of Excellence award in 1993 and the Royal Forestry Society Excellence in Forestry first prize for silviculture in 2010 were other welcome milestones. When in 2004 we won the regional "Best managed medium-sized wood" award from the Royal Agricultural and Royal Forestry Societies, the judges reported that we "would have stood head and shoulders above the competition in several other classes". Ever cautious, we had not entered those other classes on account of the entrance fees! Other gongs included the "Tourfor" Award for forest tourism, when, along with representatives of sites in Finland and Portugal, we enjoyed a ceremony at the Millennium Dome in January 2000.

In a sense, success was also measured by the reactions of visitors. We all like to feel appreciated, and reading the visitors' book would usually lift the spirits. "These woods have taken me back to my childhood – how things used to be - will come back again", suggested that our efforts were valued by the elderly. "It's absolutely brilliant. I'm defenetly going to drag my pearents up" (sic) indicated we were succeeding with the young; whereas "Trees, trees, trees" was possibly not meant as a compliment. A tired but happy child sighing "That was the best party I've ever been to", or even "This is the best day of my life", was welcome reward after a couple of hours in charge of a clutch of over-excited eight-year-olds. We also derived great satisfaction from being able to fulfil our evangelical aspirations to explain and interpret forestry and other aspects of the natural environment, and to open people's eyes to a world many may have glimpsed only on a TV screen. Again, we had plenty of positive feedback, from the many appreciative comments and letters from school groups, to the fungus hunter who remarked "I shall never see things in the same way again". What more can a teacher ask for?

The direction of our Wilderness Wood enterprise depended more on our own interests and abilities than on any carefully thought-out business plan. During the later years, when the prospect of retiring loomed, it became apparent just how much the venture was a reflection of our specialised training and interests, and that replacing us with a similar owner might be difficult.

It was clear to us that someone with sufficient money to buy the venture would probably be uninterested in running it. Conversely, a person with the skills and enthusiasm would be unlikely to have the capital to buy it. If we were to live in comfortable retirement, we would have to realise close to the market value of what was our biggest asset. Our great fear was that the wood would fall into the hands of a wealthy person looking for a country retreat, who would put up fences and "Keep Out" signs, and all we had worked for would disappear overnight. We comforted ourselves that, if events were to turn out this way, we could at least take solace that almost a million visitors had enjoyed the wood during our tenure; that we had provided worthwhile training and employment to many; and that an ancient woodland had been escorted into the twenty-first century in a state of rude viability.

With Jo and Kate well established in their careers as sustainability consultant and doctor respectively, it had never occurred to us that either might wish to take on the wood. We were therefore very pleasantly surprised when Jo and her fiancé Jonathan announced they would like to buy the wood and run it as an exemplar for their consultancy, which specialised in designing greener places. In her own right, Jo had written three books on how individuals could live more sustainably by changes to their lifestyles, and had known the wood from childhood. If we could live reasonably close by, and on hand to ease the transition, we felt this was the best solution for the wood's future, and one that would keep it in the family.

As exemplified in Sir Gerry Robinson's TV series about family businesses, "I'll show them who's boss", handing a business from one generation to the next can be fraught with difficulties. We explored briefly the possibility of building a "granny annexe" in the orchard, but soon realised our close proximity would be insufferable to a generation used to freedom for so many years. Besides, my inability to pass by a woodland task without attending to it or pointing out the deficiency would soon drive all parties insane. We therefore bought a smaller house locally, went off on a nine-week jaunt round Europe, and left the offspring to find their feet.

Jo and Jonathan were clear they wanted a smaller footfall, with fewer people spending more money than the clientele to date, some of whom had come for the day with their own food, and spent little other than admission. The Barn and kitchen were quickly updated, with better and more sophisticated food and drink on the menu. They replaced our somewhat amateur website with a very professional one, which attracted a whole new clientele, whose email addresses were assiduously collected for promoting events at the wood. These included monthly "candlelit dinners" in the Barn, with speakers on sustainability topics such as food waste, sustainable fisheries and ethical fashion. Predictably, the best-attended were when well-known TV personalities spoke, rather than often more interesting presentations on "worthy" topics.

A wider range of children's activities was added to our list, while well-established events, such as the working horse day and Anne's fungus walks, continued as ever. Accommodation in a converted horsebox, and three further camping spots, established Wilderness Wood as a "glamping" location, and woodland wedding receptions increased in number and sophistication.

A manager was inevitably required to run the business day-to-day, as Jo and Jonathan had busy professional lives in London, and this ate into the profits To change the ship's direction took longer than anticipated, and in the meantime the economy hit the rocks of recession. In 2013 Jo was head-hunted to lead the sustainability team of a large international company, an offer too good to refuse. With a baby on the way, their lives had become impossibly crowded, and, with great reluctance on all sides, we took back the management of the wood and prepared to put it on the market.

As soon as word got round that we would be selling, enquiries flooded in. We immediately made it clear that we intended to sell to a purchaser who would respect the ethos and land-use we had so assiduously established. So it was with great relief that, within a short time, we heard from a young family, via mobile 'phone from deepest France, that Wilderness Wood was just what they had been seeking for several years. Dan is an architect, intent on practical application of his skills, and his wife Emily is an educational researcher also intent on practical application of her ideas, by creating opportunities for adults and children to learn alongside each other outside the classroom. With their three young children, they are establishing a centre where local people and other visitors actively participate in learning and woodland management, both as volunteers and through courses. Dan intends to build simple timber structures from the wood grown on site to act as accommodation for courses and apprentices. School and children's activities continue, ably run by Lucy and Ed, who have already worked with Wilderness Wood for some years. Andrew, our long-term woodsman and carpenter, continues to carry out coppicing and making the wood products we so readily sold. Meanwhile, in the Barn, our tradition of simple, good-value food continues under the direction of Rachel, who, coincidently, went to school with Kate. This group will be able to develop their businesses in a familiar and benign setting, with an established market.

Such was the unanimity of purpose between vendor and buyer, we had no difficulty in persuading Dan and Emily to covenant to keeping the wood open to villagers free of charge, and to maintaining the areas of continuous cover forestry. Sadness, combined with a sense of relief, overwhelmed us as we did our last wash-up and cashing up that final Easter Monday afternoon, before the lawyers completed the sale the next morning.

Now we must stand back and pass on the baton, wherever it shall be carried.

We are such stuff
As dreams are made on, and our little life
Is rounded with a sleep.

GLOSSARY

Ancient woodland	Woodland that has existed continuously since 1600 in England.
Beating up	Replanting of failed trees in the first few years after initial planting.
Bloomery	A small, primitive clay furnace for smelting iron.
Brashing	Removal of lower branches from trees, usually up to about 2 metres.
Break	A device for holding a pole while being cleft with a froe.
Broadleaves	Trees with wide leaves, usually deciduous, yielding hardwood timber.
Cant	An area of coppice cut in one season.
Certification	Registration, usually by third parties, for forests to conform to local laws and standards of responsible management (see UKWAS).
Clear felling	The removal of all trees from an area of forest.
Cleft chestnut / cleaving	Chestnut split along the grain with a wedge or froe.
Compartment	A management unit of woodland, often of uniform composition. May be divided into sub-compartments.

Conifer	A cone-bearing tree. Usually evergreen, with needle leaves and yielding softwood timber.
Continuous cover forestry *(CCF)*	The management of a forest to promote trees of all sizes so that the ground is never cleared of trees.
Coppice	Trees cut near ground level and allowed to re-sprout with a number of stems, usually cut on a rotation of less than 20 years.
Coppice-with-standards	Coppice grown between larger trees managed on a longer rotation for timber.
Cord/cordwood	A stack of wood for use as firewood, usually measuring 4ft. x 4ft. x 8ft.
Dedication	Various grant schemes between 1947 and 1981 for covenanting land with the Forestry Commission to retain and manage it under good forestry practices.
Error of closure	In surveying, the difference between the plotted start and finishing points of a closed loop survey.
Faggots	Bundles of sticks, usually used for lighting fires or heating ovens.
Froe	A tool with a long, narrow blade at right-angles to a handle, used for splitting poles and shingles.
FSC *(Forestry Stewardship Council)*	An independent international organisation set up to promote responsible management of forests.
Hardwood	The timber of a broadleaved tree. Often used as synonym for a broadleaved tree.
Heartwood	The older, dead wood at the centre of a tree, often darker, more rot-resistant and stronger than the sapwood. Occurs in both softwood and hardwood.
High forest	Trees growing under forest conditions to their mature height, as opposed to coppice or areas of young trees, scrub or scattered trees.
Increment *(annual)*	The amount of wood added to a tree or area of land in one year by growth, eg 5 millimetres diameter, or 10 cubic metres per hectare per annum.
Layering	Propagation of a living stem so it roots into the ground where it touches. Can occur naturally, but used to create new trees as an alternative to planting.

Loess	Fine, wind-blown material forming a well-drained, usually fertile soil.
Lop and top	The tops and side branches cut off trees after felling.
Multiple use	The planned use of land to achieve more than one benefit, eg timber and recreation.
Natural regeneration	The replacement of trees by self-seeding or other natural means.
Nursery stock	Young trees grown in a nursery for planting in a wood.
Oast, oasthouse	Agricultural building for drying hops, usually with conical roof. Now popular as house conversions.
Pale	See spile.
PAWS *(Plantation on Ancient Woodland Site)*	An ancient woodland site diversified with planted trees, commonly thought to be to the detriment of wildlife interest.
Phytopthora	A fungus-like organism which can attack a variety of species. Spread by wind and rain, according to species, and thought to thrive in damp conditions.
PTO *(power take off)*	A drive-shaft at the rear of a tractor giving power to ancillary equipment.
Ride	A track or road within a wood or forest, which may be paved or otherwise.
Rotation	The time in years between planting or seeding of trees and their felling, or between the cutting of coppice.
Sapwood	The young wood, initially living, on the outermost part of a tree, which conducts water from roots to leaves. Often less rot-resistant than heartwood.
Scrub	Area of woody vegetation, dominated by young trees and shrubs. A forester's term of abuse for self-sown trees without timber value, or the result of amateur tree-planting and subsequent neglect.
Shakes/shingles	Roofing tiles made by splitting or sawing thin slices of wood.
Silviculture	The art and science of growing trees in woodlands.
Slasher	A hand tool with a sharp blade at the end of a long handle, used for clearing low scrub vegetation.

Snedding	Removal of side branches of a tree once it has been felled.
Softwood	The timber of a coniferous tree.
Soil acidity	Measured on the pH scale of 1 to 10, where 7.0 is neutral, and 5.0 to 5.5 is strongly acidic. Lime is generally used to correct acidity, and also allows release of minerals such as potassium.
Spile/pale	A split, thin pole for fencing or garden use.
Stand	An area or grove of trees, often of homogenous composition.
Standard	A tree grown as a single stem, at or near its mature height, often widely spaced from others.
Stool	The stump of a coppiced tree.
Storing	Thinning out stems on a coppice stool to favour one or more stems, to produce larger material.
Swaphook/sickle	Hand tool with a thin, curved blade for cutting grass, etc.
Thinning	Removal of trees to allow more space to their neighbours.
Transplants	Nursery trees which have been dug up and re-planted in the nursery to improve their root systems. They may also be mechanically undercut for the same reason.
Tree shelter	A tube, usually plastic and between 0.6 and 1.6 metres tall, used to protect young trees from browsing animals and chemical weedkillers, and to improve growing conditions.
UKWAS *(United Kingdom Woodland Assurance Standard)*	A framework for woodland management acceptable for Forestry Commission grants or certification.
WGS *(Woodland Grant Scheme)*	Generic term for suite of grants administered by the Forestry Commission for woodland management.
WIG *(Woodland Improvement Grant)*	Forestry Commission capital grant to enhance public benefits.

CONVERSION FACTORS

I like to use the metric system, which is used in most professions and industry, including forestry. Anne, like many in Britain, still thinks in Imperial units, so here are some equivalents.

Metric	Imperial
1 centimetre	0.39 inch
2.54 cm	1 inch
1 metre	3.28 feet
30.05 cm	1 foot
1 kilometre	0.62 mile
1.61 km	1 mile
1 hectare	2.47 acres
0.40 ha	1 acre
1 cubic metre	35.3 cubic feet
0.028 cu m	1 cu ft